DC Circuits – Vol. II
Circuit Analysis Methods

Ralph A. Oliva, Ph.D.
Texas Instruments Learning Center

Charles W. Dale, Ed.D.
Dallas County Community College District
Eastfield College

With Contributions by

David Clemens

Ross Wise

Donald W. Taylor

SECOND EDITION

This book is part of the Basic Electricity Series
from the Texas Instruments Learning Center consisting of:

Basic Electricity and DC Circuits
Basic AC Circuits

The Basic Electricity Series Published for Radio Shack
are designed as two Two-Volume Sets:

DC Circuits:
Vol. I – Basic Electricity and Circuit Concepts
Vol. II – Circuit Analysis Methods

AC Circuits:
Vol. I – Basic Circuit Concepts
Vol. II – Circuit Analysis Methods

A DIVISION OF TANDY CORPORATION
FT. WORTH, TEXAS 76102

THIRD PRINTING

IMPORTANT NOTICE REGARDING BOOK MATERIALS

Important Note to the Reader

This is a large-looking book of nearly 500 pages, but it is important to note that **about half of this book is devoted to WORKED THROUGH EXAMPLES with step-by-step solutions.** Many students learn about electricity and dc circuits most easily from problems of this sort. Students must often buy an additional book to obtain extra worked through examples; however, a wide variety of problems with solutions is included in the body of this text for you, and in a large set at the end of each lesson.

In addition, each text section uses a new **special layout** which has several distinct features:

1.   Quite a bit of blank space has been deliberately left on the text pages so that there is ample room for highlighting, extra notes, questions, etc.

2.   There are two "pathways" through the text material. One is a fast path through the essential required materials. The other path includes extra examples and detailed discussion in areas where questions are commonly raised.

The page layout and type faces are your keys to the use of these two pathways. The explanation of their use is a simple one, as is shown on the next page. It's as if you are on a railroad train and you have the option of selecting an "express route", or taking a tour through a new "sidings" of interest. Here's how it works.

- **Basic Concept #1**
- Supplemental Material
- **Basic Concept #2**

Basic Concept #1 — Basic materials are presented on the left side of printed text pages in type like this. (Figure A) The main body of the course will be presented using this layout. In key course areas, supplemental materials are inserted for you. At these points, you have the option of swinging your attention to the right side of the page, or moving straight down to the next basic concept, skipping the supplemental material.

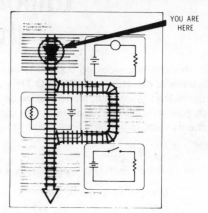

Figure A

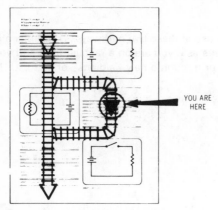

Figure B

Supplemental Material — If you are interested in "digging in" a little deeper for an extra example or more detailed discussion, swing your attention to the right, where supplemental materials are printed in a slightly lighter type like this. On these "sidings" you will hopefully find a question answered, a helpful extra example, or extra details in an area of interest to you.

Basic Concept #2 — If you move straight down the left side of the textbook pages, from basic concept to basic concept, you will have no problems with the continuity of the text or flow of material. If you have some background in basic electricity, or wish a shorter "express" pathway through the material, this is the path for you.

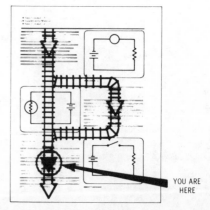

Figure C

Features of This Book

This book is designed primarily for the entry level student. No sophisticated math background or previous knowledge of electricity is assumed, and no matter what your background you can learn the basic concepts that have enabled man to harness and control dc electricity.

There are several features of this book specifically designed to increase its efficiency and aid you in grasping the principles of predicting and controlling dc electricity.

1. There is plenty of blank space near each text passage and figure for your notes, calculations or sketches. Keep your notes here in the book so they can serve as a handy reference.

2. At the beginning of each lesson, on a shaded page, detailed OBJECTIVES are listed for you. These objectives state, step-by-step, what new things you should be able to do upon successful completion of each chapter. (The things you will actually be doing are printed in *italics; write, sketch, calculate, predict, construct, explain, etc.)*

3. At the end of each lesson there are three types of examples for your use:

    First, in addition to those examples in the text, there is a set of examples with detailed step-by-step solutions. These WORKED THROUGH EXAMPLES *apply* the theory in each lesson to typical situations involving dc electricity. In this way you are led from *knowledge* of the concepts you need to know, to the *application* of those concepts in circuits you will build and handle.

    Second, you are provided with a complete set of PRACTICE PROBLEMS with answers on the back of each page. These problems will give you the opportunity to *try* your new skills and *test* your accuracy.

    Finally, a set of questions without solutions or answers is arranged as a two-page QUIZ, and will take you less than an hour to complete. Your quiz will serve as an indicator of areas where you need further review of key concepts and principles.

    The quizzes and the worked through problems were taken from the most asked questions in TI's instructor conducted course on Basic Electricity and DC Circuits.

Contents

Important Note to Reader iii
Sample Text Page iv
Features of this Book v

Lesson 8   **Parallel-Series Circuits**   **8-1**
            Objectives 8-3
            Text 8-5
            Worked Through Examples 8-35
            Practice Problems 8-43
            Quiz 8-57

Lesson 9   **Series-Parallel Circuits**   **9-1**
            Objectives 9-3
            Text 9-5
            Worked Through Examples 9-35
            Practice Problems 9-45
            Quiz 9-77

Lesson 10   **Voltage Dividers and Power**   **10-1**
            Objectives 10-3
            Text 10-5
            Worked Through Examples 10-43
            Practice Problems 10-53
            Quiz 10-71

Lesson 11   **Introduction to Kirchhoff's Laws**   **11-1**
            Objectives 11-3
            Text 11-5
            Worked Through Examples 11-43
            Practice Problems 11-53
            Quiz 11-67

Lesson 12   **Advanced Methods of DC Circuit Analysis**   **12-1**
            Objectives 12-3
            Text 12-5
            Worked Through Examples 12-37
            Practice Problems 12-55
            Quiz 12-65
            Supplement   **12-67**

Lesson 13   Capacitors and the RC Time Constant   13-1
               Objectives 13-3
               Text 13-5
               Worked Through Examples 13-33
               Practice Problems 13-41
               Quiz 13-47

Lesson 14   Inductors and the L/R Time Constant   14-1
               Objectives 14-3
               Text 14-5
               Worked Through Examples 14-27
               Practice Problems 14-31
               Quiz 14-35

Appendices   A-1
Appendix 1   Interpreting the Resistor Color Code A-2
Appendix 2   Preferred Values for Resistors and Capacitors A-3
Appendix 3   Resistor Size Comparison A-4
Appendix 4   Scientific Notation and Metric Prefixes A-5
Appendix 5   Basic Schematic Symbols A-6
Appendix 6   How to Use Square Root Tables A-7
Appendix 7   How to Extract Square Roots Manually A-10
Appendix 8   The Universal Time Constant Graph A-14
Appendix 9   Charge and Discharge Curve Calculations A-17
Appendix 10   Capacitor Color Codes A-18
                    Mica Capacitors A-19
                    Ceramic Capacitors A-20
Appendix 11   Unit Conversion Charts A-22
Appendix 12   The Greek Alphabet A-25
Appendix 13   Basic Formulas of Basic Electricity A-26

Bibliography   B-1

Glossary   G-1

Index   I-1

Quiz Answers   Q-1

Lesson 8

Parallel-Series Circuits

Now that series and parallel circuit analyses have been introduced, this lesson begins discussing how these methods may be combined to analyze circuits that are a simple combination of the two: PARALLEL-SERIES circuits. The techniques discussed are essentially an extension of the principles covered in Lessons 5, 6, and 7. The circuit examples discussed find many applications in everyday life, including the basic layout of the automotive wiring system.

LESSON 8. PARALLEL-SERIES CIRCUITS

● **Objectives**

This lesson begins to put together the techniques of parallel and series circuit analysis and to apply them to a more complex circuit, the parallel-series circuit. The basic principles covered are essentially a logical extension of those you have learned thus far. The circuit examples you will work with in this lesson include a basic automotive wiring system. At the end of this lesson you should find yourself able to:

1. *Define* parallel-series circuit and given a series of schematics, *distinguish* which represent series, parallel, series-parallel, and parallel-series circuits.

2. Given a schematic diagram of the type shown below, *use circuit reduction techniques* to *calculate* the total equivalent resistance of the circuit.

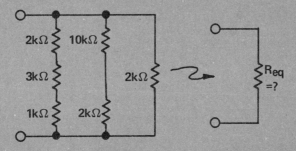

3. Given a schematic diagram of the type shown, you should be able to use *circuit reduction techniques* and Ohm's law to: *calculate* the voltage across and current through each resistor in the circuit, *find* the total current in the circuit, and *calculate* the circuit's equivalent resistance.

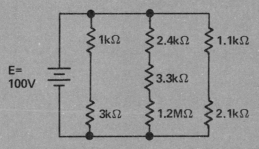

4. Given a schematic diagram of the type shown and using *current reduction techniques* and Ohm's law, you should be able to: *calculate* all unknown currents, voltages, and resistances.

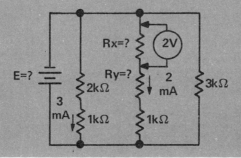

LESSON 8: PARALLEL-SERIES CIRCUITS

- **Series-Parallel Circuit**
- **Parallel-Series Circuit**

In Lessons 5, 6 and 7, series and parallel circuits were discussed. The essential features differentiating these two basic types of circuit were outlined along with the specific rules that describe the operation of each type of circuit.

In this lesson you will see how several of the key features of parallel circuits may be combined with those of series circuits in forming what is called a *parallel-series circuit*. Later on in Lesson 9, another circuit type, the *series-parallel circuit*, will be covered. These new circuit names, series-parallel and parallel-series, sound pretty much alike, but there are some key distinctions between these two types of circuits that will affect the methods used in analyzing them. In presenting their analysis it is important that you distinguish the two types in your mind.

Series-Parallel Circuit — Figure 8.1 shows the *series-parallel* circuit which will be covered in detail in Lesson 9. This circuit is called a series-parallel circuit because at least one circuit component, in this case R_1, lies in *series* with the total current. Notice that in this schematic, resistor R_1 is connected so that the total circuit current flows through it. It is wired in series with other circuit components which may include parallel wired combinations of resistors such as R_2 and R_3.

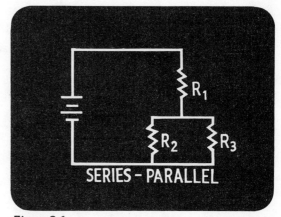

Figure 8.1

Parallel-Series Circuit — Figure 8.2 shows a *parallel-series* circuit. The key difference between this type of circuit and the series-parallel circuit is that there is *no* single component that lies in the path of the total circuit. This circuit consists of several branches wired in parallel, but notice that each of the parallel branches may contain one or more resistors connected in series with one another. The circuit contains several parallel branches which may each contain several resistors wired in series; hence, this is called a parallel-series circuit.

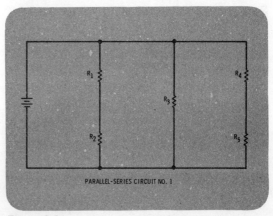

Figure 8.2

- Series Voltage Law and Formula
- Series Current Law and Formula

In order to analyze circuits of this type, you will be applying both the series and parallel circuit laws. To help keep these laws in mind, review them now briefly before examining your first parallel-series circuit.

Series Voltage Law and Formula — Series circuit behavior is summarized in three rules. Recall that as far as voltage behavior is concerned the rule to use is, "The sum of the individual voltage drops around a series circuit is equal to the total applied voltage." Putting this law in formula form, the law appears as shown in Figure 8.3:

$$E_T = E_{R1} + E_{R2} + E_{R3}.$$

LAWS OF SERIES CIRCUITS

1. THE SUM OF THE INDIVIDUAL VOLTAGE DROPS AROUND A SERIES CIRCUIT EQUALS THE APPLIED VOLTAGE

$$E_T = E_{R1} + E_{R2} \ E_{R3} + \ldots$$

Figure 8.3

Series Current Law and Formula — The current behavior of series circuits is summarized in a law which states "The current has the same value at any point within a series circuit," as shown in Figure 8.4. The current law for series circuits written as a formula indicates that the total circuit current is the same as that current through each of the circuit resistors: $I_T = I_{R1} = I_{R2} = I_{R3}.$

2. CURRENT HAS THE SAME VALUE AT ANY POINT WITHIN A SERIES CIRCUIT

$$I_T = I_{R1} = I_{R2} = I_{R3} = \ldots$$

Figure 8.4

- Series Resistance Law and Formula
- Parallel Voltage Law and Formula
- Parallel Current Law and Formula

Series Resistance Law and Formula — The law governing the behavior of resistance in series circuits states: "The sum of the individual resistances within a series circuit equals the total resistance of the circuit." To find the total (or equivalent) resistance of a string of resistors wired in series, simply add the resistance of each series wired resistor, as shown in Figure 8.5.

As you recall, three similar laws governing the operation of parallel circuits have also been covered. The laws point out the key differences between series and parallel circuit behavior.

3. THE SUM OF THE INDIVIDUAL RESISTANCES WITHIN A SERIES CIRCUIT EQUALS THE TOTAL RESISTANCE OF THE CIRCUIT

$$R_T = R_1 + R_2 + R_3 + \ldots$$

Figure 8.5

Parallel Voltage Law and Formula — The law describing voltage behavior in parallel circuits states: "The total applied voltage in a parallel circuit is the same across each branch of that circuit." This law may be written in formula form as shown in Figure 8.6. Note that in the formula the subscripts have been changed from E_{R1} to E_{B1}. The "B" subscript is used to indicate "Branch" in this formula, and it will be of help to focus your attention on the behavior of parallel *branches* in this lesson. Notice that the only real difference between "regular" parallel circuits and parallel-series circuits is that *parallel-series circuits may contain several resistors in any branch*.

LAWS FOR PARALLEL CIRCUITS

1. THE TOTAL VOLTAGE OF A PARALLEL CIRCUIT IS THE SAME ACROSS EACH BRANCH OF THAT CIRCUIT

$$E_T = E_{B1} = E_{B2} = E_{B3}$$

Figure 8.6

Parallel Current Law and Formula — The law governing current behavior in a parallel circuit states, "The total (or main line) current in a parallel circuit is equal to the sum of the individual branch currents." Figure 8.7 shows how this law is written in formula form. Notice once again a "B" subscript is used to indicate branch.

2. THE TOTAL CURRENT IN A PARALLEL CIRCUIT IS EQUAL TO THE SUM OF THE INDIVIDUAL BRANCH CURRENTS.

$$I_T = I_{B1} + I_{B2} + I_{B3} + \ldots$$

Figure 8.7

- **Parallel Resistance Law**
- **Parallel Resistance Formula**
- **Circuit Laws**

Parallel Resistance Law — Finally, the law governing resistance in parallel circuits states, "The total resistance of a parallel circuit is always less than, or approximately equal to, that of the smallest resistive branch (Figure 8.8).

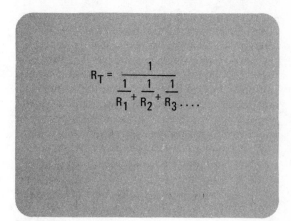

3. THE TOTAL RESISTANCE IN A PARALLEL CIRCUIT IS ALWAYS LESS THAN OR APPROXIMATELY EQUAL TO THE SMALLEST RESISTIVE BRANCH.

Figure 8.8

Parallel Resistance Formula — The most general formula used in determining parallel resistance is "Sum of the Reciprocals Formula," shown in Figure 8.9. This formula can be used in calculating equivalent resistance of any parallel resistor combination.

$$R_T = \frac{1}{\frac{1}{R_1} + \frac{1}{R_2} + \frac{1}{R_3} \cdots}$$

Figure 8.9

Circuit Laws — The parallel and series circuit rules will be the basic tools you will need as you proceed to analyze any parallel-series circuit. The only other formulas you will need will be those given you by Ohm's law. The real key to analyzing more complex parallel-series circuits boils down to the question, "How do I know which circuit laws to apply and where to apply them?" The answer to this question is fairly straightforward, as you might have guessed. Simply apply the series circuit laws to those portions of the circuits that are wired in series (Figure 8.10). Those parts of the circuits you encounter that are connected in parallel are subject to the parallel circuit laws.

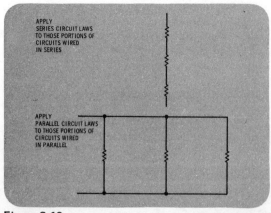

APPLY SERIES CIRCUIT LAWS TO THOSE PORTIONS OF CIRCUITS WIRED IN SERIES

APPLY PARALLEL CIRCUIT LAWS TO THOSE PORTIONS OF CIRCUITS WIRED IN PARALLEL

Figure 8.10

All of these problems depend on your ability to recognize various parts of circuits as being in either series or parallel with other circuit components. Hopefully, by now you can fairly easily guess at the one sure way to gain expertise in this area. Practice! Your "circuit sense," that is, your ability to just examine a circuit and sense what is going on right away, develops only after you have examined many different types of circuits.

Basic Parallel-Series Circuit — Figure 8.11 shows a basic parallel-series circuit. First, focus your attention on the fact that R_1 and R_2 are connected in series with each other, and that R_3 and R_4 are also connected in series with each other. Now, focus on the whole circuit. Notice that branch 1, which contains R_1 and R_2, is in *parallel* with branch 2, which contains R_3 and R_4.

To solve for voltage, current, and resistance in this circuit, you must simply apply the series circuit rules to the series-connected *resistors*, and then the parallel-circuit rules to the parallel-connected *branches*. Remember, your general aim is to solve for all the voltage drops, currents, and total resistance of the circuit. Also, recall that once the circuit's total or equivalent resistance is known, this value can be used to help you find the total or main line current it draws.

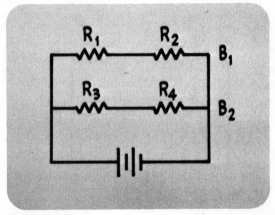

Figure 8.11

- **Ohm's Law**
- **Basic Parallel-Series Circuit (Circuit Reduction)**
- **Basic Parallel-Series Circuit (First Reduction)**

Ohm's Law — The procedure for finding the total current simply involves using Ohm's law as shown in Figure 8.12. Total current I_T equals the applied voltage, E_A, divided by the circuit's total equivalent resistance, R_{eq}.

The process by which the total equivalent resistance, R_{eq}, is found is called *circuit reduction*. The term "circuit reduction" refers to the processes by which a complex circuit is reduced to one that is simpler. A circuit is reduced by alternately applying the series and parallel circuit laws.

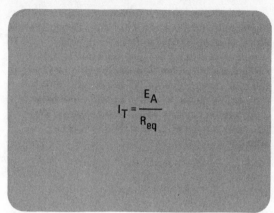

$$I_T = \frac{E_A}{R_{eq}}$$

Figure 8.12

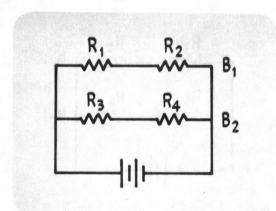

Figure 8.13

Basic Parallel-Series Circuit (Circuit Reduction) — How do you begin the process of circuit reduction? A good idea is to begin with the simplest parts of the circuit focusing your attention on how they may be further simplified. For example, in the basic parallel-series circuit shown in Figure 8.13 the simplest thing you can do immediately is to add the series resistors in each branch using the series circuit rule. You could then replace the two resistors in each branch with one equivalent resistor whose value is the sum of the two resistances. The sum of the values of R_1 and R_2 is labeled R_{1-2}. The sum of the resistances R_3 and R_4 is R_{3-4}.

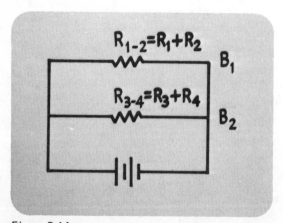

Figure 8-14

Basic Parallel-Series Circuit (First Reduction) — You can redraw the circuit as shown in Figure 8.14 using the reduced values, R_{1-2} and R_{3-4}. Notice that you now have a simple parallel circuit with a single resistor in each branch. You can proceed to further reduce this circuit to a circuit containing one single resistance by combining R_{1-2} and R_{3-4} using the law for adding resistances in parallel. The final single resistance R_{eq} can be obtained using the formula:

$$R_{eq} = \frac{1}{\frac{1}{R_{1-2}} + \frac{1}{R_{3-4}}}$$

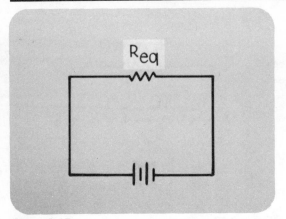

Figure 8.15

Parallel-Series Circuit No. 2 (Third Reduction) —
This finally reduces the circuit to the simple form
shown in Figure 8.15. Now you may easily solve
for the total or main line current that would flow
in this circuit. This current value will then aid in
solving for the *rest* of the voltages and currents in
this circuit.

Reexamine this same circuit but this time
consider the circuit reduction using realistic ohmic
values for the four resistors.

Parallel-Series Circuit No. 2 — Figure 8.16 shows
the same basic parallel-series circuit with resistance
values inserted. Branch 1 consists of resistor R_1
with 1 kilohm of resistance in series with resistor
R_2, which is a 2-kilohm resistor. Resistors R_3 and
R_4 in the second branch have resistance values of
3 kilohms and 1 kilohm, respectively. First focus
on the upper branch of this circuit, between
points C and D. Resistors R_1 and R_2 may be
combined using the law for addition of series
resistances. This enables you to replace R_1 and R_2
with *one* equivalent resistance, R_{1-2}.

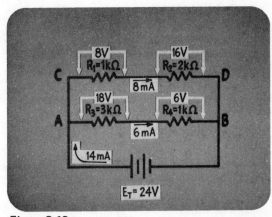

Figure 8.16

Series Resistance Formula — Using the resistance
law to find R_{1-2} (as shown in Figure 8.17), R_{1-2} =
$R_1 + R_2$ or R_{1-2} = 1 kilohm + 2 kilohms for a
total of 3 kilohms.

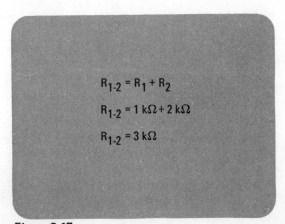

$$R_{1-2} = R_1 + R_2$$

$$R_{1-2} = 1\ k\Omega + 2\ k\Omega$$

$$R_{1-2} = 3\ k\Omega$$

Figure 8.17

- **Basic Parallel-Series Circuit (First Reduction)**
- **Series Resistance Formula**
- **Basic Parallel-Series Circuit (Second Reduction)**

Basic Parallel-Series Circuit (First Reduction) —
The two resistors in the upper branch may be replaced with one single resistor, R_{1-2}, of 3 kilohms. Similarly, the second branch may be simplified by the combination of R_3 and R_4 resulting in an equivalent resistance R_{3-4} as you can see in Figure 8.18.

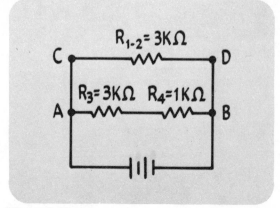

Figure 8.18

Series Resistance Formula — Again applying the series circuit resistance formula, R_{3-4} equals 3 kilohms plus 1 kilohm or 4 kilohms (Figure 8.19).

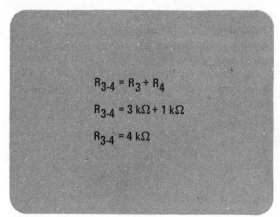

$$R_{3-4} = R_3 + R_4$$

$$R_{3-4} = 3\ k\Omega + 1\ k\Omega$$

$$R_{3-4} = 4\ k\Omega$$

Figure 8.19

Basic Parallel-Series Circuit (Second Reduction) —
Resistors R_3 and R_4 may be replaced by one resistor, R_{3-4}, having a resistance of 4 kilohms and illustrated in Figure 8.20.

At this point, notice that this circuit may be further reduced because it is now a simple parallel circuit. Since this circuit has only *two* resistors in parallel, the product-over-the-sum formula can be used to calculate the total equivalent resistance.

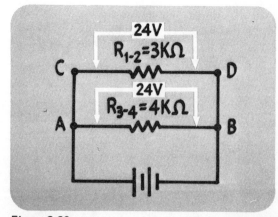

Figure 8.20

- **Parallel Resistance Formula**
- **Basic Parallel-Series Circuit (Final Reduction)**
- **Ohm's Law (I_T)**

Parallel Resistance Formula — All necessary calculations are shown in Figure 8.21. Begin with the product-over-the-sum-formula and substitute the correct circuit values to get 3 kilohms *times* 4 kilohms *over 3 kilohms plus* 4 kilohms. Having done the indicated multiplication and addition, you will get 12 X 10^6, divided by 7 X 10^3. Completing the calculation, the total equivalent resistance is found to be equal to 1.714 X 10^{+3}, or 1.71 kilohms (Figure 8.21).

$$R_{eq} = \frac{R_{1-2} \times R_{3-4}}{R_{1-2} + R_{3-4}}$$

$$R_{eq} = \frac{3k \times 4k}{3k + 4k}$$

$$R_{eq} = \frac{12 \times 10^6}{7 \times 10^3}$$

$$R_{eq} = 1.714 \times 10^3 = 1.71 \ k\Omega$$

Figure 8.21

Basic Parallel-Series Circuit (Final Reduction) — This 1.71 kilohms of equivalent resistance can be placed into a new circuit that, as far as total resistance is concerned, is equivalent to the original circuit. The new resistor has been labeled R_{eq} for equivalent. Notice that by using the process of circuit reduction or circuit simplification, the complex parallel-series circuit you began with has now been reduced to a circuit that contains only one resistor (Figure 8.22).

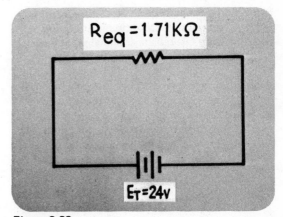

Figure 8.22

Ohm's Law (I_T) — Using this equivalent resistance, you can find the total or main line current that will flow in this circuit. The voltage applied to the circuit is 24 volts. The circuit's total resistance is also known, 1.71 kilohms. These values can be substituted into the Ohm's law formula $I_T = E_T/R_{eq}$ to find the total current (Figure 8.23). Divide 24 volts by 1.71 kilohms and you will find that 14 milliamps of main line current is flowing in the circuit.

To proceed to the next part of the circuit analysis, look at the reduced circuit carefully. It can be seen that the entire 24 volts is dropped across the equivalent resistance, R_{eq}. Now, here's a

$$I_T = \frac{E_T}{R_{eq}}$$

$$I_T = \frac{24 \ V}{1.71 \ k\Omega}$$

$$I_T = \frac{24 \ V}{1.71 \times 10^3}$$

$$I_T = 14 \times 10^{-3} = 14 \ mA$$

Figure 8.23

key method of procedure in circuit analysis: back up one step at this point.

Basic Parallel-Series Circuit (Second Reduction) — Figure 8.24 shows the same circuit just before it was reduced to one resistance showing two resistive branches, each with a single resistor. Recall that the parallel circuit rules state that the voltage is the same across all branches of a parallel circuit. In this case both branches each have 24 volts applied across them. This bit of information is very significant because the voltage across each branch may simply be divided by the branch resistance to find the current flowing through each branch.

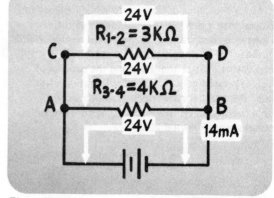

Figure 8.24

Ohm's Law (I_{1-2}) — Consider branch 1. At this point you know that E_{R1-2} is equal to 24 volts and that R_{1-2} is 3 kilohms. If these values are used in an appropriate Ohm's law formula, as shown in Figure 8.25, a current value of 8 milliamps through R_{1-2} can be calculated. (Notice this is the current flowing through resistor R_{1-2}, and, hence, this is the current that flows *throughout* branch 1.)

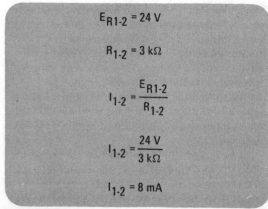

Figure 8.25

- Ohm's Law (I_{3-4})
- Basic Parallel-Series Circuit
- Ohm's Law (E_{R1})

Ohm's Law (I_{3-4}) — The current flowing through the second branch containing R_{3-4} may be calculated in the same manner. The voltage across this branch is also 24 volts, and the branch resistance in this case is 4 kilohms. Using Ohm's law again, as shown in Figure 8.26, 24 volts is divided by 4 kilohms to equal 6 milliamps of current through R_{3-4}, and, *hence, all of branch 2.*

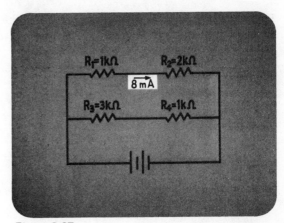

$$I_{3-4} = \frac{E_{R3-4}}{R_{3-4}}$$

$$I_{3-4} = \frac{24 \text{ V}}{4 \text{ k}\Omega}$$

$$I_{3-4} = 6 \text{ mA}$$

Figure 8.26

Basic Parallel-Series Circuit — Now that the current flow through both branches is known, the original circuit diagram can be used to find the voltages dropped across each individual resistor (Figure 8.27). For example, in branch 1, you know that 8 milliamps of current is flowing through *both* R_1 and R_2. Why? Notice that both these resistors are connected in *series.* Throughout any series-connected branch, whatever current is flowing in one resistor, flows in all of them. So, whatever current flows in the equivalent resistor R_{eq}, is flowing through all the series resistors that make it up.

You can proceed to calculate the voltage drop across R_1 and R_2 now that you know the current flowing through the top branch.

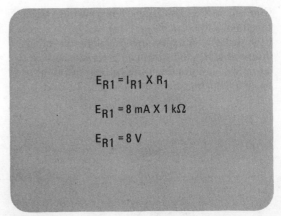

Figure 8.27

Ohm's Law (E_{R1}) — Using Ohm's law, E_{R1} can be found by simply multiplying I_{R1} by R_1 (Figure 8.28). Substituting the circuit values into the equation and completing the mathematics yields 8 milliamps times 1 kilohm, or 8 volts for the voltage across R_1.

Notice that once E_{R1} is known to be 8 volts, the series circuit voltage law may be applied to find E_{R2}. Recall that in a series circuit the sum of the individual voltage drops is equal to the applied voltage. Again recall that the total voltage applied to this branch is 24 volts.

$$E_{R1} = I_{R1} \times R_1$$

$$E_{R1} = 8 \text{ mA} \times 1 \text{ k}\Omega$$

$$E_{R1} = 8 \text{ V}$$

Figure 8.28

- **Series Voltage Formula (E$_{R2}$)**
- **Basic Parallel-Series Circuit**
- **Ohm's Law (E$_{R3}$)**

Series Voltage Formula (E$_{R2}$) — Consequently, E$_{R1}$, which is 8 volts, plus E$_{R2}$ must equal 24 volts. Subtracting 8 volts from 24 volts yields 16 volts, which is the voltage dropped across R$_2$ (Figure 8.29).

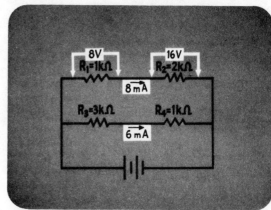

$$E_{R1} + E_{R2} = E_T$$
$$8V + E_{R2} = 24V$$
$$E_{R2} = 24V - 8V$$
$$E_{R2} = 16V$$

Figure 8.29

Basic Parallel-Series Circuit — The same procedure may now be used to calculate the voltage drops across R$_3$ and R$_4$. Previously, it was calculated that 6 milliamps flows through the second branch, and thus flows through R$_3$ and R$_4$ because of their series connection (Figure 8.30).

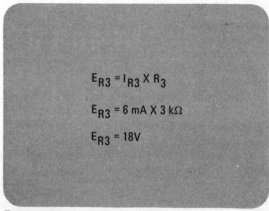

Figure 8.30

Ohm's Law (E$_{R3}$) — Using Ohm's law once again, this time in the form E$_{R3}$ = I$_{R3}$ X R$_3$ (Figure 8.31), you may now calculate the voltage drop across R$_3$. Substituting the resistance and current values into the formula, E$_{R3}$ is found to equal 6 milliamps times 3 kilohms or 18 volts.

$$E_{R3} = I_{R3} \times R_3$$
$$E_{R3} = 6\ mA \times 3\ k\Omega$$
$$E_{R3} = 18V$$

Figure 8.31

- Series Voltage Formula (R$_4$)
- Basic Parallel-Series Circuit
- Automotive Electrical System

Series Voltage Formula (R$_4$) — Now that you know 18 of the 24 volts applied to this branch are dropped across R$_3$, by subtracting E$_{R3}$ (which is 18 volts) from 24 volts, the voltage dropped across R$_4$ may be found. As shown in Figure 8.32, E$_{R4}$ is 6 volts.

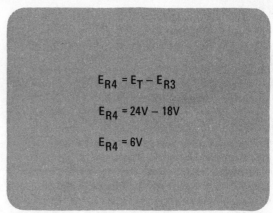

$$E_{R4} = E_T - E_{R3}$$
$$E_{R4} = 24V - 18V$$
$$E_{R4} = 6V$$

Figure 8.32

Basic Parallel-Series Circuit — Through this logical step-by-step procedure, you have seen how the voltage across and current through every component in this circuit can be calculated (Figure 8.33). The technique of circuit reduction, which you have seen illustrated, will become an important part of your "bag of tricks" as you analyze circuits. Why? One reason to learn circuit reduction as applied to parallel-series circuits is because many common electronic circuits you will encounter in your everyday life will have this general configuration. A particularly important example can be found in the typical automobile wiring system.

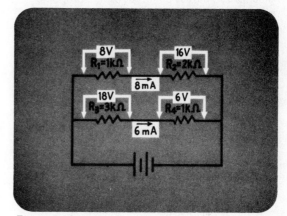

Figure 8.33

Automotive Electrical System — Figure 8.34 shows a schematic diagram of several key parts of an automobile. Notice that in this automotive situation all of the circuit branches are powered by the car's standard 12-volt battery. The branch closest to the battery contains a headlight and a switch. The headlight is designed to operate at 12 volts and will receive the total battery voltage when the switch is closed.

The second branch is a series circuit which contains a spark coil and spark plug, a resistor called a "dropping resistor," and a momentary contact switch which simulates the switching action of the points in an automobile distributor.

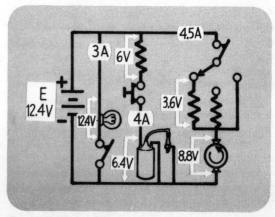

Figure 8.34

Branch 3 consists of a heater fan motor, a fan speed control switch which can be turned to one of three positions, and an on-off switch. Notice that there are resistors connected to two of the three fan speed control switch positions. These resistors are also called "dropping resistors" as is the resistor connected in series with the coil.

The term "dropping resistor" has cropped up quite a bit. Consider the function of these dropping resistors in the circuit. In many automotive applications, devices are designed to operate at a *lower voltage* than the usual 12 volts supplied by the car battery. To enable these devices to operate properly, some other device is needed which will "drop" some of the circuit voltage. This is how the "dropping resistor" got its name. In automotive applications, the dropping resistor value is selected so that when the 12 volts from the battery is applied to the branch, enough voltage is dropped across the resistor to allow a device such as the spark coil to receive the correct voltage.

Automotive Electrical System (Equivalent Schematic) — To simplify this discussion of the automotive electrical system, the circuit pictorial diagram shown in Figure 8.34 can be reduced to an equivalent circuit schematic consisting solely of resistors, as shown in Figure 8.35.

In this schematic the headlight resistance is drawn as a simple resistor in the first branch, and the spark coil is shown as a resistance in series with its dropping resistor in the second branch. In the third branch, the motor resistance is shown connected in series with a speed control dropping resistor. Examining this circuit as a whole, you can recognize this as a parallel-series circuit.

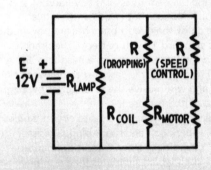

Figure 8.35

Automotive Wiring System — Figure 8.36 shows a drawing of the actual circuit. The 12-volt battery supplies power to branch 1, consisting of the headlamp and its on-off switch, branch 2 which contains the dropping resistor, on-off switch, spark coil, and spark plug. Branch 3 consists of an on-off switch, a three-pole switch, two resistors, and an automobile heater fan motor.

Imagine at this point that you need to analyze this automotive electrical system in detail. You need to calculate the total current it demands, I_T, as well as the individual branch currents, I_1, I_2, and I_3, and the voltage drop across each individual component including the dropping resistors.

When you begin your analysis of the circuit, you know absolutely nothing about it except for the total applied voltage. You will need something more than that, so how do you proceed? In this example, it will be assumed that some of the circuit voltages and currents can be *measured*, while other circuit values will have to be *calculated* using circuit laws. In analyzing or troubleshooting real circuits, you may often have to proceed in this manner. In some cases, you may have a schematic in the auto's service manual showing you generally how various components are wired throughout the car. Some of these actual components may be easily accessible allowing you convenient access for voltage or current measurements. Some components, however, may be quite inaccessible, enclosed in cabinets or in operating positions deep inside your car. As you will see, it is possible to utilize *measurements*, giving you some known values, *combined with* calculations to give information about inaccessible circuit components.

To measure voltages, remember that an appropriate voltmeter must be inserted *across* the circuit component being tested (in parallel with it). For any current values that are needed, the circuit must be broken and an ammeter inserted in *series*, so that the current being measured passes through it. For example, the voltage across the first branch may be easily measured. Notice that the voltage across this branch will be equal to the source voltage since the headlamp is connected in parallel or directly across the battery.

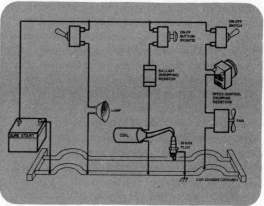

Figure 8.36

Automotive Wiring System — Suppose that the voltage measured across the branch containing lamp, E_L, was 12.4 volts and suppose you needed to find the current flowing through the lamp when it is operating. To do this you must connect an ammeter in series with the lamp. A convenient means of measuring the current would be to connect the ammeter directly across the lamp on-off switch terminals. If the switch is initially open, connecting the meter across its terminals will complete the circuit and allow the full branch current to flow through the ammeter as required for the measurement.

If you performed this measurement in a typical branch of this type containing a single headlamp, as shown in Figure 8.37, you would find that the current flowing through the lamp was about 3 amperes.

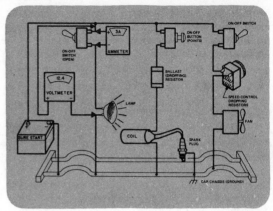

Figure 8.37

Ohm's Law (R_L) — From the two values, 12.4 volts and 3 amps, you may calculate the resistance of the lamp when in operation. Using Ohm's law in the form R equals E over I and substituting your measured values, you have 12.4 volts divided by 3 amps which is equal to 4.13 ohms (Figure 8.38). Incidentally, if you were to measure the resistance of this headlamp directly with an ohmmeter, you would read a significantly lower value for R_L. This is because as the filaments of the bulb heat up, their resistance also increases. So, in order to be accurate, the resistance of the lamp should be calculated while the lamp is operating, rather than measured while it is off.

$$R_L = \frac{E}{I}$$

$$R_L = \frac{12.4 \text{ V}}{3 \text{ A}}$$

$$R_L = 4.13 \ \Omega$$

Figure 8.38

Automotive Wiring System — By applying the rules for a parallel circuit (Figure 8.39), you know that the voltage across branch 2 should be the same as the source vol+age, 12.4 volts. This total voltage applied to branch 2 will be divided between the dropping resistor and the coil. To get a picture of this voltage behavior, the voltage across the dropping resistor can be measured while the coil is in operation. Then once the voltage across the resistor is known, this value may be subtracted from the total voltage applied to the branch, and the remainder is the voltage that is dropped across the coil.

If you were to connect your voltmeter across a typical automotive ballast or dropping resistor while the switch or points were closed, you would typically find that 6 volts are dropped across the resistor.

Knowing that 6 volts are dropped across the ballast resistor, you then know that the remainder of the total voltage applied to the branch is dropped across the ignition coil.

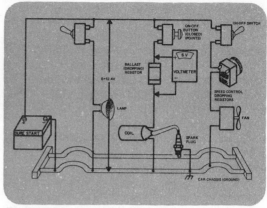

Figure 8.39

Series Voltage Formula — Subtracting the 6 volts dropped across the resistor, E_R from the 12.4 volts applied to the branch, E_T, you would find that a voltage of 6.4 volts is dropped across the coil as shown in the equation in Figure 8.40. Since any branch in this circuit is actually a series circuit, the sum of the individual voltage drops in the branch is equal to the total applied branch voltage.

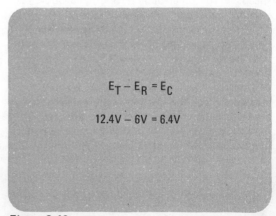

$$E_T - E_R = E_C$$

$$12.4V - 6V = 6.4V$$

Figure 8.40

Automotive Wiring System — Moving on in your measurement and analysis of this circuit, pictured in Figure 8.41, you know that by connecting an ammeter in series with this branch, the branch current can be found. One way to perform this measurement would be to place the ammeter across the open switch, completing the circuit and allowing the total current to flow through the ammeter. Typically, this branch current would read about 4 amps. You would also notice that each time the circuit containing the coil was activated and then deactivated, the spark plug would "spark." This important electronic phenomenon involving sparks and coils is a key effect used in automotive ignition systems, and will be covered in detail in a later lesson.

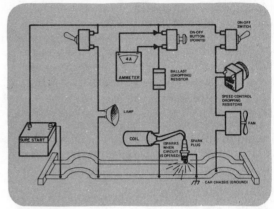

Figure 8.41

Automotive Wiring System — You could employ the same procedures to find the individual voltage drops and branch current in branch 3. Imagine for a moment, however that the heater fan was inside an enclosure that was difficult to get to. A direct voltage measurement in a case like this would require lots of disassembling. In this case, instead of measuring the voltage drop across the motor, you could calculate it after making some other measurements in the circuit. Assume that the fan motor speed control is set in the medium speed position as you begin your work (Figure 8.42).

First of all, the total branch current may be found by connecting your ammeter across the open on-off switch, thus completing the circuit. With one type of typical fan motor and motor speed control (on medium setting), you would read a branch current in the neighborhood of 4.5 amps.

While the ammeter is still connected, you could vary the setting of the motor speed control and observe its effect on current flow in this branch. You should note that when a larger value of dropping resistance is switched in, the motor slows down and the ammeter reads a lower value. When a smaller value of resistance is selected, the motor speeds up and the ammeter indicates that more current is flowing.

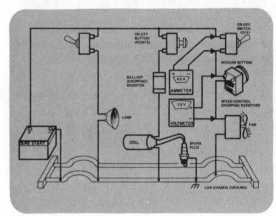

Figure 8.42

With the motor speed switch set at its medium speed position, the smaller of the two dropping resistors is in operation. In typical circuit situations, you may measure 3.6 volts dropped across this resistor. Units of this type may be mounted right behind your dashboard and be fairly accessible for measurement.

Series Voltage Formula — Since the total branch voltage is known, the voltage dropped across the speed control resistor can be subtracted from the total voltage, and the remainder will be the voltage dropped across the motor. As shown in Figure 8.43, 12.4 volts minus 3.6 volts gives a voltage of 8.8 volts across the motor.

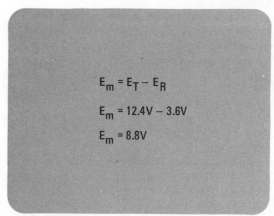

$$E_m = E_T - E_R$$

$$E_m = 12.4V - 3.6V$$

$$E_m = 8.8V$$

Figure 8.43

Automotive Wiring System — At this point and shown in Figure 8.44, the voltage drop across each component in this automotive circuit is known along with all of the branch currents. The total or main line current the battery is providing to this circuit may be found by simply adding the individual branch currents.

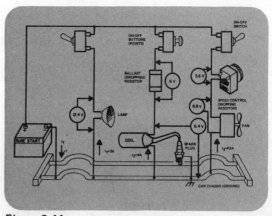

Figure 8.44

Parallel Current Formula — Using the formula for finding main line currents shown in Figure 8.45, add 3 amps of current flowing in branch 1, 4 amps flowing in branch 2, and 4.5 amps flowing through branch 3. The total current flowing in the circuit is 11.5 amps.

Your analysis of this automotive circuit example is now complete. All the voltage drops have been found, the branch currents have been measured and added together to find the total current. This example illustrates a common technique used in analyzing actual circuits. Some circuit values were first measured and then by applying the three laws governing series circuits, the three laws governing parallel circuits, and Ohm's law, the other needed values were calculated.

If you keep the laws governing series and parallel circuits firmly in your mind and practice, you will encounter little difficulty as you move on the more complex circuit.

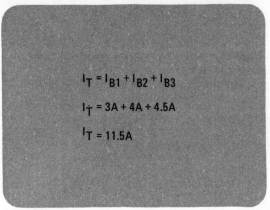

$$I_T = I_{B1} + I_{B2} + I_{B3}$$

$$I_T = 3A + 4A + 4.5A$$

$$I_T = 11.5A$$

Figure 8.45

As you have seen, your automobile is a good place to learn about dc electricity and to get some practice in handling and studying dc circuits. In a way, your car is like your own private dc circuits lab, and many laboratory and circuit analysis techniques can be learned and practiced right in your car. Be sure, as always, to use *extreme caution* when working with automotive circuitry. Also, please realize that the circuit studied in this lesson presents only part of what is happening in the average automobile electrical system, and the measured values shown in this example were only *typical* values. Actual circuit voltages and currents will vary from car to car as you might expect.

Details on automotive wiring are discussed in further detail in automotive shop manuals and repair texts that are available. You will find that most of the electrical systems in your car, gauges, charging, starting, ignition, etc., involve the basic principles of parallel-series circuit analysis that have been discussed in this lesson. Also, keep in mind that on most cars the frame or body of the car forms part of all electrical circuits completing the circuit path to the battery. This "chassis ground" is usually connected to the *negative* battery terminal in most American cars.

Before completing this lesson, one more circuit will be analyzed for you in detail. This circuit will put you through some different types of analyses and manipulation than before, but you will still be using the old standby, Ohm's law and the laws governing series and parallel circuits. This circuit, unlike the first you analyzed, will have a variety of unknown quantities and will be presented in a slightly different schematic form.

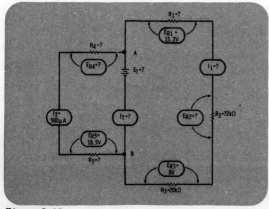

Figure 8.46

Parallel-Series Circuit — The circuit in Figure 8.46 is clearly a little different looking than those you have handled previously. The voltage source is drawn in the center of the circuit, and the branches are drawn around to either side of it. By now you should be able to recognize this as a parallel-series circuit with two branches, and you should be able to redraw this circuit if you desire in a more familiar form. Notice that the total potential difference is applied to points A and B and from there to each branch. If you can imagine for a moment that the wires in this circuit were as flexible as rubber bands, you could take the left-hand branch and stretch it back up and over the voltage source to the right of the right-hand branch without changing any circuit connections.

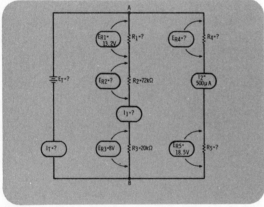

Figure 8.47

Equivalent Parallel-Series Circuit — The circuit drawn in Figure 8.46 is entirely identical to the more recognizable one shown in Figure 8.47. The knack of redrawing circuits such as this comes easily with practice and can greatly simplify complicated looking circuits into simpler ones. Doing the practice problems included at the end of this lesson will help you learn this.

Examine the known and unknown quantities in this circuit. In branch 1, the voltage across R_1 is known, but its value in ohms is not. The value of R_2 is known, but you do not know the voltage across R_2. Both the voltage across and the resistance of R_3 are known.

The branch current in the second branch is known to be 500 microamps, and the voltage across R_5 is also known. Nothing else is given. Where do you go from here? Focus your attention on the left-hand branch of this circuit and look for a component about which two values are known so that you can apply Ohm's law. R_3 fits this description. The voltage across it and its resistance value are known and thus you can use Ohm's law to find the current through it.

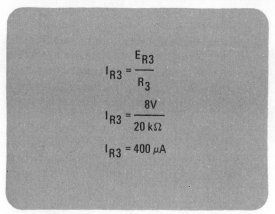

$$I_{R3} = \frac{E_{R3}}{R_3}$$

$$I_{R3} = \frac{8V}{20\ k\Omega}$$

$$I_{R3} = 400\ \mu A$$

Figure 8.48

Ohm's Law — Using Ohm's law in the form I equals E divided by R and substituting the known values for R_3, 8 volts divided by 20 kilohms yields a calculated current flowing through R_3 of 400 microamps as you can see in Figure 8.48.

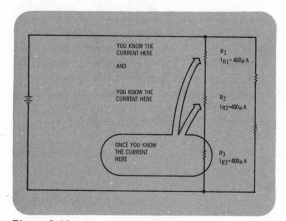

Figure 8.49

Series Current Analysis — The law for current behavior in series circuits says that current is the *same* at all points in a series circuit. Notice in Figure 8.49 that R_1, and R_2 and R_3 are all in series. Once you know the current flowing through any of these resistors, you know that the same current is flowing throughout that branch. You know 400 microamps are flowing in R_3, so you also know that the current flowing throughout branch 1 is 400 microamps. This now enables you to find the voltage across R_2, because you know that 400 microamps is flowing through R_2, and R_2 has an ohmic value of 72 kilohms.

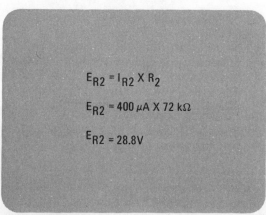

$$E_{R2} = I_{R2} \times R_2$$

$$E_{R2} = 400\ \mu A \times 72\ k\Omega$$

$$E_{R2} = 28.8V$$

Figure 8.50

Ohm's Law (E_{R2}) — The voltage across R_2 can be calculated using Ohm's law in the form E_{R2} equals the current in branch 1 times the value of R_2, which is 400 microamps times 72 kilohms which yields a voltage value of 28.8 volts as shown in Figure 8.50. With this voltage calculated, you now know the voltage drop for each resistor in branch 1.

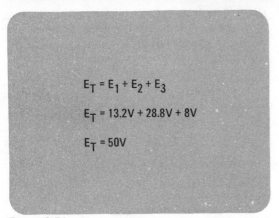

$$E_T = E_1 + E_2 + E_3$$

$$E_T = 13.2V + 28.8V + 8V$$

$$E_T = 50V$$

Figure 8.51

Series Circuit Voltage Law — Recall that the voltage law for series circuits says that the sum of the individual voltage drops in any series circuit equals the total applied voltage. Branch 1 is itself a series circuit. By adding the individual voltage drops, as shown in Figure 8.51, the total voltage across branch 1 is calculated to be 50 volts.

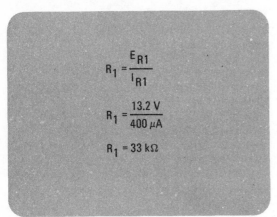

$$R_1 = \frac{E_{R1}}{I_{R1}}$$

$$R_1 = \frac{13.2\ V}{400\ \mu A}$$

$$R_1 = 33\ k\Omega$$

Figure 8.52

Ohm's Law (R_1) — The only unknown quantity remaining in the first branch is R_1. Using Ohm's law in the form R =E/I, R_1 may be calculated since you know that 13.2 volts is dropped across R_1, and 400 microamps are flowing through it. Working this problem out as shown in Figure 8.52, 13.2 volts divided by 400 microamps gives 33 kilohms of resistance for the value of R_1.

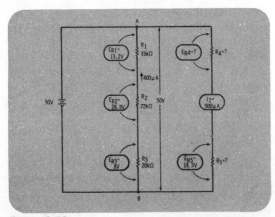

Figure 8.53

Parallel-Series Circuit: Branch 2 — In moving from one parallel branch to another, keep in mind the voltage law for parallel circuits which states that the voltage across all of the branches in any parallel circuit is the same.

Since you know there are 50 volts across branch 1, as illustrated in Figure 8.53, there must also be a 50-volt drop across branch 2. In fact, 50 volts must be the total voltage applied to this circuit by the battery or power supply.

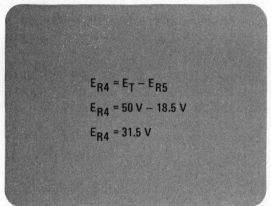

$$E_{R4} = E_T - E_{R5}$$

$$E_{R4} = 50\,V - 18.5\,V$$

$$E_{R4} = 31.5\,V$$

Figure 8.54

Calculation of E_{R4} — Since you know that there are 50 volts across branch 2 and 18.5 volts across R_5, you can readily solve for the voltage across R_4 (Figure 8.54). For a series branch such as this one, you know that the total applied voltage, $E_T = $ 50 volts, equals the sum of individual voltage drops. One of the voltage drops, E_{R5}, is 18.5 volts, so the other, E_{R4}, must equal $E_T - E_{R5}$, which is 50 minus 18.5 or 31.5 volts.

$$R_4 = \frac{E_{R4}}{I_{R4}}$$

$$R_4 = \frac{31.5V}{500\,\mu A}$$

$$R_4 = 63\,k\Omega$$

Figure 8.55

Ohm's Law (R_4) — You can proceed to solve for the resistance value of R_4, as shown in Figure 8.55, because the voltage across it and the current through it are known. This time you will use Ohm's law in the form R equals E over I. Substituting the known voltage and current values into the formula yields 31.5 volts divided by 500 microamps which gives a calculated resistance of 63 kilohms for R_4.

$$R_5 = \frac{E_{R5}}{I_2}$$

$$R_5 = \frac{18.5\,V}{500\,\mu A}$$

$$R_5 = 37\,k\Omega$$

Figure 8.56

Ohm's Law (R_5) — R_5 may now be calculated quite easily. Using R = E/I and substituting the known values E_{R5} = 18.5 volts and I_2 = 500 microamps, as shown in Figure 8.56, R_5 is calculated as 37 kilohms.

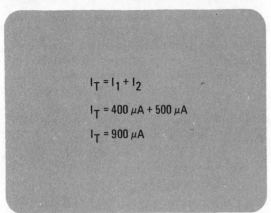

$$I_T = I_1 + I_2$$

$$I_T = 400\,\mu A + 500\,\mu A$$

$$I_T = 900\,\mu A$$

Figure 8.57

Parallel Current Formula — Now you know all there is to know about each one of the individual branches, so it will be easy to calculate the total amount of current flowing in the circuit. Use the law for parallel current which says "the sum of the individual branch currents equals the total current" in formula form, I_T equals I_1 plus I_2 (Figure 8.57). Substituting the branch currents into the formula and adding these together, 900 microamps of total current is found to be flowing in this circuit.

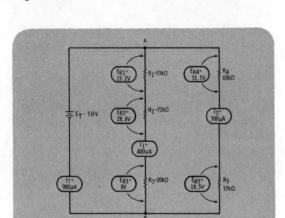

Figure 8.58

Analyzed Parallel-Series Circuit — The fully analyzed circuit with all of the known values inserted is shown in Figure 8.58 for your reference. With several of these circuit analyses behind you and the practice provided by the problems at the end of this lesson, you should be able to carry out a detailed analysis on any circuit of this type.

As you see, there are several alternative ways to proceed through each calculation and the best way to really learn how to use them is to practice these techniques.

As has been mentioned, at the end of this lesson there are several practice problems designed to enable you to really learn and practice the methods.

If you should get bogged down, there are also several additional worked through examples showing how to solve these circuits.

Procedural Steps for Parallel-Series Circuits — This lesson has shown you how to use the laws governing series and parallel circuits along with Ohm's law to analyze *parallel-series* circuits (Figure 8.59). The technique of circuit reduction was also introduced, and you have a bit of practice behind you in that area.

Basically, when you first encounter a parallel-series circuit problem, carefully examine the known or given values on the schematic and then clearly mark those circuit values that you need to calculate. Focus your attention on each circuit component and what is *known* about it. From this you may be able to draw some immediate conclusions.

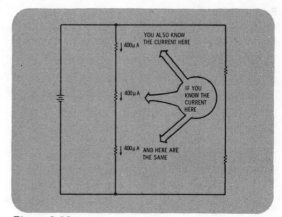

Figure 8.59

Current Through Series Resistors — As an example, see Figure 8.60. If a resistor is in a series branch and the current through it is known, then the same current flows through all resistors in that branch because of the law for currents in a series circuit.

Figure 8.60

Voltage in Parallel — Remember also that once the voltage across any one complete branch is known, the parallel circuit voltage laws say that the same voltage must also be dropped across all of the circuit branches. This is shown in Figure 8.61.

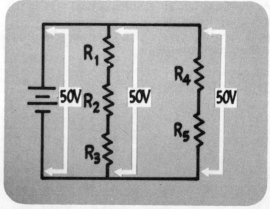

Figure 8.61

Total Current Methods — Also recall that the total or main line current in a parallel-series circuit is the sum of all of the branch currents and is also equal to the applied circuit voltage divided by the circuit's equivalent resistance. This equation is shown in Figure 8.62.

$$I_T = I_{B1} + I_{B2} + \ldots$$

$$= \frac{E_a}{R_{eq}}$$

Figure 8.62

Parallel-Series Circuit — The equivalent resistance may be found for a circuit such as the one in Figure 8.63 by systematically applying the method of circuit reduction.

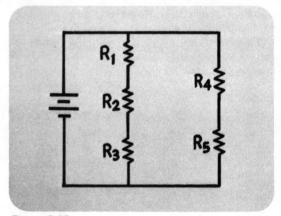

Figure 8.63

Parallel-Series Circuit (First Reduction) — First, reduce *each series branch* to a single resistance value using the rules for adding resistances in series as shown in Figure 8.64.

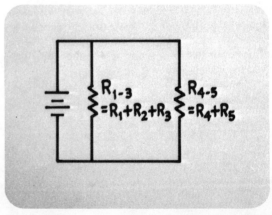

Figure 8.64

Parallel-Series Circuit (Second Reduction) — Then *combine the parallel branch resistances* into a single equivalent resistance using the reciprocal formula, product-over-sum formula, or other appropriate technique as shown in Figure 8.65.

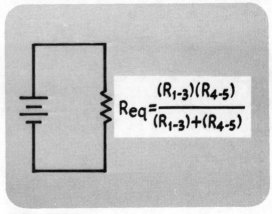

Figure 8.65

Power in Parallel-Series Circuits — Consider how to calculate the *total power dissipated* in the parallel-series circuit shown in Figure 8.66. You will find that in all dc resistive circuits power is an additive quantity. Each resistor in any circuit dissipates a certain amount of power, and to find the total power dissipated, you simply add all these individual power dissipations.

Alternatively, once a circuit has been fully analyzed, such as the circuit in the illustration, you can use the total circuit values E_T, I_T, and R_T in one of the three power formulas you have been given, and you will obtain the same result for the power dissipated.

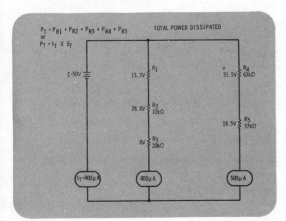

Figure 8.66

$$P = I \times E$$
$$P_{R1} = I_{R1} \times E_{R1} = (400 \times 10^{-6})(13.2)$$
$$= 5.28 \text{ MILLIWATTS}$$
$$P_{R2} = 11.52 \text{ mW}$$
$$P_{R3} = 3.2 \text{ mW}$$
$$P_{R4} = 15.8 \text{ mW}$$
$$P_{R5} = \underline{9.25 \text{ mW}}$$
$$P_T = 45.1 \text{ mW}$$
$$\text{OR}$$
$$P_T = I_T \times E_T = (900 \times 10^{-6})(50) = 45 \text{ mW}$$

Figure 8.67

Example — In the circuit of Figure 8.66 you could apply the formula $P = I \times E$ to each resistor as shown in Figure 8.67. Adding all the powers dissipated by each resistor yields a total dissipated power of 45.1 milliwatts. Alternatively, applying the formula $P_T = E_T \times I_T$ and substituting the total circuit values of 900 microamps and 50 volts, you obtain approximately 45 milliwatts.

• **Worked Through Examples**

1. Solve for all voltages and currents in the circuit shown below.

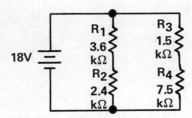

First of all, you need to simplify or reduce the circuit in order to find its equivalent resistance. The values of resistors R_1 and R_2 may be added since they are connected in series, 3.6 kilohms plus 2.4 kilohms is equal to 6.0 kilohms. This means that resistors R_1 and R_2 can be replaced by an equivalent resistance, $R_{1\text{-}2}$ equal to 6 kilohms. The same procedure may be followed with resistors R_3 and R_4. When 1.5 kilohms and 7.5 kilohms are added, you get an equivalent resistance, $R_{3\text{-}4}$ equal to 9.0 kilohms. The circuit redrawn to include these two equivalent resistances appears as shown below.

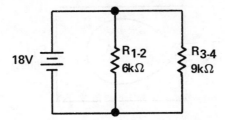

The circuit now appears as a simple parallel circuit. $R_{1\text{-}2}$ and $R_{3\text{-}4}$ may be combined using one of the parallel resistance formulas. This time the produce-over-the-sum formula will be used.

$$R_T = \frac{R_{1\text{-}2} \times R_{3\text{-}4}}{R_{1\text{-}2} + R_{3\text{-}4}}$$

Substitute the circuit values into the formula in powers of ten form:

$$R_T = \frac{6 \times 10^3 \times 9 \times 10^3}{(6 \times 10^3) + (9 \times 10^3)}$$

Multiply and add:

$$R_T = \frac{54 \times 10^6}{15 + 10^3}$$

Now divide:

$$R_T = \frac{54 \times 10^{6\text{-}3}}{15}$$

$$R_T = \frac{54 \times 10^3}{15}$$

$$R_T = 3.6 \times 10^3 = 3{,}600 \; \Omega$$

The total equivalent resistance of this circuit is 3,600 ohms. Now that you know the total equivalent resistance and the total applied voltage, Ohm's law may be used to find the total current flowing in this circuit.

$$I_T = E_T/R_{eq}$$

$$I_T = 18 \; V/3{,}600 \; \Omega$$

$$I_T = 0.005 \; A = 5 \; mA$$

The equivalent circuit now looks like this:

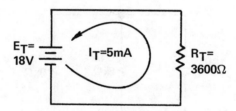

Now, an important point, back up a step. Draw the circuit as it appeared just before the final equivalent resistance was found. The circuit will look like this:

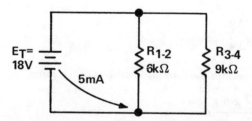

The total circuit current flows to the junction of the two resistances and splits. Some amount of current flows through the 9-kilohm resistance, and the rest flows through the other resistance. How can the exact amounts be found? This question is answered simply by applying the parallel circuit rule that says, "The voltage is the same across all branches of a parallel circuit." Since resistances $R_{1\text{-}2}$ and $R_{3\text{-}4}$ are connected in parallel with the source voltage, the voltage across them will be the same as the source voltage, 18 volts. Ohm's law may now be used to calculate the current flowing through each branch of the circuit.

For branch 1:

$$I_{1\text{-}2} = E_{1\text{-}2}/R_{1\text{-}2}$$

$$I_{1\text{-}2} = 18 \text{ V}/6 \text{ k}\Omega$$

$$I_{1\text{-}2} = 3 \text{ mA}$$

At this point, one of two approaches may be taken to arrive at the value of current flowing through $R_{3\text{-}4}$. Ohm's law may be used again, or a circuit law may be employed. This time, the circuit law that says "The total current in a parallel circuit is equal to the sum of the individual branch currents," will be used. The total current is equal to 5 milliamps. If 3 milliamps flow through branch 1 ($R_{1\text{-}2}$), then the rest of the current, 2 milliamps, must be flowing through the second branch ($R_{3\text{-}4}$). In formula form, the law appears like this:

$$I_T = I_{1\text{-}2} + I_{3\text{-}4}$$

To find $I_{3\text{-}4}$, $I_{1\text{-}2}$ must be subtracted from both sides of the equation to produce:

$$I_T - I_{1\text{-}2} = I_{1\text{-}2} + I_{3\text{-}4} - I_{1\text{-}2}$$

$$I_T - I_{1\text{-}2} = I_{3\text{-}4}$$

Now plug the correct values into the formula:

$$5 \text{ mA} - 3 \text{ mA} = I_{3\text{-}4}$$

$$2 \text{ mA} = I_{3\text{-}4}$$

Therefore, 2 milliamps of current flow through the resistance $R_{3\text{-}4}$. Label these current values on the original schematic.

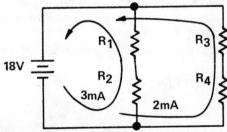

Since the current flowing through and the resistance of each resistor is known, Ohm's law may be used to find the voltage dropped across each individual resistor. R_1 is equal to 3.6 kilohms. I_1 is 3 milliamps. Ohm's law in the form $E = I \times R$ may be used to solve this problem.

$$E_{R1} = I_{R1} \times R_1$$

$$E_{R1} = 3 \text{ mA} \times 3.6 \text{ k}\Omega$$

$$E_{R1} = 3 \times 10^{-3} \times 3.6 \times 10^{+3}$$

$$E_{R1} = 10.8 \text{ V}$$

The same procedure may be used to find E_{R2}, or a circuit law may be employed. You know that in a series circuit ($R_1 + R_2$ are in series with each other) the sum of the individual voltage drops is equal to the source voltage. Written in formula form:

$$E_{R1} + E_{R2} = E_T$$

To find E_{R2}, E_{R1} must be subtracted from both sides of the equation producing:

$$E_{R1} + E_{R2} - E_{R1} = E_T - E_{R1}$$
$$E_{R2} = E_T - E_{R1}$$

Substitute in the circuit values:

$$E_{R2} = 18 \text{ V} - 10.8 \text{ V}$$
$$E_{R2} = 7.2 \text{ V}$$

The same procedure will be followed in solving for E_{R3} and E_{R4}. First E_{R3} may be found by using Ohm's law. R_3 is known to be 1.5 kilohms. The current flowing through R_3 is 2 milliamps. Substitute these values into an Ohm's law formula and solve for E_{R3}.

$$E_{R3} = I_{R3} \times R_3$$
$$E_{R3} = 2 \text{ mA} \times 1.5 \text{ k}\Omega$$
$$E_{R3} = 2 \times 10^{-3} \times 1.5 \times 10^{+3}$$
$$E_{R3} = 3.0 \text{ V}$$

You know that 3 volts are dropped across resistor R_3. The rest of the 18 volts applied to this branch must be dropped across R_4. The voltage equation may be rearranged to solve this problem by subtracting the known value of E_{R3} from both sides:

$$E_T = E_{R3} + E_{R4}$$
$$-E_{R3} + E_T = E_{R3} + E_{R4} - E_{R3}$$
$$-E_{R3} + E_T = E_{R4}$$

Substitute in the circuit values and subtract:

$$-3 \text{ V} + 18 \text{ V} = E_{R4}$$
$$15 \text{ V} = E_{R4}$$

Place all known values on the schematic, and the circuit analysis is complete.

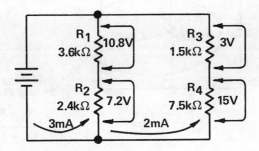

2. Solve for all of the voltages and currents in the following circuit.

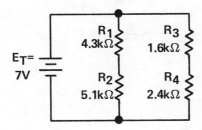

Since this circuit has the same configuration as the last example the same analysis methods will be employed in abbreviated form.

First, reduce or simplify the circuit to its equivalent resistance.

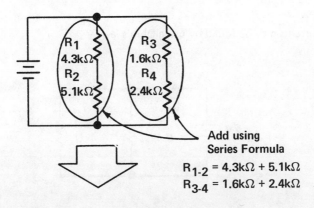

Add using
Series Formula

$R_{1-2} = 4.3k\Omega + 5.1k\Omega$
$R_{3-4} = 1.6k\Omega + 2.4k\Omega$

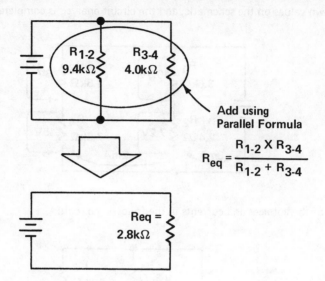

Add using
Parallel Formula

$$R_{eq} = \frac{R_{1-2} \times R_{3-4}}{R_{1-2} + R_{3-4}}$$

Req =
2.8kΩ

Find I_T by using Ohm's law:

$$I_T = E_T/R_{eq}$$

$$I_T = 7 \text{ V}/2.8 \text{ k}\Omega$$

$$I_T = \frac{7.0 \times 10^0}{2.8 \times 10^{+3}}$$

$$I_T = \frac{7.0 \times 10^{-3}}{2.8}$$

$$I_T = 2.5 \times 10^{-3} = 2.5 \text{ mA}$$

The branch currents may be found by using Ohm's law.

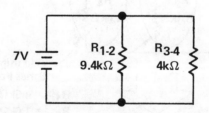

$$I_{R1\text{-}2} = \frac{E_{R1\text{-}2}}{R_{1\text{-}2}}$$

$$I_{R1\text{-}2} = \frac{7\ V}{9.4\ k\Omega}$$

$$I_{R1\text{-}2} = \frac{7 \times 10^0}{9.4 \times 10^{+3}}$$

$$I_{R1\text{-}2} = \frac{7 \times 10^{-3}}{9.4 \times 10}$$

$$I_{R1\text{-}2} = 0.745 \times 10^{-3} = 0.745\ mA$$

$$I_{R3\text{-}4} = \frac{E_{R3\text{-}4}}{R_{3\text{-}4}}$$

$$I_{R3\text{-}4} = \frac{7\ V}{4\ k\Omega} = \frac{7 \times 10^0}{4 \times 10^3}$$

$$I_{R3\text{-}4} = \frac{7 \times 10^{0\text{-}3}}{4}$$

$$I_{R3\text{-}4} = 1.75 \times 10^{-3}$$

$$I_{R3\text{-}4} = 1.75\ mA$$

Now that the branch currents are known, the individual voltage drops may be calculated using Ohm's law.

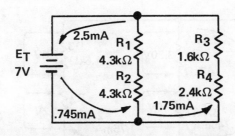

Ohm's law:

$$E_{R1} = I_{R1} \times R_1$$

$$E_{R1} = 0.745 \text{ mA} \times 4.3 \text{ k}\Omega$$

$$E_{R1} = 0.745 \times 10^{-3} \times 4.3 \times 10^{+3}$$

$$E_{R1} = 3.20 \text{ V}$$

$$E_{R2} = I_{R2} \times R_2$$

$$E_{R2} = 0.745 \text{ mA} \times 5.1 \text{ k}\Omega$$

$$E_{R2} = 0.745 \times 10^{-3} \times 5.1 \times 10^{+3}$$

$$E_{R2} = 4.0 \text{ V}$$

Moving to the right-hand branch, and again using Ohm's law:

$$E_{R3} = I_{R3} \times R_3$$

$$E_{R3} = 1.75 \text{ mA} \times 1.6 \text{ k}\Omega$$

$$E_{R3} = 1.75 \times 10^{-3} \times 1.6 \times 10^{+3}$$

$$E_{R3} = 2.8 \text{ V}$$

$$E_{R4} = I_{R4} \times R_4$$

$$E_{R4} = 1.75 \text{ mA} \times 2.4 \text{ k}\Omega$$

$$E_{R4} = 1.75 \times 10^{-3} \times 2.4 \times 10^{+3}$$

$$E_{R4} = 4.2 \text{ V}$$

Placing these values on the circuit schematic, the analysis is complete.

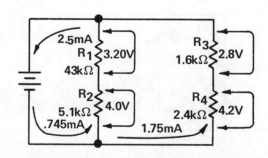

LESSON 8. PARALLEL-SERIES CIRCUITS

• **Practice Problems**

The key objective of this lesson has been achieved if you can solve for the total resistance of any parallel-series circuit using the techniques of circuit reduction, and if given any parallel-series circuit schematic with known values labeled, you can solve for any unknowns required. The following problems are designed to give you practice in both of these areas. Check your progress and accuracy by folding over the page as indicated.

Depending upon the approach you use in solving these problems and how you round off intermediate results, your answers may vary slightly from those given here. However, any differences you encounter should only occur in the third significant digit of your answer. If the first two significant digits of your answers do not agree with those given here, recheck your calculations.

1. Find the total equivalent resistance, R_{eq}, for each of these circuits.   **Fold Over**

a.

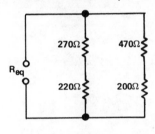

R_{eq} = _____

b.

R_{eq} = _____

c.

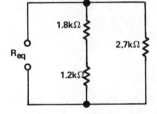

R_{eq} = _____

d.

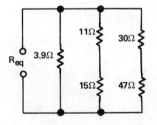

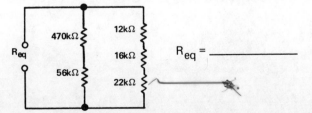

R_{eq} = _____

8-43

Answers

1.a. 283 Ω

1.b. 1.42 kΩ

1.c. 3.2 Ω

1.d. 45.7 kΩ

1. (Continued)   **Fold Over**

e.

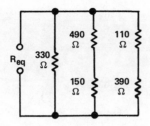

$R_{eq} = $ _____

f.

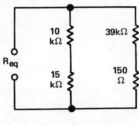

$R_{eq} = $ _____

g.

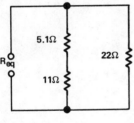

$R_{eq} = $ _____

h.

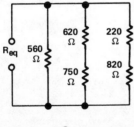

$R_{eq} = $ _____

i.

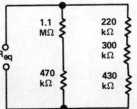

$R_{eq} = $ _____

Answers

1.e. 152 Ω

1.f. 15.3 kΩ

1.g. 9.29 Ω

1.h. 287 Ω

1.i. 591 kΩ

- **Practice Problems**

1. (Continued)

Fold Over

j.

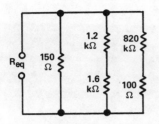

R_{eq} = _____

k.

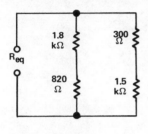

R_{eq} = _____

l.

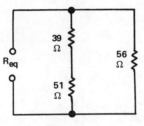

R_{eq} = _____

m.

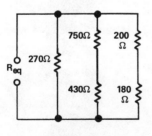

R_{eq} = _____

n.

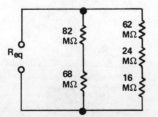

R_{eq} = _____

Answers

1.j. 142 Ω

1.k. 1.06 kΩ

1.l. 34.5 Ω

1.m. 139 Ω

1.n. 60.7 MΩ

1. (Continued)   **Fold Over**

o.

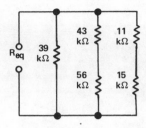

R_{eq} = _____

2.   In each of the following circuits, calculate the voltage across and current
     through each resistor as well as the circuit's total current, total resistance,
     and total power dissipation.

a.

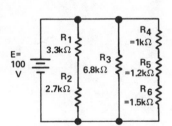

E_{R1} = _____ I_{R1} = _____

E_{R2} = _____ I_{R2} = _____

E_{R3} = _____ I_{R3} = _____

E_{R4} = _____ I_{R4} = _____

E_{R5} = _____ I_{R5} = _____

E_{R6} = _____ I_{R6} = _____

I_T =   _____

R_T =   _____

P_T =   _____

b.

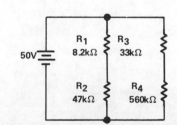

E_{R1} = _____ I_{R1} = _____

E_{R2} = _____ I_{R2} = _____

E_{R3} = _____ I_{R3} = _____

E_{R4} = _____ I_{R4} = _____

I_T =   _____

R_T =   _____

P_T =   _____

Answers

1.o. 13.5 kΩ

2.a. E_{R1} = 54.9 V I_{R1} = 16.7 mA

    E_{R2} = 45.1 V I_{R2} = 16.7 mA

    E_{R3} = 100 V I_{R3} = 14.7 mA

    E_{R4} = 27 V I_{R4} = 27.0 mA

    E_{R5} = 32.4 V I_{R5} = 27.0 mA

    E_{R6} = 40.5 V I_{R6} = 27.0 mA

    I_T = 58.4 mA

    R_T = 1.71 kΩ

    P_T = 5.84 W

2.b. E_{R1} = 7.43 V I_{R1} = 906 μA

    E_{R2} = 42.6 V I_{R2} = 906 μA

    E_{R3} = 2.78 V I_{R3} = 84.3 μA

    E_{R4} = 47.2 V I_{R4} = 84.3 μA

    I_T = 990 μA

    R_T = 50.5 kΩ

    P_T = 49.5 mW

2. (Continued)

c.

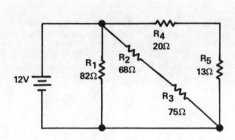

$E_{R1} =$ _____ $I_{R1} =$ _____

$E_{R2} =$ _____ $I_{R2} =$ _____

$E_{R3} =$ _____ $I_{R3} =$ _____

$E_{R4} =$ _____ $I_{R4} =$ _____

$E_{R5} =$ _____ $I_{R5} =$ _____

$I_T =$ _____

$R_T =$ _____

$P_T =$ _____

d.

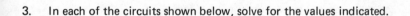

$E_{R1} =$ _____ $I_{R1} =$ _____

$E_{R2} =$ _____ $I_{R2} =$ _____

$E_{R3} =$ _____ $I_{R3} =$ _____

$E_{R4} =$ _____ $I_{R4} =$ _____

$E_{R5} =$ _____ $I_{R5} =$ _____

$I_T =$ _____

$R_T =$ _____

$P_T =$ _____

3. In each of the circuits shown below, solve for the values indicated.

a.

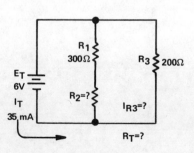

$R_T =$ _____

$R_2 =$ _____

$I_{R3} =$ _____

Answers

2.c. $E_{R1} = +12$ V $I_{R1} = 146$ mA

   $E_{R2} = 5.71$ V $I_{R2} = 83.9$ mA

   $E_{R3} = 6.29$ V $I_{R3} = 83.9$ mA

   $E_{R4} = 7.28$ V $I_{R4} = 364$ mA

   $E_{R5} = 4.73$ V $I_{R5} = 364$ mA

   $I_T = 594$ mA

   $R_T = 20.2$ Ω

   $P_T = 7.13$ W

2.d. $E_{R1} = 17.7$ V $I_{R1} = 31.6$ mA

   $E_{R2} = 12.3$ V $I_{R2} = 31.6$ mA

   $E_{R3} = 30$ V $I_{R3} = 136$ mA

   $E_{R4} = 6.1$ V $I_{R4} = 50.8$ mA

   $E_{R5} = 23.9$ V $I_{R5} = 50.8$ mA

   $I_T = 218.8$ mA

   $R_T = 137$ Ω

   $P_T = 6.55$ W

3.a. $R_T = 171$ Ω

   $R_2 = 900$ Ω

   $I_{R3} = 30$ mA

3. (Continued)   Fold Over

b.

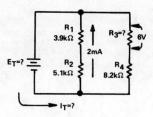

$E_T =$ _____

$I_T =$ _____

$R_3 =$ _____

c.

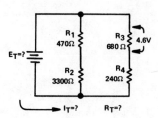

$E_T =$ _____

$I_T =$ _____

$R_T =$ _____

d.

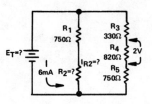

$E_T =$ _____

$R_2 =$ _____

$I_{R2} =$ _____

e.

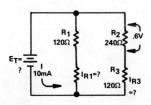

$E_T =$ _____

$I_{R1} =$ _____

$I_{R3} =$ _____

f.

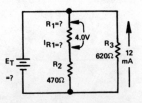

$E_T =$ _____

$I_{R1} =$ _____

$R_1 =$ _____

Answers

3.b. $E_T = 18$ V

     $I_T = 3.46$ mA

     $R_3 = 4.1$ kΩ

3.c. $E_T = 6.22$ V

     $I_T = 8.42$ mA

     $R_T = 739.5$ Ω

3.d. $E_T = 4.64$ V

     $R_2 = 550$ Ω

     $I_{R2} = 3.56$ mA

3.e. $E_T = 900$ mV

     $I_{R1} = 7.5$ mA

     $I_{R3} = 2.5$ mA

3.f. $E_T = 7.44$ V

     $I_{R1} = 7.32$ mA

     $R_1 = 546$ Ω

3. (Continued)   **Fold Over**

g.

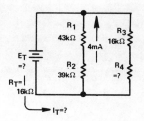

E_T = _____

I_T = _____

R_4 = _____

h.

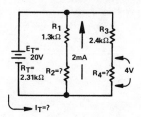

R_2 = _____

R_4 = _____

I_T = _____

i.

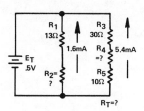

R_2 = _____

R_4 = _____

R_T = _____

j.

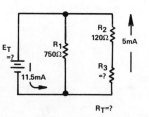

E_T = _____

R_T = _____

R_3 = _____

Answers

3.g. E_T = 328 V

I_T = 20.5 mA

R_4 = 3.87 kΩ

3.h. R_2 = 8.7 kΩ

R_4 = 600 Ω

I_T = 8.66 mA

3.i. R_2 = 300 Ω

R_4 = 52.6 Ω

R_T = 71.4 Ω

3.j. E_T = 4.87 V

R_T = 424 Ω

R_3 = 854 Ω

LESSON 8 — QUIZ

Identify the following circuits as being series (S), parallel (P), series-parallel (SP), or parallel-series (PS).

1.

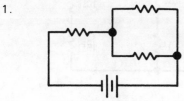

_____

2.

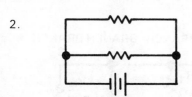

_____

3.

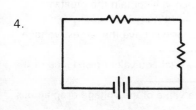

_____

4.

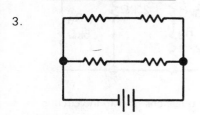

_____

5.

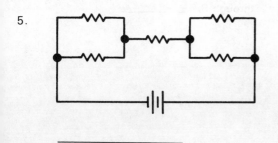

_____

6.

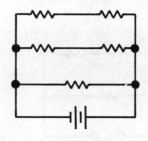

_____

7.

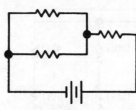

_____

8.

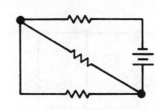

_____

9.

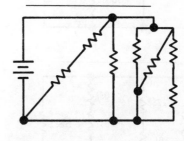

_____

10.

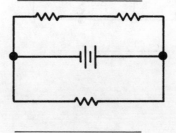

_____

Calculate Rfor the following circuits:

11.

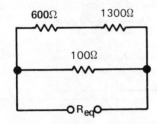

600Ω   1300Ω

100Ω

R_eq

_____

12.

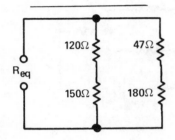

120Ω   47Ω

R_eq

150Ω   180Ω

_____

13.

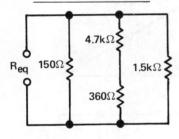

4.7kΩ

R_eq   150Ω   1.5kΩ

360Ω

_____

14.

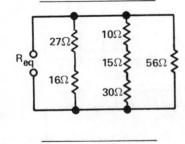

27Ω   10Ω

R_eq

16Ω   15Ω   56Ω

30Ω

_____

15.

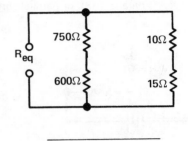

750Ω   10Ω

R_eq

600Ω   15Ω

_____

BRANCH   BRANCH   BRANCH
   1   2   3

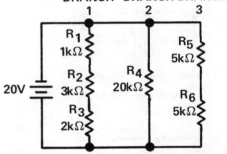

20V

R_1 1kΩ   R_5 5kΩ
R_2 3kΩ   R_4 20kΩ   R_6 5kΩ
R_3 2kΩ

The following questions refer to the circuits above.

16. Which branch will contain the greatest amount of current?_____

17. Which resistor will have the largest voltage drop?_____

18. What is the total equivalent resistance of the circuit?_____

19. What is the value of the voltage drop across R_6_____

20. What is the value of the current flowing through R_4?_____

8-58

Lesson 9
Series-Parallel Circuits

This lesson will deal with the recognition and description of series-parallel circuits. The student will also learn to recognize series and parallel circuit configurations when they are part of larger, more complex circuits. The laws governing series and parallel circuits will be used to solve more complex circuits by applying them to one circuit segment at a time.

LESSON 9. SERIES-PARALLEL CIRCUITS

● **Objectives**

1. Given a series of schematics, *select* which represents series, parallel, series-parallel, and parallel-series circuits.

2. *Write* an explanation, using sketches, of the distinguishing features of parallel-series and series-parallel circuits.

3. Given a schematic of the type shown, *calculate* the total equivalent resistance R_{eq} for the network, using the techniques of circuit reduction.

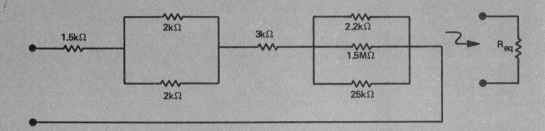

4. Using Ohm's law and circuit reduction techniques, *calculate* all of the unknown voltages and currents in any series-parallel circuit of the type shown below, given the applied voltage and resistance values as illustrated on the schematic.

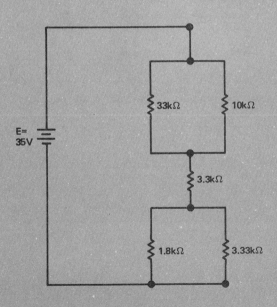

5. Using Ohm's law and circuit reduction techniques, *calculate* all unknown voltages, currents, and resistances in any series and parallel circuit of the type shown below, given a combination of known circuit values as illustrated in the schematic below.

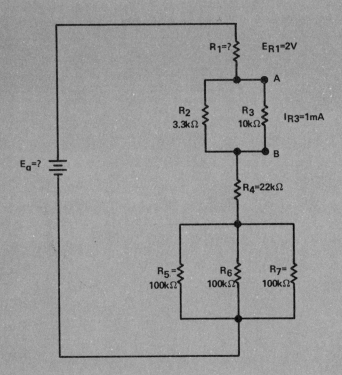

LESSON 9. SERIES-PARALLEL CIRCUITS

- **Parallel-Series Circuit**
- **Series-Parallel Circuit**

In Lesson 8, two new circuits were introduced, parallel-series and series-parallel circuits. The essential differences between these circuits were explained with an emphasis on how different approaches are used in solving for the voltages, currents, and resistances in these two different circuit configurations. Lesson 8 focused in deep detail on the procedures to follow in analyzing parallel-series circuits. Several example circuits were worked through in detail for you, including several circuits taken from automotive applications. In this lesson your attention will be focused on the series-parallel circuit. You will see several circuits of this type and be shown how they may be identified. You will also learn the steps to follow in analyzing this type of circuit.

An important objective of this lesson, as well as this entire course, is to enable you to recognize simple series and parallel circuit configurations when they are part of larger and more complex circuits. At the end of this lesson you should be able to use the laws governing series and parallel circuits to solve the more complex series-parallel circuits by applying the basic laws correctly to one circuit segment at a time.

To begin, the basic difference between the parallel-series circuit discussed in Lesson 8 and the series-parallel circuit discussed in this lesson is that in *series-parallel circuits* there is *either one resistor or equivalent resistance connected in series with the total current*. In the parallel-series circuit, no single element contains the total current flowing in the circuit.

Parallel-Series Circuit — To further understand the features of these two types of circuits, examine Figure 9.1 which shows one of the parallel-series circuits of the type discussed in Lesson 8. Notice that in this circuit there is no single circuit element that must carry the total or mainline current. This circuit essentially consists of several parallel branches, each of which may contain one resistor or several resistors in series.

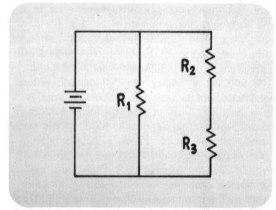

Figure 9.1

Series-Parallel Circuit — Series-parallel circuits which will be the topic for discussion in this lesson contain one circuit element (or an equivalent resistance) that lies in the path of the total current, as shown in Figure 9.2. In this series-parallel circuit, the series component is resistor R_1, and the entire circuit current will flow through it.

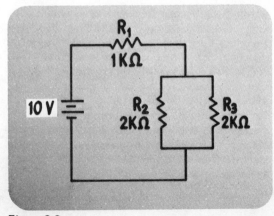

Figure 9.2

9-5

- **Two Parallel Circuits in Series**
- **Solving Parallel-Series Circuits Review**
- **Solving Series-Parallel Circuits**

Two Parallel Circuits in Series — Notice that the definition of a series-parallel circuit specifies that the element in series with the total circuit current may be an equivalent resistance. This equivalent resistance may be made up of several resistors in parallel. For this reason, a series-parallel circuit may appear as two or more parallel circuits wired in series, as shown in Figure 9.3. The analysis of circuits with this configuration will also be discussed for you in this lesson.

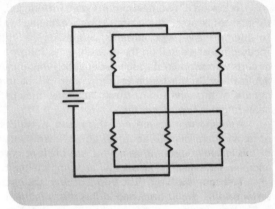

Figure 9.3

Solving Parallel-Series Circuits Review — As far as the techniques you will learn in this lesson are concerned, you will find that many of the same techniques used to solve parallel-series circuits will also be employed to solve series-parallel circuits. The only real difference is that these basic various techniques will be applied in a different order.

You may recall that when voltage, current, and resistance values in parallel-series circuits were calculated, each of the branches was examined first, as shown in Figure 9.4. The three series circuit laws were initially applied to each branch to reduce the circuit to the fewest possible elements. Then the parallel circuit laws were used to further reduce the number of elements in the circuit.

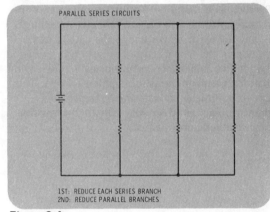

Figure 9.4

Solving Series-Parallel Circuits — When working with series-parallel circuits, you will find that the analysis will in general proceed in the reverse direction from that of parallel-series circuits (Figure 9.5). The parallel circuit "clusters" will first be reduced using the parallel circuit laws. The series circuit laws are then used to reduce the remaining series resistors and parallel equivalent resistances to one final equivalent resistance. Once the equivalent resistance is known, the total circuit current can be found and used to find the voltage across each component.

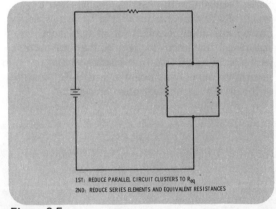

Figure 9.5

Basic Series-Parallel Circuit — Before actually going through the mechanics of a detailed circuit solution, consider in general the path of current flow in a simple series-parallel circuit. The circuit in Figure 9.6 contains one resistor connected in series with two other resistors which are connected in parallel. (This is actually the most simple form of series-parallel circuit.)

Electron current flows from the negative side of the power supply to point B where it divides, then flows through the two resistors, R_3 and R_4, in parallel. At point A, the current recombines and comes back to a single path and flows through the single resistor, R_1, and back to the other side of the power supply. Notice again that all the current in this circuit must pass through the single resistor, R_1.

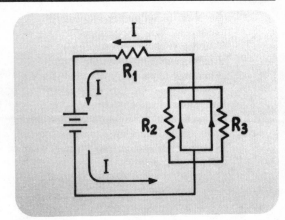

Figure 9.6

Steps in Analyzing Series-Parallel Circuits — How would you go about analyzing an actual circuit of this type? The procedural steps are listed in Figure 9.7.

1. Find the equivalent resistance of the circuit. This may be done by simplifying or reducing the circuit down to a single component. As has been mentioned, the best way to do this is to first identify those portions of the circuit that are connected in parallel, and using the rules for combining parallel resistances, reduce those parallel "clusters" to single equivalent resistors. Then using series circuit rules, combine all the series

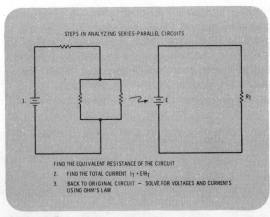

STEPS IN ANALYZING SERIES-PARALLEL CIRCUITS

FIND THE EQUIVALENT RESISTANCE OF THE CIRCUIT
2. FIND THE TOTAL CURRENT $I_T = E/R_T$
3. BACK TO ORIGINAL CIRCUIT — SOLVE FOR VOLTAGES AND CURRENTS USING OHM'S LAW

Figure 9.7

elements, including the equivalent resistances, to a single resistance.

2. Find the total current flowing in the circuit using Ohm's law. Once the total circuit resistance is known, Ohm's law may be used in the form $I_T = E/R_T$ to find the total current.

3. Go back to the original circuit and, once again, using Ohm's law, calculate the voltage across and current through each circuit component.

Basic Series-Parallel Circuit Example — With these steps in mind, consider the circuit shown in Figure 9.8. In this circuit the value of resistor R_1 is 1 kilohm and R_2 and R_3 are each 2 kilohms. Following the steps in the analysis outlined above, you will begin by reducing this circuit to a single equivalent resistance, beginning with the parallel resistors R_2 and R_3.

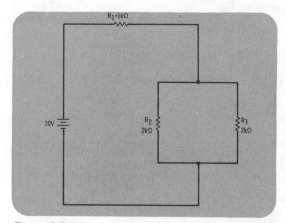

Figure 9.8

Parallel Resistance Reduction Shortcut — Note that since both of these resistors are 2 kilohms, a shortcut formula may be used to determine the equivalent resistance as was discussed in a previous lesson. The shortcut rule (Figure 9.9) states: The equivalent resistance of two equal resistors in parallel is one-half the value of one of the resistors.

THE RESISTANCE OF TWO RESISTORS IN PARALLEL, WHICH HAVE THE SAME VALUE, IS ONE-HALF THE VALUE OF ONE OF THE RESISTORS

Figure 9.9

- **Equal Resistance Formula**
- **Simple Series-Parallel Circuit Reduced to Two Resistances**
- **Series Resistance Rule and Formula**

Equal Resistance Formula — In formula form as shown in Figure 9.10, this rule translates to, $R_{eq} = R_s/N$. When the resistance values for R_2 and R_3 are substituted into the formula, the result is 2 kilohms divided by 2, because these two equal value resistors are connected in parallel. The result is 1 kilohm, that is, resistors R_2 and R_3 are equivalent to a single 1-kilohm resistor.

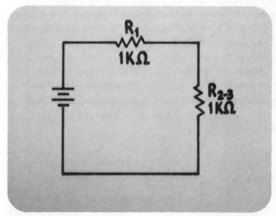

Figure 9.10

Simple Series-Parallel Circuit Reduced to Two Resistances — This is the first reduction of this circuit, and it appears as shown in Figure 9.11. The circuit consists of resistance R_1 which is 1 kilohm, in series with the equivalent resistance R_{2-3}, which is also 1 kilohm.

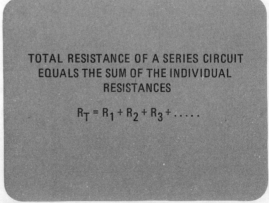

Figure 9.11

Series Resistance Rule and Formula — This circuit may be reduced even further using the law for series resistance (Figure 9.12), which states that the total equivalent resistance of a series circuit equals the sum of the individual resistances.

TOTAL RESISTANCE OF A SERIES CIRCUIT EQUALS THE SUM OF THE INDIVIDUAL RESISTANCES

$$R_T = R_1 + R_2 + R_3 + \ldots\ldots$$

Figure 9.12

- R_T = 2 kilohms
- Simple Series-Parallel Circuit Reduced to a Single Resistance
- Calculating Total Current

R_T = 2 kilohms — In the circuit of Figure 9.13, R_T, the total equivalent resistance, simply equals R_1 plus R_{2-3}. One kilohm plus 1 kilohm equals 2 kilohms for the total circuit resistance.

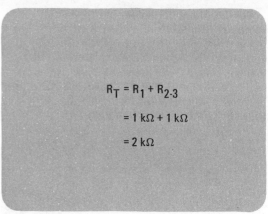

$$R_T = R_1 + R_{2-3}$$
$$= 1\ k\Omega + 1\ k\Omega$$
$$= 2\ k\Omega$$

Figure 9.13

Simple Series-Parallel Circuit Reduced to a Single Resistance — At this point it is important to point out once again that in solving for these circuit values, the first step is most usually to reduce the circuit to a single equivalent resistance as shown in Figure 9.14. Keep in mind that no matter how complex these circuits may appear at first, they reduce down to a single equivalent resistance.

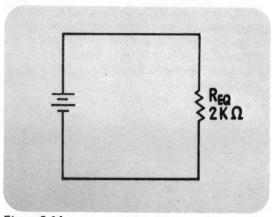

Figure 9.14

Calculating Total Current — Now that the equivalent resistance of this circuit is known, it can be used to find the total circuit current using Ohm's law in the form $I_T = E_T/R_T$ (as shown in Figure 9.15). Substituting 10 volts for the applied voltage and 2 kilohms for R_{eq}, I_T is calculated to be 5 milliamps. This 5 milliamps flows through R_{eq}. Keeping this in mind, take the circuit back to the second reduction where it was seen as two resistors in series.

Figure 9.15

9-10

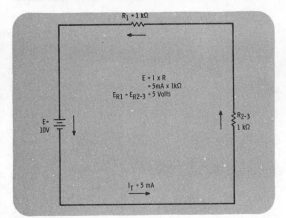

Figure 9.16

Determining Voltage Drops — In Figure 9.16 you can see that the total current, I_T, flows through both R_1 and R_{2-3}. Since both these resistors' values are known, the voltage drop across each can be calculated using Ohm's law in the form $E = I \times R$. Since each resistor's value is the same, the result for the voltage across each is easily seen to be 5 volts.

Notice the voltage across R_{2-3} is 5 volts, *and R_{2-3} is made up of two parallel resistors, R_2 and R_3.* This means that you now know the voltage across R_2 and R_3 to be 5 volts because in any parallel circuit the voltage across each branch is the same.

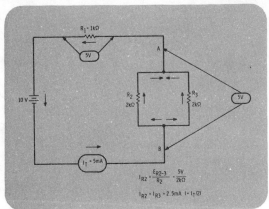

Figure 9.17

Determining the Branch Currents — At this point you are ready to put what you know about the circuit on the original unreduced schematic as shown in Figure 9.17. The currents through R_2 and R_3 are the only values remaining to be calculated, and there are two ways this can be done. Using Ohm's law in the form $I_{R2} = E_{R2-3}/R_2$, you can find the current through R_2 and also R_3 since R_2 and R_3 have the same value. Dividing 5 volts by 2 kilohms yields 2.5 milliamps for I_{R2} and I_{R3}. Consider the fact that the total current must divide at point B, to flow through two branches of equal resistance. Because of this equal resistance, exactly 1/2 of I_T must flow in each branch, and $I_T/2$ is 2.5 milliamps.

Two Parallel Circuits Connected in Series — The circuit analyzed above is actually the simplest form of a series-parallel circuit. If the single resistor R_1 were actually an equivalent resistance made up of several resistors in parallel, the circuit would appear initially more complex and resemble the circuit of Figure 9.18. As you proceed through the analysis of this circuit, however, you will see that using the same steps to do the job, the analysis is not much more complex than before. This circuit consists of a 35-volt power supply, resistors R_1 and R_2 in parallel, and resistors R_3, R_4, and R_5 which are also in parallel with each other. These two parallel circuits are then wired in series with each other.

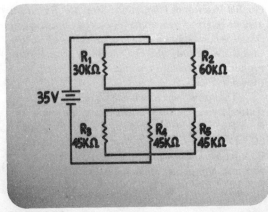

Figure 9.18

• Parallel Resistance Reduction: Step 1

Before beginning the actual circuit analysis, it will be helpful to generally block out the steps you will be taking. The first step in solving this problem is to reduce the circuit to its equivalent resistance. Then you can use the equivalent resistance to calculate the total current flowing in the circuit. Using the value of the total current, the rest of the voltage drops, and currents in the circuit may be calculated.

In reducing this circuit to a single equivalent resistance, you must begin by first reducing the two parallel circuit clusters. The parallel combination of R_1 and R_2 may first be reduced to an equivalent resistance, and also the combination of R_3, R_4, and R_5 can be reduced to their equivalent resistance. Then, these two equivalent resistances, which are connected in series, may be added to arrive at the total equivalent resistance for the circuit.

Parallel Resistance Reduction: Step 1 – R_1 and R_2 may be reduced to a single resistance by using the rules for combining parallel resistors. Since in this case there are only two resistances in parallel, the product-over-the-sum technique will be used, as shown in Figure 9.19.

The equivalent resistance equals R_1 times R_2 divided by R_1 plus R_2. Substituting the value for $R_1 + R_2$ yields 30 kilohms (or $3 \times 10^{+4}$) times 60 kilohms (or $6 \times 10^{+4}$) over 30 kilohms plus 60 kilohms. Carrying out the multiplication and addition, this equals $18 \times 10^{+8}$ divided by $9 \times 10^{+4}$. The result is $2 \times 10^{+4}$, or 20 kilohms.

$$R_{T1\text{-}2} = \frac{R_1 \times R_2}{R_1 + R_2}$$

$$= \frac{(3 \times 10^{+4})(6 \times 10^{+4})}{(3 \times 10^{+4}) + (6 \times 10^{+4})}$$

$$= \frac{18 \times 10^{+8}}{9 \times 10^{+4}}$$

$$= 2 \times 10^{+4}$$

$$= 20\ \text{k}\Omega$$

Figure 9.19

- **Parallel Resistors 1 and 2 Reduced to a Single Resistance**
- **Equal Value Parallel Resistance Reduction**
- **Circuit with R_{1-2} and R_{3-5}**

Parallel Resistors 1 and 2 Reduced to a Single Resistance — The equivalent resistance of resistors R_1 and R_2 is 20 kilohms and is labeled R_{1-2} as shown in Figure 9.20.

The parallel combination of resistors R_3, R_4, and R_5 may be reduced, and this equivalent resistance will be labeled R_{3-5}.

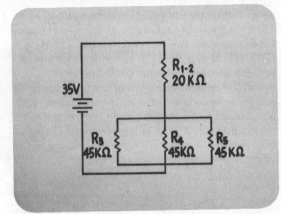

Figure 9.20

Equal Value Parallel Resistance Reduction — Since resistors R_3, R_4 and R_5 are equal in value, this parallel combination can be reduced using the shortcut formula as shown in Figure 9.21. R_{3-5} equals R_s, which is the value of one of these equal size resistors, divided by N, the total number of resistors. Substituting the values from the schematic diagram into the formula yields 45 kilohms divided by 3, which equals 15 kilohms for the equivalent resistance R_{3-5}.

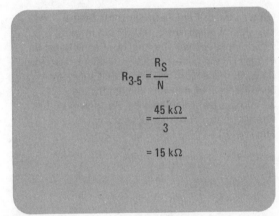

$$R_{3-5} = \frac{R_S}{N}$$

$$= \frac{45 \text{ k}\Omega}{3}$$

$$= 15 \text{ k}\Omega$$

Figure 9.21

Circuit with R_{1-2} and R_{3-5} — As seen in Figure 9.22, the two parallel resistor combinations have been reduced to their equivalent resistances, and the equivalent circuit simply consists of two resistors connected in series. At this point, another reduction can be performed using the law for combining series resistances.

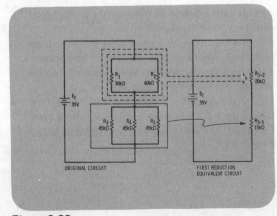

Figure 9.22

Series Resistance Formula (Final Reduction) —
The total equivalent resistance of this circuit equals
the sum of these two equivalent resistances. R$_{1-2}$
(20 kilohms) plus R$_{3-5}$ (15 kilohms) yields a total
circuit equivalent resistance of 35 kilohms as
shown in Figure 9.23. Now that the total resistance
and the total voltage in the circuit are known, you
can proceed to the second step in analyzing this
circuit, using Ohm's law to determine the circuit's
total current.

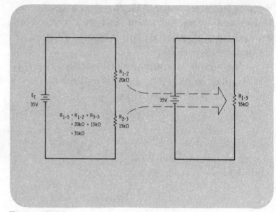

Figure 9.23

Ohm's Law to Find Total Current: Step 2 — As
you should recall, the total current in this
situation, I$_T$, equals the total applied voltage, E$_T$,
divided by the circuit's total equivalent resistance,
R$_{1-5}$. In this circuit you know that there are
35 volts applied, and this divided by the
35 kilohms just calculated for R$_{1-5}$ gives you a
total current of 1 milliamp, as shown in
Figure 9.24.

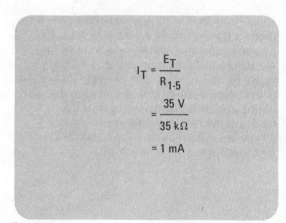

$$I_T = \frac{E_T}{R_{1-5}}$$

$$= \frac{35 \text{ V}}{35 \text{ k}\Omega}$$

$$= 1 \text{ mA}$$

Figure 9.24

Circuit with Equivalent Resistor R$_{1-5}$ — At this
point it is time to recall that an equivalent circuit
has the same essential characteristics of the larger,
more complex circuit from which it originated. An
equivalent circuit has the same amount of applied
voltage, the same total equivalent resistance, and
the same total current flowing. The only difference
is that the many resistive components have been
reduced to a single resistive component as shown in
Figure 9.25.

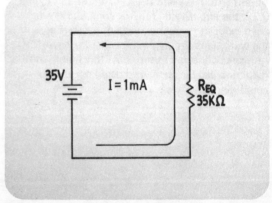

Figure 9.25

Two Parallel Circuits Connected in Series: Step 3 —
The circuit in Figure 9.25 is electrically equivalent
to the original circuit shown again in Figure 9.26.
Now that the voltage, current, and resistance of the
equivalent circuit are known, the third step in
completing the analysis of this circuit is to work
your way back to this original circuit, following
the same steps as in circuit reduction, but this time
in reverse. As you proceed you will determine all
the unknown voltage drops in the circuit and the
branch currents for each branch.

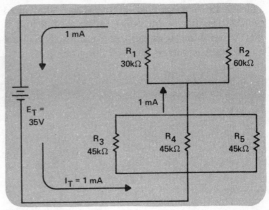

Figure 9.26

Circuit with R_{1-2} and R_{3-5} — Consider the circuit
shown in Figure 9.27(B). Recall that this circuit
was the next to last step in the circuit reduction,
just before the circuit was reduced to a single
equivalent resistor, Figure 9.27(A). You now know
that the total current flowing in this circuit is
1 milliamp. The current law governing series
circuits states that the current must have the same
value at any point in a series circuit. Thus,
Figure 9.27 shows that 1 milliamp of current is
flowing through both the equivalent resistance
R_{1-2} and through the equivalent resistance R_{3-5}.
You know the current flowing through these
resistors and their value in ohms; thus, using Ohm's
law the voltage drops across R_{1-2} and R_{3-5} can be
found.

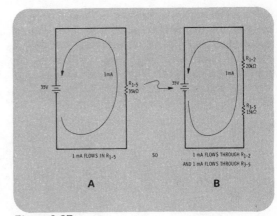

Figure 9.27

Ohm's Law (E_{R1-2}) — The voltage drop across the
entire equivalent resistance R_{1-2} is found by using
the Ohm's law formula as shown in Figure 9.28,
E_{R1-2} equals I_T times R_{1-2}. Substituting the
circuit figures into this formula, 1 milliamp times
20 kilohms equals 20 volts dropped across R_{1-2}.

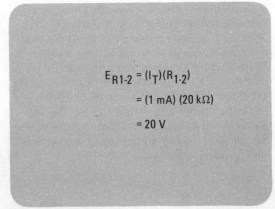

Figure 9.28

- **Ohm's Law ($E_{R3\text{-}5}$)**
- **Voltage Across Series Resistors**
- **Back to Original Circuit**

Ohm's Law ($E_{R3\text{-}5}$) — Using the same formula and substituting the circuit values for $R_{3\text{-}5}$, you find that 15 volts is dropped across $R_{3\text{-}5}$, the equivalent resistance as shown in Figure 9.29.

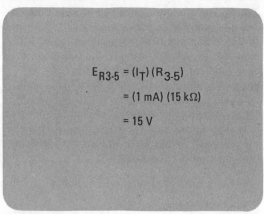

$$E_{R3\text{-}5} = (I_T)(R_{3\text{-}5})$$
$$= (1\ mA)(15\ k\Omega)$$
$$= 15\ V$$

Figure 9.29

Voltage Across Series Resistors — These calculations may be checked by adding the voltage dropped across $R_{1\text{-}2}$, which is 20 volts, and the voltage dropped across $R_{3\text{-}5}$, which is 15 volts. The sum of these voltages is 35 volts and this is equal to the total applied voltage as shown in Figure 9.30.

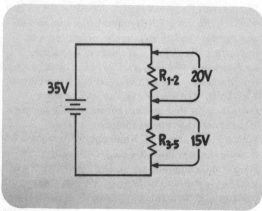

Figure 9.30

Back to Original Circuit — Now that these two voltage drops are known, you can go back to the original circuit and complete the circuit analysis. First of all, since you know that there is a drop of 20 volts across $R_{1\text{-}2}$, you also automatically know that there is a 20-volt drop across both R_1 and R_2 since these are connected in parallel. Likewise you know that there are 15 volts across R_3, R_4, and R_5, as shown in Figure 9.31. With these facts, you can calculate the current flowing through each of the individual resistors.

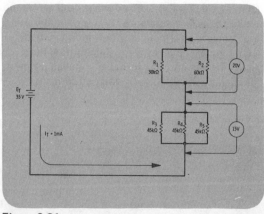

Figure 9.31

- Ohm's Law (I_{R1})
- Parallel Circuit Current Law
- Ohm's Law (I_{R2})

Ohm's Law (I_{R1}) – The current flowing through R_1 may be found by using Ohm's law as shown in Figure 9.32. Dividing 20 volts by 30 kilohms yields 666 microamps of calculated current flowing through R_1.

$$I_{R1} = \frac{E_{R1}}{R_1} = \frac{20\text{ V}}{30\text{ k}\Omega} = 666\ \mu\text{A}$$

Figure 9.32

Parallel Circuit Current Law – You know that the total current flowing in the circuit is 1 milliamp. Since R_1 is passing 666 microamps and since resistor R_2 affords the only other path for the remainder of the current flow, at this point in the circuit, the current through R_2 may be found by subtracting the current through R_1 from the total current flowing in the circuit. Following the procedure shown in Figure 9.33, 1 milliamp plus 666 microamps equals 333 microamps of current for the current flowing through R_2.

$$I_{R2} = I_T - I_{R1} = 1\text{ mA} - 666\ \mu\text{A} = 333\ \mu\text{A}$$

Figure 9.33

Ohm's Law (I_{R2}) – A second method may also be used to find the current flowing through R_2 which involves simply using Ohm's law. Twenty volts are being dropped across R_2 which is a 60-kilohm resistor. Ohm's law says that the current through R_2 equals 20 volts divided by 60 kilohms, as shown in Figure 9.34. Hence this calculation also yields a current of 333 microamps flowing through R_2, which agrees with the previous result.

$$I_{R2} = \frac{E_{R2}}{R_2} = \frac{20\text{ V}}{60\text{ k}\Omega} = 333\ \mu\text{A}$$

Figure 9.34

- **Calculating Lower Branch Currents**
- **Ohm's Law (I_{R3})**
- **Complete Circuit Solution**

Calculating Lower Branch Currents — Figure 9.35 shows the original circuit with all the calculated values for the upper parallel resistor cluster labeled. Ohm's law may be used once again to calculate the current flowing through the three individual resistors in the lower cluster, R_3, R_4, and R_5. From your previous analysis of the equivalent circuit, it was shown that 15 volts were being dropped across this lower parallel resistor combination.

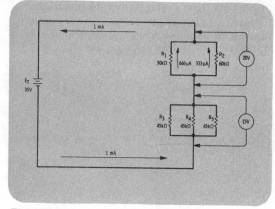

Figure 9.35

Ohm's Law (I_{R3}) — The current through R_3 can be calculated using Ohm's law in the form $I_{R3} = E_{R3}/R_3$, as shown in Figure 9.36. Plugging in the circuit values yields 15 volts across R_3, divided by the value of R_3, 45 kilohms, which equals 333 microamps of current for I_3.

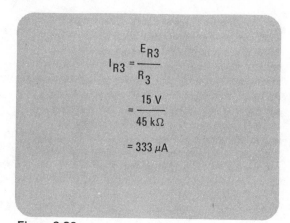

$$I_{R3} = \frac{E_{R3}}{R_3}$$

$$= \frac{15\ V}{45\ k\Omega}$$

$$= 333\ \mu A$$

Figure 9.36

Complete Circuit Solution — Determining the current flowing through resistors R_4 and R_5 is now relatively easy because these resistors all have the same value as R_3. Since 1 milliamp of current enters the parallel combination of the identical resistors R_3, R_4, and R_5, all the resistors must have one-third of 1 milliamp flowing through them. Thus each resistor in the lower parallel cluster has 333 microamps of current flowing through it, as shown in Figure 9.37.

Keep in mind, however, that if the resistors in the lower parallel cluster had different resistive values, Ohm's law could have been used to solve for the current through each individual resistor.

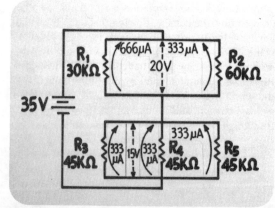

Figure 9.37

Review of Circuit Analysis — This is a good time to look back and review just how the analysis took place.

Originally, only the applied voltage and the values of the various resistors were known as shown in Figure 9.38(A).

By using parallel circuit laws, the parallel resistor combinations were reduced to their equivalent resistances illustrated in Figure 9.38(B).

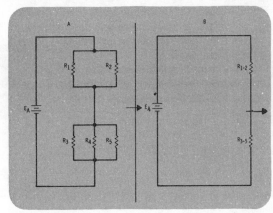

Figure 9.38

As you can see in Figure 9.39(A), the series circuit laws were then used to determine one single equivalent resistance for the circuit.

This equivalent resistance was then used to determine the total current flowing in the circuit as in Figure 9.39(B).

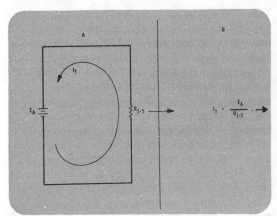

Figure 9.39

Once the total current was known, the individual resistances, and the series and parallel circuit laws were used to determine the voltage drops across the two parallel resistor combinations as you can see in Figure 9.40(A).

Once the voltage drops were known, this information was used to calculate the current flowing through each of the individual resistors in the circuit in Figure 9.40(B).

It is simply a process of:
1. Reducing the resistances
2. Determining the total current

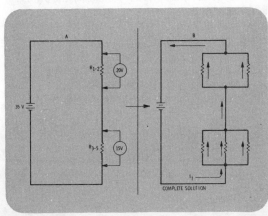

Figure 9.40

3. Using this information to determine the voltage drops across and current flowing through each of the individual components.
This procedure is basic to solving any series-parallel circuit where all the resistance values and the total applied voltage are known.

Lamp Demonstration Circuit — At this point the basic steps in solving series-parallel circuits have been set down and demonstrated and a few circuits have been analyzed. More circuit examples will be worked through for you but for now it will be helpful to consider a real-life example of a series-parallel circuit to watch and get the feel of them in actual operation. The demonstration circuit that will be discussed is an easy one to set up in the laboratory and will provide you with some insight as to how these circuits behave.

Figure 9.41 shows a schematic diagram of a series-parallel circuit that consists of four switches and four lamps. Notice that lamp 1 and switch 1 are in series with the total current, and that lamps 2, 3, and 4 are connected in parallel with each other. Each lamp is controlled by the switch in series with it.

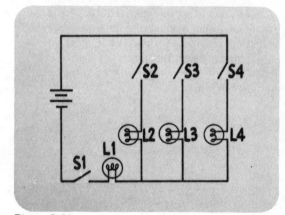

Figure 9.41

Switch S$_1$ Closed — Consider what would happen in this circuit if S$_1$ alone were closed. Would there be any current flow in the circuit? A quick examination of Figure 9.42 should tell you there would be no current flow. Trace the electron current flow out of the negative power supply terminal. With S$_1$ alone closed, current could flow through it, through lamp 1, and then as you can see, with S$_2$, S$_3$, and S$_4$ open, there is no complete path for current flow further.

If any one or all of these remaining switches are closed, the circuit will be completed and current will flow.

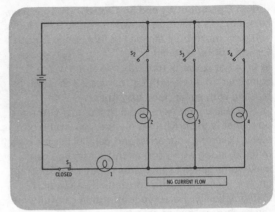

Figure 9.42

Picture of Circuit Operation — Consider what will happen if switches S$_1$ and S$_2$ are closed in Figure 9.43 which is a sketch of what this actual circuit might look like. With switches S$_1$ and S$_2$ closed, lamps L$_1$ and L$_2$ will be lit.

Electron current will flow from the power supply, through S$_1$, L$_1$, L$_2$, S$_2$, and then return to the power supply. With S$_1$ and S$_2$ closed, this circuit acts as a simple series circuit. Because these lamps are identical, they have the same amount of current flowing through them because they are connected in series, and they should produce the same amount of light as indicated in the figure. Equal currents through these identical lamps produce equal light output. (Also, because these two lamps are identical, they have the same resistance, and therefore the voltage drop across each is the same.)

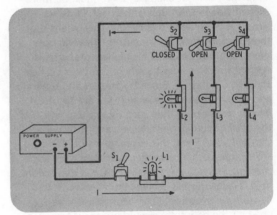

Figure 9.43

Circuit Operation: S_2 and S_3 Closed — If S_3 is now closed in this circuit, as shown in Figure 9.44, L_1 will glow much brighter than before, while L_2 and L_3 will not be as bright as L_1. Lamp 2 will not be as bright as it was before, when it alone was connected in series with L_1. Lamps 2 and 3 will be burning with equal (low) brightness.

If this circuit were wired in front of you right now, that is the brightness picture you would be seeing. Keeping your series and parallel circuit laws in mind, along with some circuit sense, you can make some general statements about what is going on in this circuit before you actually analyze it mathematically. Focus your attention carefully on the brightness level of each lamp. Lamp 1 is burning more brightly than before; so since the lamp itself has not changed, there must be more current flowing through it than before. Since lamp 1 is in series in this circuit, this means that there is more total circuit current flowing now than there was before. This higher total circuit current flows on past L_1 where it *divides* to flow through L_2 and L_3. Since L_2 and L_3 are in parallel and have the same resistance (they are identical lamps, remember), they each must carry *one-half* the total circuit current. Now think, what does that tell you? First, this explains why L_2 and L_3 are of equal brightness, they each carry the same current. Second, L_2 is dimmer than it was before, so it is receiving *less* current than before in this new circuit situation. (This also means that one-half the new total circuit current is less than the old total circuit current.)

Those are a few general deductions. Now consider how these can be backed up by circuit analysis.

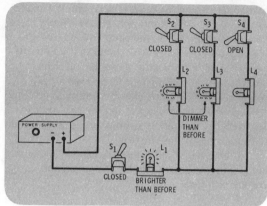

Figure 9.44

Lamp One Glows More Brightly — Why does L_1 glow more brightly when L_3 is switched on? As was mentioned, it must be because more current is flowing through it which means the total circuit current must increase. To calculate this increase, go back and consider the resistances in these two circuits as shown schematically in Figure 9.45.

When L_1 and L_2 were connected in series, the circuit contained a certain amount of resistance. For typical resistance in laboratory lamps you might use about 40 ohms. With two of these lamps in series, the total resistance of the first circuit would be 80 ohms.

When L_3 was switched into the circuit, the circuit's total resistance was reduced. Why? Notice that L_2 and L_3 are connected in *parallel*. Recall that one of the parallel resistance rules says that two resistors of equal value connected in parallel have a total resistance equal to half the value of one of the resistors.

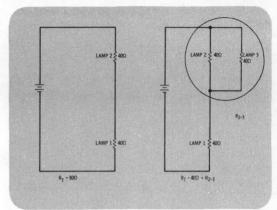

Figure 9.45

Calculating New Resistance — According to the parallel resistance rule, shown in Figure 9.46, the equivalent resistance of lamps L_2 and L_3 in parallel is equal to R_S over N, which equals 40 over 2 or 20 ohms. Now the total circuit resistance, R_T, equals 40 ohms plus R_{2-3}, or 40 ohms plus 20 ohms, which is 60 ohms.

Therefore, the circuit resistance dropped from 80 ohms to 60 ohms when L_3 was switched on. This is a decrease of 20 ohms or 20/80 (or 1/4 or 25%) *drop* in resistance. Since the resistance has dropped by 25%, the total current flowing will *rise* by 25%, because as you should recall, current and resistance are inversely related. So L_1, which is

$$R_{2-3} = \frac{R_S}{N}$$

$$R_{2-3} = \frac{40}{2} = 20 \ \Omega$$

$$R_T = 40 \ \Omega + R_{2-3}$$

$$R_T = 40 \ \Omega + 20 \ \Omega$$

$$R_T = 60 \ \Omega$$

Figure 9.46

carrying the total current, will glow brighter than before.

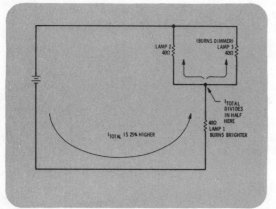

Figure 9.47

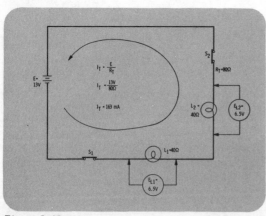

Figure 9.48

Lamps Two and Three Burn Dimmer — This new 25% higher current flows on to L_2 and L_3 where it divides, half flowing through each lamp (Figure 9.47). Although 25% more total current is flowing in this circuit, because it is divided by 2 as it flows through L_2 and L_3, these two lamps each receive less current than L_2 did previously. This is why L_2 and L_3 glow less brightly now than in the first circuit.

Circuit Calculation: Circuit 1 — To check this discussion, you could quickly calculate all the currents and voltages flowing in these circuits using the techniques covered in this lesson. In a laboratory demonstration of this type, the first circuit (shown in Figure 9.48) contains a 13-volt supply, and the two lamps L_1 and L_2 are in series. The total circuit resistance has already been calculated as 80 ohms, so the total circuit current is just 13 volts divided by 80 ohms which is 163 milliamps. The voltage dropped across each bulb equals this circuit current times the bulb's resistance, 163 milliamps times 40 ohms which is 6.5 volts. Each bulb drops one-half of the supply voltage.

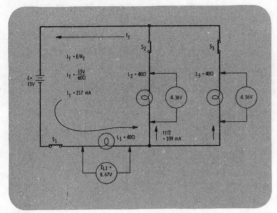

Figure 9.49

Circuit Calculation: Circuit 2 — In the second circuit everything is the same except another bulb, L_3, has been switched in across L_2, as shown in Figure 9.49. The total resistance in this case has been calculated as 60 ohms. The total circuit current is just 13 volts divided by 60 ohms or 217 milliamps. This is flowing through L_1, so the voltage across L_1 equals 217 milliamps times 40 ohms or 8.67 volts. This current divides so that half of it flows through L_2 and half through L_3, 217/2 is 109 milliamps. With 109 milliamps flowing through each of these 40-ohm bulbs, you can calculate that 109 milliamps times 40 ohms, or 4.36 volts is across each of L_2 and L_3. This gives you a complete picture of how these circuits differ in operation, and what happens when switch 3 is thrown bringing a third lamp into the circuit.

Fourth Lamp in Circuit — You should be able to predict what would happen if a fourth lamp were switched into the circuit, as shown in Figure 9.50. Lamp 1, which is in series, should glow more brightly, and L_2, L_3, and L_4 should glow less brightly than before.

    This effect occurs because L_4 is put into the circuit in parallel, which *decreases* the total resistance of the circuit. This decrease again causes an increase in the total circuit current, which passes through lamp 1.

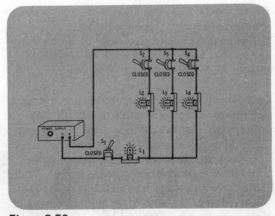

Figure 9.50

Fuse Action — The circuit has actually demonstrated an important circuit situation in electricity and electronics, that of the series-wired fuse. As has been discussed in earlier lessons, fuses are designed to be protective devices. They are usually made of a special resistive material that will melt if a prescribed current flows through it. If a circuit protected by a fuse were to draw too much current, the fuse would open the circuit.

In the demonstration circuit of Figure 9.51, L_1 is in the position that would normally be occupied by a fuse. All circuit current flows through it. In fact, L_1 may actually act as a fuse. If the current carrying capability of the lamp is exceeded, the lamp will burn out, opening the circuit just as a fuse would if the circuit exceeded its current rating.

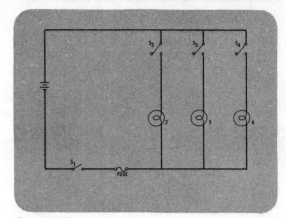

Figure 9.51

Circuit Switch Operation — Quite a lot has been reviewed concerning this demonstration circuit. Before leaving it completely, focus your attention on one final factor, the action of the switches in this circuit. By examining the schematic in Figure 9.52, you can see that S_1 controls the operation of all the circuit lamps because it is series with the total current. With S_1 closed, the other switches can then be used to activate L_2, L_3, and L_4 in the circuit branches.

Consider the behavior of the voltage across S_1. If this circuit were built for you in the laboratory, the voltage drop across S_1 could be measured simply by placing the voltmeter leads directly across the switch.

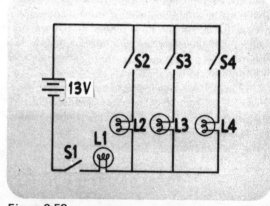

Figure 9.52

Open Switch: Maximum Voltage Drop — Let's check the operation of the circuit by closing switches S_1 and S_2. Lamps L_1 and L_2 will light. If S_1 is now opened, as in Figure 9.53, both lights will go out and no current will flow in the circuit. If you placed a voltmeter across this open switch, as shown in the figure, the meter would indicate approximately 13 volts, the total power supply voltage. This value is indicated because in the "open" position, the switch offers maximum opposition to current flow. Because of this, no current flows anywhere in the circuit, so there is no voltage dropped anywhere in this circuit. Across the point where the circuit is broken, the full supply voltage appears. It is not enough voltage, however, to force current to flow through the very high resistance of the open switch.

    If the switch S_1 is closed, the voltmeter would read zero volts and the lamps will light.

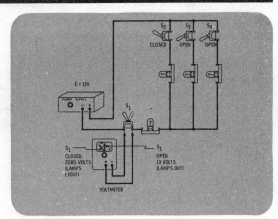

Figure 9.53

Ohm's Law and Switches — Figure 9.54 shows Ohm's law applied to a switch. The voltage drop across a device and the device's resistance vary directly. For an open switch, the resistance to current flow is infinite, so the voltage across it is at a maximum and it permits no current to flow. A closed switch offers zero resistance to current flow. Thus, if the resistance is zero ohms, the voltage drop across the resistance must be zero volts. The resistance of a closed switch is very close to zero ohms, so there's no voltage drop across it.

	E	$=$	I	$\times$	R
$R = \infty$ $I = 0$ $E = MAX$ OPEN SWITCH		FULL SUPPLY VOLTAGE	ZERO		∞ INFINITY
$R = 0$ $I = FULL FLOW$ $E = 0$ CLOSED SWITCH		ZERO	FULL CURRENT FLOW		ZERO

Figure 9.54

Voltage Across a Switch — This is an important point to remember: *voltage is always maximum or equal to the applied voltage across an open switch and minimum across a closed switch, as shown in Figure 9.55.*

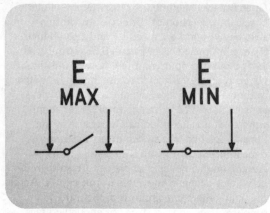

Figure 9.55

Before leaving this lesson, it will be helpful to extend your knowledge of and skill in handling series-parallel circuits by discussing a different type of example.

Up to this point, you have seen circuit reduction techniques used to determine voltages and currents in series-parallel circuits. In these examples you were given only the applied voltage and resistance values at the beginning of the problem. There will be times when you will know more about the circuit as you begin to analyze it than you did in the previous examples in this lesson. In some of these cases, the circuit analysis may proceed in a little more straightforward fashion.

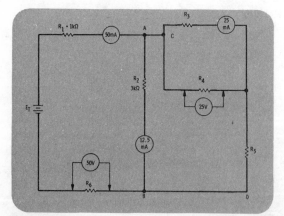

Figure 9.56

Series Parallel Circuit with Known Values — To see how this may be done, consider the circuit in Figure 9.56. Going through the solution to solve this circuit will help develop your circuit sense, because it is a tricky circuit. But, it is a circuit type often encountered and you should know how to handle it.

First of all, take a moment to analyze this circuit. You should recognize it as a series-parallel circuit, because in this case there are two resistors, R_1 and R_6, that are in series with the total circuit current.

You can also see that resistor R_2 is a parallel component. The function of resistors R_3, R_4, and R_5 in the circuit may not be clear to you at first.

This circuit can be redrawn in a slightly different fashion to clarify the operation of the right-hand side.

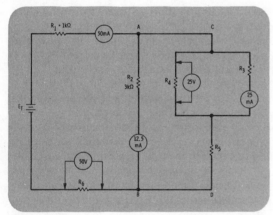

Figure 9.57

Redrawn Circuit — It is fairly easy to recognize in this redrawn circuit (Figure 9.57), that R_3 and R_4 are in parallel with each other, and that this parallel combination of R_3 and R_4 is in series with resistor R_5. In addition, the parallel combination of R_3 and R_4 *plus* the series resistor R_5 are all in *parallel* with resistor R_2. Hence, in this circuit you can see that there is a parallel-series element (R_3, R_4, and R_5) in parallel with another component, R_2. This entire resistor cluster is in series with the components R_1 and R_6.

Now focus your attention on the known quantities in this circuit as labeled on the schematic. You know that R_1 is 1 kilohm, and that the current flowing through this leg of the circuit is 50 milliamps. You know that resistor R_2 is 3 kilohms, and the current flowing through its branch is 12.5 milliamps. The current through the branch containing R_3 is 25 milliamps, and the voltage drop across R_4 is 25 volts. Finally, you are given that the voltage drop across R_6 is 50 volts.

E	I	R
E_{R1} =	I_{R1} = 50 mA	R_1 = 1 kΩ
E_{R2} =	I_{R2} = 12.5 mA	R_2 = 3 kΩ
E_{R3} =	I_{R3} = 25 mA	R_3 =
E_{R4} = 25 V	I_{R4} =	R_4 =
E_{R5} =	I_{R5} =	R_5 =
E_{R6} = 50 V	I_{R6} =	R_6 =
E_T =	I_T =	R_T =

Figure 9.58

Known Circuit Values Chart — This example is really a little different from the others that have been analyzed in this lesson, except there are a few more knowns and unknowns, and they are sort of "scrambled." To help you keep track of the knowns and the unknowns as you determine them, you can use a chart such as the one shown in Figure 9.58. This chart lists all the possible voltages, currents, and resistances in the particular circuit you are going to solve. When you complete your calculations, all of the spaces will be filled in, and you can check your values since each voltage listed should equal the current times the resistance across each line of the chart.

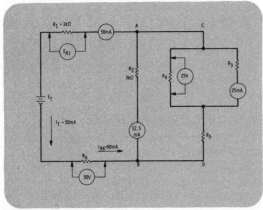

Figure 9.59

Solution: Begin with R_1 — There are several ways to begin the solution of this problem, but in general when solving series-parallel circuits, it is a good idea to determine the total current flowing in the circuit as soon as possible. Focus your attention on R_1 in Figure 9.59. Since R_1 is in series with the total current, and you are given that 50 milliamps is flowing through it, you immediately know that the total current flowing in this circuit, I_T, is also 50 milliamps. Also, since R_6 is in series with the total current, it too must have 50 milliamps flowing through it. With these values in mind, you can now use Ohm's law to calculate the voltage across R_1 (E_{R1}) and the resistance of R_6.

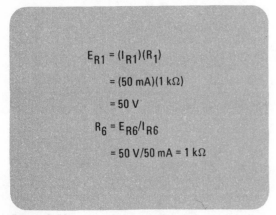

$$E_{R1} = (I_{R1})(R_1)$$
$$= (50 \text{ mA})(1 \text{ k}\Omega)$$
$$= 50 \text{ V}$$
$$R_6 = E_{R6}/I_{R6}$$
$$= 50 \text{ V}/50 \text{ mA} = 1 \text{ k}\Omega$$

Figure 9.60

Calculation of E_{R1} and R_6 — Using Ohm's law in the correct form, as shown in Figure 9.60 E_{R6} and R_6 can be calculated. E_{R1} is 50 volts and R_6 turns out to be identical to R_1, 1 kilohm.

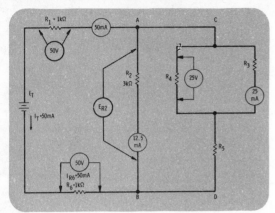

Figure 9.61

Solution: Branch Containing R_2 — Turn your attention to the branch containing resistor R_2 in Figure 9.61. You know two things about R_2: its resistance is 3 kilohms and the current flow through it is 12.5 milliamps. Using Ohm's law in the form $E_{R2} = I_{R2} \times R_2$, you can calculate the voltage across R_2, 12.5 milliamps times 3 kilohms is 37.5 volts for E_{R2}. Remember this important fact, the voltage across R_2 is also the voltage across the right-hand branch (between points C and D), since these two branches are connected in parallel. Therefore, E_{R2} (37.5 volts) is the voltage across the entire parallel-connected cluster of resistors. At this point you know:

1. The voltage across R_1 is 50 volts.
2. Connected in series with R_1 is the parallel cluster containing resistors R_2, R_3, R_4, and R_5, and the voltage across that cluster (E_{R2-5}) is 37.5 volts.
3. Connected in series with R_{2-5} is R_6 and the voltage across R_6 is 50 volts.

What do these three facts tell you? The total voltage, E_T, is the sum of these three voltages:

$$E_T = E_{R1} + E_{R2-5} + E_{R6}$$

or

$$E_T = 50 + 37.5 + 50$$
$$E_T = 137.5 \text{ V}$$

Chart with Calculated Values — You are now quite well into the analysis of the operation of this circuit. Your chart of values at this point should look like the one in Figure 9.62. By inspecting the chart carefully, you can decide on your next step. First of all, since E_T and I_T, the total applied voltage and current, are known, you can calculate R_T, the total equivalent resistance of this circuit, using Ohm's law. Notice that *no* circuit reduction was involved in this case since you were given different types of known values at the start of this problem than in previous cases. Using Ohm's law in the form $R_T = E_T/I_T$, and substituting, yields R_T = 137.5 volts divided by 50 milliamps, which equals a value of 2.75 kilohms. Looking at the

E	I	R
E_{R1} = 50 V	I_{R1} = 50 mA	R_1 = 1 kΩ
E_{R2} = 37.5 V	I_{R2} = 12.5 mA	R_2 = .3 kΩ
E_{R3} =	I_{R3} = 25 mA	R_3 =
E_{R4} = 25 V	I_{R4} =	R_4 =
E_{R5} =	I_{R5} =	R_5 =
E_{R6} = 50 V	I_{R6} = 50 mA	R_6 = 1 kΩ
E_T = 137.5 V	I_T = 50 mA	R_T =

Figure 9.62

other blank spaces in your chart should tell you that it is time to move your attention to the right-hand branch of the circuit which contains R_3, R_4, and R_5.

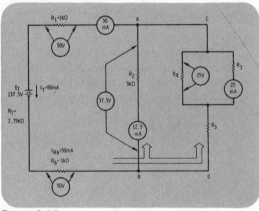

Figure 9.63

Circuit Solution: Right-Hand Branch — All you know about the branch in Figure 9.63 is that the voltage across it equals E_{R2}, 37.5 volts. What else can you calculate about it? The law for currents in a parallel circuit states that the total or main line current must equal the sum of the branch currents. Here, 50 milliamps is flowing through R_6 to point B, where it divides. You know that 12.5 milliamps out of this 50 milliamps flows through R_2, so the rest must flow in the right-hand branch. Fifty milliamps minus 12.5 milliamps yields 37.5 milliamps flowing in this branch. Automatically you know that this is I_{R5}, the current through R_5 since R_5 is in series in this branch and hence must carry all the branch current. Also, this branch current of 37.5 milliamps flowing past R_5 must again branch to go through R_3 and R_4. Twenty-five out of those 37.5 milliamps flow through R_3 so what is left must go through R_4. This 37.5 milliamps minus 25 milliamps leaves 12.5 milliamps for the current through R_4, I_{R4}. Immediately, your mind should "click." E_{R4} and I_{R4} are now known. Therefore, R_4 can be calculated with Ohm's law in the form $R_4 = E_{R4}/I_{R4}$. Substituting, $R_4 = 25$ volts/12.5 milliamps, or R_4 equals 2 kilohms.

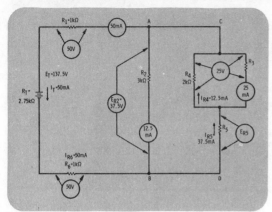

Figure 9.64

Circuit Solution R$_3$ and R$_5$ — Where do you proceed from here? Look at Figure 9.64. You need to "finish off" R$_3$ and R$_5$. What do you know about R$_3$? You are given that 25 milliamps of current flows through it. Also, notice that it is in *parallel* with R$_4$, so the voltage across R$_4$ is also the voltage across R$_3$, 25 volts. This enables you to calculate R$_3$:

$$R_3 = E_{R3}/I_{R3}$$
$$R_3 = 25 \text{ V}/25 \text{ mA}$$

which equals 1 kilohm.

Proceed to R$_5$. You have already calculated that I$_{R5}$ is 37.5 milliamps. You know that the total voltage across the right-hand branch, between points C and D, is 37.5 volts. Twenty-five volts of that is dropped across the parallel cluster containing R$_3$ and R$_4$, and the remainder must be dropped across R$_5$. This means that 37.5 volts minus 25 volts results in 12.5 volts for E$_{R5}$. With E$_{R5}$ and I$_{R5}$ known, you can now calculate

$$R_5 = E_{R5}/I_{R5}$$
$$= 12.5 \text{ V}/37.5 \text{ mA}$$

which equals 333 ohms.

Complete Analysis — Your analysis should be complete and the completed chart of values for this circuit is given in Figure 9.65 for your reference.

E	I	R
E$_{R1}$ = 50 V	I$_{R1}$ = 50 mA	R$_1$ = 1 kΩ
E$_{R2}$ = 37.5 V	I$_{R2}$ = 12.5 mA	R$_2$ = 3 kΩ
E$_{R3}$ = 25 V	I$_{R3}$ = 25 mA	R$_3$ = 1 kΩ
E$_{R4}$ = 25 V	I$_{R4}$ = 12.5 mA	R$_4$ = 2 kΩ
E$_{R5}$ = 12.5 V	I$_{R5}$ = 37.5 mA	R$_5$ = 333 Ω
E$_{R6}$ = 50 V	I$_{R6}$ = 50 mA	R$_6$ = 1 kΩ
E$_T$ = 137.5 V	I$_T$ = 50 mA	R$_T$ = 2.75 kΩ

Figure 9.65

Final Note-Power in Series-Parallel Circuits — As was the case for parallel-series circuits and *all* dc resistive circuits, the power dissipated by the circuit is an additive quantity. To find the total power a series-parallel circuit dissipates, you could:

1.   Find the power dissipated by each resistor and add them all.
2.   Apply a power formula to the total circuit quantities E_T, I_T, or R_T.

For the circuit that has just been analyzed then, as shown in Figure 9.66, the total dissipated power can be calculated using the formula $P_T = I_T \times E_T$. Substituting the circuit total values into the formula:

$$P_T = 50 \text{ mA} \times 137.5 \text{ V}$$
$$P_T = 6.88 \text{ W}$$

More information concerning the calculation of dissipated power in complex circuits will be covered in Lesson 10.

During this lesson quite a lot concerning the series-parallel circuit has been covered. These circuits were first discussed in general with attention to how they may be recognized and what the outstanding features of these operations are. Several simple circuits were analyzed where you were given the applied voltages and resistance values and where to calculate all voltages and currents. In cases such as this, three steps to follow in the circuit analysis were set down. A "live" example then demonstrated some of the peculiarities in the behavior of these circuits for you. Finally, an example involving a "detective" approach was covered for you. In cases such as the last one, you proceed through the circuit armed with your "circuit sense," building your analysis as you go along.

Practice, as usual, is the best way to develop the knack for handling these circuits. An extensive set of worked through examples and practice problems is included at the end of this lesson for your use. If you work with these problems, you will find yourself capable of solving these circuits very quickly. Also, you should begin to enjoy the "detective" aspect involved in predicting the behavior of voltages and currents in this complex circuit situation.

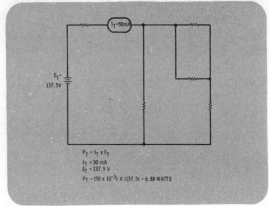

Figure 9.66

LESSON 9. SERIES-PARALLEL CIRCUITS

- **Worked Through Examples**

---

1. In the series-parallel circuit shown, calculate the total equivalent resistance and all unknown voltages and currents using Ohm's law and circuit reduction techniques.

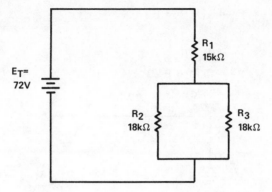

First, you can find R_T by circuit reduction techniques. Since R_2 and R_3 are of equal value and are connected in parallel, the equivalent resistance, $R_{2,3}$ can be found with the formula:

$$R_{eq} = \frac{R_s}{N}$$

R_s equals 18 kilohms and N equals 2, so:

$$R_{2,3} = R_{eq} = \frac{R_s}{N} = \frac{18 \text{ k}\Omega}{2}$$

$$R_{2,3} = 9 \text{ k}\Omega$$

After the first circuit reduction, the circuit now consists of R_1 in series with $R_{2,3}$ as shown.

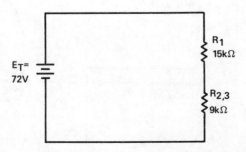

You can find the total resistance of the circuit by simply using the series circuit law which says that the total resistance of a series circuit equals the sum of the individual resistances. In formula form:

$$R_T = R_1 + R_2 + R_3 + \ldots$$

or in this case:

$$R_T = R_1 + R_{2,3}$$
$$R_T = 15 \text{ k}\Omega + 9 \text{ k}\Omega$$
$$R_T = 24 \text{ k}\Omega$$

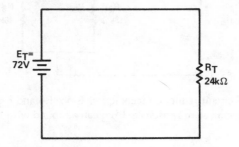

Once you know the total resistance, you can find the total current by using Ohm's law in the form $I_T = E_T/R_T$. Substituting the appropriate values in the formula gives:

$$I_T = \frac{E_T}{R_T} = \frac{72 \text{ V}}{24 \text{ k}\Omega}$$

$$I_T = 3 \text{ mA}$$

This total current can be used to find the voltage across R_1. Remember, since R_1 is in series with the rest of the circuit, the total current must flow through R_1. If you use Ohm's law in the form $E = I \times R$ and substitute the appropriate values, you get:

$$E_{R1} = I_T \times R_1$$

$$E_{R1} = 3 \text{ mA} \times 15 \text{ k}\Omega$$

$$E_{R1} = 45 \text{ V}$$

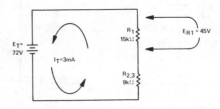

- **Worked Through Examples**

Remember that in a series circuit the total voltage equals the sum of the individual voltage drops. You know the total voltage and the voltage across R_1; the remainder of the voltage must be dropped across $R_{2,3}$. In formula form:

$$E_{R2,3} = E_T - E_{R1}$$
$$E_{R2,3} = 72\,V - 45\,V$$
$$E_{R2,3} = 27\,V$$

You can find the current through R_2 or R_3 by using Ohm's law in the form $I = E/R$. Remember, R_2 and R_3 are in parallel, so they have the same 27 volts dropped across them.

$$I_{R2} = \frac{E_{R2}}{R2} = \frac{27\,V}{18\,k\Omega}$$
$$I_{R2} = 1.5\,mA$$

Since R_2 and R_3 have the same resistance value and the same voltage across them, they have the same current flow through them. You could have found the current through R_2 and R_3 by simply realizing that they must divide the total current of 3 milliamps equally between them.

$$I_{R2} = I_{R3} = \frac{I_T}{2} = \frac{3\,mA}{2}$$
$$I_{R2} = I_{R3} = 1.5\,mA$$

If R_2 and R_3 did not have the same resistance value, you could have found the current through R_3 by subtraction. You know the total current and you know the current through R_2, so the remainder of the current must flow through R_3.

$$I_{R3} = I_T - I_{R2}$$
$$I_{R3} = 3 \text{ mA} - 1.5 \text{ mA}$$
$$I_{R3} = 1.5 \text{ mA}$$

and the circuit is completely solved.

2. In the series-parallel circuit shown, calculate the total equivalent resistance and all unknown voltages and currents using Ohm's law and circuit reduction techniques.

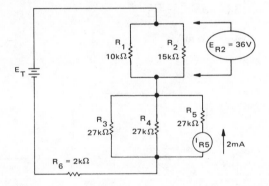

In order to keep track of all the knowns and unknowns, make a chart as shown below and fill in the known values. Then you can fill in the unknown values as you calculate them.

E	I	R
$E_{R1} = $ 36 V	$I_{R1} = $	$R_1 = 10 \text{ k}\Omega$
$E_{R2} = $ 36 V	$I_{R2} = $	$R_2 = 15 \text{ k}\Omega$
$E_{R3} = $	$I_{R3} = $	$R_3 = 27 \text{ k}\Omega$
$E_{R4} = $	$I_{R4} = $	$R_4 = 27 \text{ k}\Omega$
$E_{R5} = $	$I_{R5} = $ 2 mA	$R_5 = 27 \text{ k}\Omega$
$E_{R6} = $	$I_{R6} = $	$R_6 = $ 2 kΩ
$E_T = $	$I_T = $	$R_T = $

Notice that since R_1 and R_2 are in parallel, the voltage across them is the same.

You can use Ohm's law in the form $I = E/R$ to calculate I_{R1} and I_{R2}.

$$I_{R1} = \frac{E_{R1}}{R_1} \qquad\qquad I_{R2} = \frac{E_{R2}}{R_2}$$

$$I_{R1} = \frac{36\ V}{10\ k\Omega} \qquad\qquad I_{R2} = \frac{36\ V}{15\ k\Omega}$$

$$I_{R1} = 3.6\ mA \qquad\qquad I_{R2} = 2.4\ mA$$

You know that the total current in a parallel circuit equals the sum of the individual branch currents. In this circuit, the total current flows through the combination of R_1 and R_2; you can add I_{R1} and I_{R2} to get I_T.

$$I_T = I_{R1} + I_{R2}$$
$$I_T = 3.6\ mA + 2.4\ mA$$
$$I_T = 6.0\ mA$$

You can now fill in these calculated values on the chart as shown.

E	I	R
E_{R1} = 36 V	I_{R1} = 3.6 mA	R_1 = 10 kΩ
E_{R2} = 36 V	I_{R2} = 2.4 mA	R_2 = 15 kΩ
E_{R3}	I_{R3}	R_3 = 27 kΩ
E_{R4}	I_{R4}	R_4 = 27 kΩ
E_{R5}	I_{R5} = 2 mA	R_5 = 27 kΩ
E_{R6}	I_{R6}	R_6 = 2 kΩ
E_T	I_T = 6.0 mA	R_T

Looking at the chart or the circuit, you can see that you know two things about R_5, you know its resistance, and you know the current flow through it. You can use Ohm's law in the form $E = I \times R$ to find E_{R5}.

$$E_{R5} = I_{R5} \times R_5$$
$$E_{R5} = 2\ mA \times 27\ k\Omega$$
$$E_{R5} = 54\ V$$

Because R_3, R_4, and R_5 are in parallel, they have 54 volts dropped across them. If they all have the same voltage across them and they all have the same resistance value, then the current must be the same through all of them. Since I_{R5} equals 2 milliamps, then I_{R3} and I_{R4} also equal 2 milliamps each.

E	I	R
E_{R1} = 36 V	I_{R1} = 3.6 mA	R_1 = 10 kΩ
E_{R2} = 36 V	I_{R2} = 2.4 mA	R_2 = 15 kΩ
E_{R3} = 54 V	I_{R3} = 2 mA	R_3 = 27 kΩ
E_{R4} = 54 V	I_{R4} = 2 mA	R_4 = 27 kΩ
E_{R5} = 54 V	I_{R5} = 2 mA	R_5 = 27 kΩ
E_{R6}	I_{R6}	R_6 = 2 kΩ
E_T	I_T = 6.0 mA	R_T

You could check your work at this point by adding I_{R3}, I_{R4} and I_{R5} to see that they do add up to the total current of 6 milliamps.

Because R_6 is in series with the rest of the circuit, the total current must flow through it. Thus I_{R6} equals 6 milliamps and you can now use this information to find E_{R6}.

$$E_{R6} = I_{R6} \times R_6$$
$$E_{R6} = 6 \text{ mA} \times 2 \text{ kΩ}$$
$$E_{R6} = 12 \text{ V}$$

As shown, you know the voltage across and current flow through each portion of the circuit.

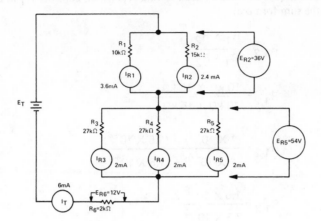

The voltage across R_1 and R_2 is the same; $E_{R1,2}$ equals 36 volts. The voltage is also the same across R_3, R_4, and R_5; $E_{R3,4,5}$ equals 54 volts. You also know the voltage across R_6; E_{R6} equals 12 volts. From series circuit laws, these voltages can be added to find the total voltage applied to the circuit.

$$E_T = E_{R1,2} + E_{R3,4,5} + E_{R6}$$

$$E_T = 36\ V + 54\ V + 12\ V$$

$$E_T = 102\ V$$

The only unknown quantity remaining to be calculated is the total resistance. This can be found in either of two ways. One way is to use Ohm's law in the form:

$$R_T = \frac{E_T}{I_T}$$

When you substitute the appropriate values in the formula, you obtain:

$$R_T = \frac{102\ V}{6\ mA}$$

$$R_T = 17\ k\Omega$$

Circuit reduction techniques can also be used to find R_T. First, consider R_1 in parallel with R_2. Using the product-over-the-sum formula:

$$R_{1,2} = \frac{R_1 \times R_2}{R_1 + R_2}$$

$$R_{1,2} = \frac{10\ k\Omega \times 15\ k\Omega}{10\ k\Omega + 15\ k\Omega}$$

$$R_{1,2} = \frac{(1 \times 10^{+4}) \times (1.5 \times 10^{+4})}{(1 \times 10^{+4}) + (1.5 \times 10^{+4})}$$

$$R_{1,2} = \frac{1.5 \times 10^{+8}}{2.5 \times 10^{+4}}$$

$$R_{1,2} = 0.6 \times 10^{+4} = 6\ k\Omega$$

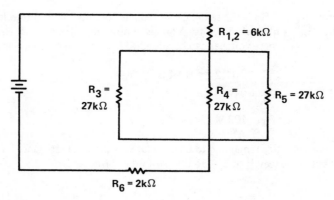

Because R_3, R_4 and R_5 all have the same resistance value, they can be reduced to an equivalent resistance by using the formula:

$$R_{eq} = \frac{R_s}{N}$$

$$R_{eq} = \frac{27\ k\Omega}{3}$$

$$R_{eq} = 9\ k\Omega$$

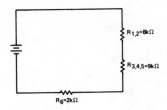

These three resistances are now in series and can be added to find R_T.

$$R_T = R_{1,2} + R_{3,4,5} + R_6$$

$$R_T = 6 \text{ k}\Omega + 9 \text{ k}\Omega + 2 \text{ k}\Omega$$

$$R_T = 17 \text{ k}\Omega$$

and this agrees with the previous calculation.

The chart can be filled in as shown, and the circuit is completely solved.

E	I	R
$E_{R1} =$ 36 V	$I_{R1} =$ 3.6 mA	$R_1 =$ 10 kΩ
$E_{R2} =$ 36 V	$I_{R2} =$ 2.4 mA	$R_2 =$ 15 kΩ
$E_{R3} =$ 54 V	$I_{R3} =$ 2 mA	$R_3 =$ 27 kΩ
$E_{R4} =$ 54 V	$I_{R4} =$ 2 mA	$R_4 =$ 27 kΩ
$E_{R5} =$ 54 V	$I_{R5} =$ 2 mA	$R_5 =$ 27 kΩ
$E_{R6} =$ 12 V	$I_{R6} =$ 6 mA	$R_6 =$ 2 kΩ
$E_T =$ 102 V	$I_T =$ 6 mA	$R_T =$ 17 kΩ

● **Practice Problems**

The key objective of this lesson has been achieved if you can analyze any series parallel circuit in a variety of situations such as:

1. Given a series-parallel wired network of resistors, calculate their equivalent resistance, R_{eq}.
2. Given a series-parallel circuit with all of the resistor values and the applied voltage labeled, calculate any or all of the voltages across and currents through each resistor, as well as the total circuit current and equivalent resistance.
3. Given a series-parallel circuit schematic with several known values labeled, calculate any unknown values required.

The practice problems that follow are designed to give you as much practice as you may need in these areas. It is suggested that you work enough of these to enable you to approach and analyze any series-parallel circuit without referring back to the lesson. Fold over the page to check your answers

Depending upon the approach you use in solving these problems and how you round off intermediate results, your answers may vary slightly from those given here. However, any differences you encounter should only occur in the third significant digit of your answer. If the first two significant digits of your answers do not agree with those given here, recheck your calculations.

1. Find R_{eq} for the following circuits. **Fold Over**

a.

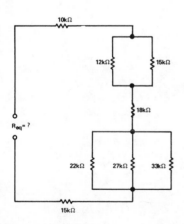

$$R_{eq} = \underline{\hspace{2cm}}$$

Answers

1.a. $R_{eq} = 58.5 \text{ k}\Omega$

b.   **Fold Over**

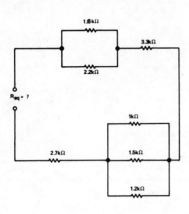

$$R_{eq} = \text{_____}$$

c.

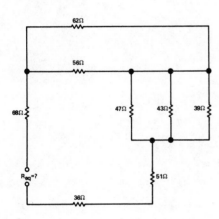

$$R_{eq} = \text{_____}$$

Answers

1.b. $R_{eq} = 7.39 \text{ k}\Omega$

1.c. $R_{eq} = 199 \ \Omega$

d.

Fold Over

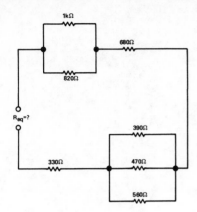

$$R_{eq} = \underline{\hspace{2cm}}$$

e.

$$R_{eq} = \underline{\hspace{2cm}}$$

Answers

1.d. R_{eq} = 1.61 kΩ

1.e. R_{eq} = 76.9 kΩ

f.

Fold Over

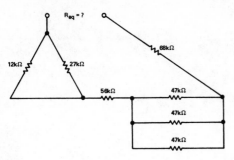

$R_{eq} =$ _____

g.

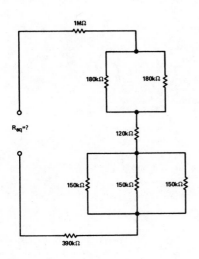

$R_{eq} =$ _____

Answers

1.f. R_{eq} = 148 kΩ

1.g. R_{eq} = 1.65 MΩ

h.   **Fold Over**

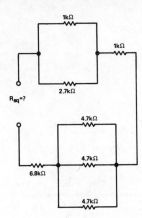

$$R_{eq} = \underline{\hspace{2cm}}$$

i.

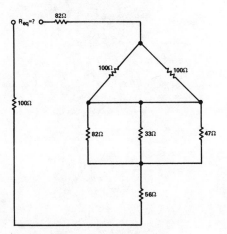

$$R_{eq} = \underline{\hspace{2cm}}$$

Answers

1.h. $R_{eq} = 10.1 \text{ k}\Omega$

1.i. $R_{eq} = 304 \ \Omega$

j.

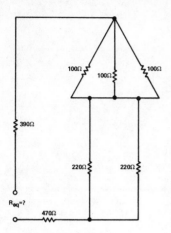

$R_{eq} = $ _____

Fold Over

k.

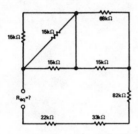

$R_{eq} = $ _____

Answers

1.j. $R_{eq} = 1 \ k\Omega$

1.k. $R_{eq} = 154 \ k\Omega$

l.

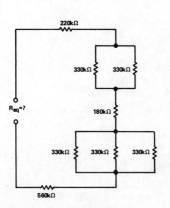

R_{eq}=?

1.5kΩ

4.7kΩ

4.7kΩ

1kΩ

1.2kΩ

8.2kΩ

5.6kΩ

R_{eq} = _____

m.

220kΩ

330kΩ   330kΩ

R_{eq}=?

180kΩ

330kΩ   330kΩ   330kΩ

560kΩ

R_{eq} = _____

Answers

1.l. R_{eq} = 5.82 kΩ

1.m. R_{eq} = 1.24 MΩ

n.

Fold Over

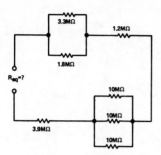

$R_{eq} =$ _____

o.

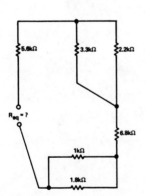

$R_{eq} =$ _____

Answers

1.n. $R_{eq} = 9.60 \text{ M}\Omega$

1.o. $R_{eq} = 14.4 \text{ k}\Omega$

p.

Fold Over

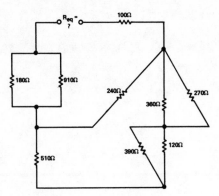

$$R_{eq} = \underline{\hspace{2cm}}$$

Answers

1.p. R_{eq} = 432 Ω

Practice Problems

2. Using Ohm's law and circuit reduction techniques, calculate the requested voltages and currents in the following circuits.

Fold Over

a.

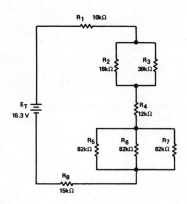

$I_{R2} =$ _____

$E_{R4} =$ _____

$I_{R5} =$ _____

b.

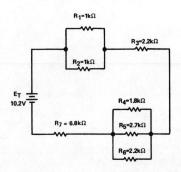

$I_{R3} =$ _____

$E_{R4} =$ _____

$I_{R6} =$ _____

Answers

2.a. $I_{R2} = 137\ \mu A$

$E_{R4} = 2.40\ V$

$I_{R5} = 66.7\ \mu A$

2.b. $I_{R3} = 1\ mA$

$E_{R4} = 724\ mV$

$I_{R6} = 329\ \mu A$

c.

Fold Over

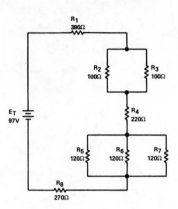

$E_{R1} =$ —————

$I_{R2} =$ —————

$E_{R6} =$ —————

d.

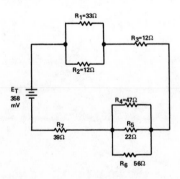

$E_{R1} =$ —————

$E_{R5} =$ —————

$I_{R7} =$ —————

Answers

2.c. E_{R1} = 39 V

 I_{R2} = 50 mA

 E_{R6} = 4.0 V

2.d. E_{R1} = 44.0 mV

 E_{R5} = 59.0 mV

 I_{R7} = 5.0 mA

e.

Fold Over

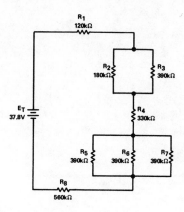

$E_{R1} = $ _____

$E_{R2} = $ _____

$I_{R6} = $ _____

f.

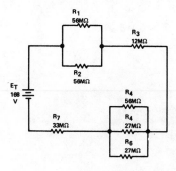

$E_{R3} = $ _____

$I_{R4} = $ _____

$E_{R6} = $ _____

Answers

2.e. $E_{R1} = 3.6$ V

$E_{R2} = 3.69$ V

$I_{R6} = 10.0 \mu A$

2.f. $E_{R3} = 24.0$ V

$I_{R4} = 389$ nA

$E_{R6} = 21.8$ V

g.

Fold Over

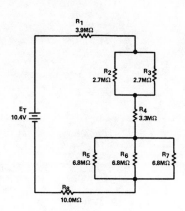

I_{R1} = _____

I_{R3} = _____

I_{R6} = _____

h.

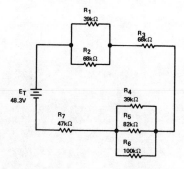

E_{R1} = _____

E_{R4} = _____

E_{R7} = _____

Answers

2.g. $I_{R1} = 500$ nA

$I_{R3} = 250$ nA

$I_{R6} = 167$ nA

2.h. $E_{R1} = 7.44$ V

$E_{R4} = 6.27$ V

$E_{R7} = 14.1$ V

3. Calculate the requested voltages, currents, and resistances in the following circuits.

Fold Over

a.

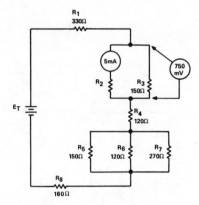

$R_2 =$ _____

$I_{R3} =$ _____

$E_{R7} =$ _____

$E_T =$ _____

b.

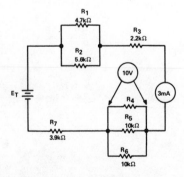

$I_{R1} =$ _____

$R_4 =$ _____

$E_{R7} =$ _____

$E_T =$ _____

Answers

3.a. $R_2 = 150\ \Omega$

   $I_{R3} = 5\ mA$

   $E_{R7} = 535\ mV$

   $E_T = 7.58\ V$

3.b. $I_{R1} = 1.63\ mA$

   $R_4 = 10.0\ k\Omega$

   $E_{R7} = 11.7\ V$

   $E_T = 36.0\ V$

c.   **Fold Over**

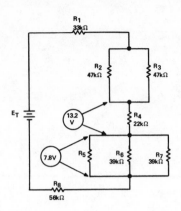

$I_{R2} =$ _____

$I_{R4} =$ _____

$R_5 =$ _____

$E_T =$ _____

d.

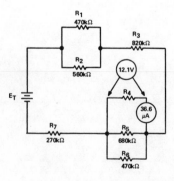

$I_{R1} =$ _____

$E_{R3} =$ _____

$R_4 =$ _____

$E_T =$ _____

Answers

3.c. $I_{R2} = 300 \, \mu A$

$I_{R4} = 600 \, \mu A$

$R_5 = 39 \, k\Omega$

$E_T = 88.5 \, V$

3.d. $I_{R1} = 43.6 \, \mu A$

$E_{R3} = 65.8 \, V$

$R_4 = 330 \, k\Omega$

$E_T = 120 \, V$

e. **Fold Over**

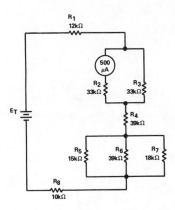

$E_{R1} = \underline{\hspace{2cm}}$

$E_{R5} = \underline{\hspace{2cm}}$

$I_{R6} = \underline{\hspace{2cm}}$

$E_T = \underline{\hspace{2cm}}$

f.

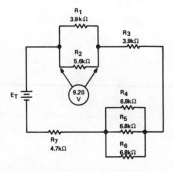

$I_{R1} = \underline{\hspace{2cm}}$

$I_{R4} = \underline{\hspace{2cm}}$

$E_{R5} = \underline{\hspace{2cm}}$

$E_T = \underline{\hspace{2cm}}$

Answers

3.e. $E_{R1} = 12$ V

$E_{R5} = 6.76$ V

$I_{R6} = 173\ \mu A$

$E_T = 84.3$ V

3.f. $I_{R1} = 2.36$ mA

$I_{R4} = 1.33$ mA

$E_{R5} = 9.04$ V

$E_T = 52.7$ V

Identify the following circuits as series (S), parallel (P), series-parallel (SP), or parallel series (PS).

1.

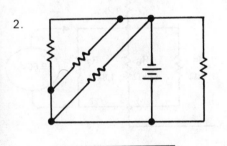

_____

2.

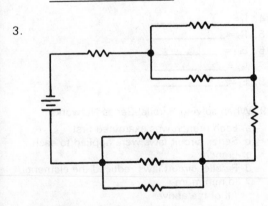

_____

3.

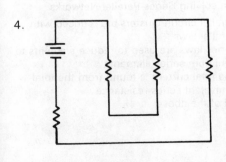

4.

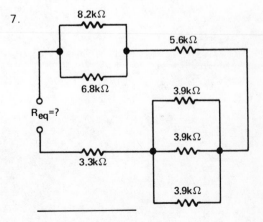

_____

5.

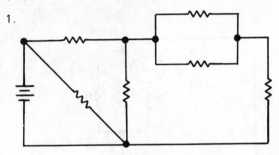

_____

Find R_{eg} for the following circuits:

6.

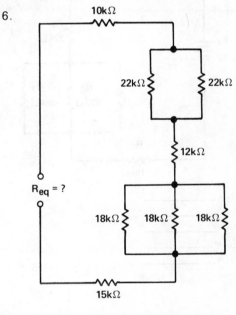

10kΩ

22kΩ   22kΩ

12kΩ

R_{eq} = ?

18kΩ   18kΩ   18kΩ

15kΩ

_____

7.

8.2kΩ

5.6kΩ

6.8kΩ

3.9kΩ

R_{eq}=?

3.9kΩ

3.3kΩ

3.9kΩ

_____

Find the requested voltages and currents and the total resistance for the following circuit.

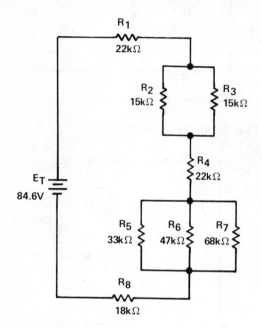

Find the requested voltages, currents, and resistances in the following circuit.

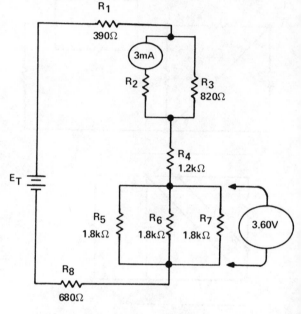

9. $R_T =$ _____
10. $I_T =$ _____
11. $I_{R2} =$ _____
12. $E_{R5} =$ _____
13. $I_{R7} =$ _____

14. $I_T =$ _____
15. $R_2 =$ _____
16. $E_{R4} =$ _____
17. $I_{R6} =$ _____
18. $E_T =$ _____

19. When solving Parallel-Series Networks:
    a. Each branch was examined first
    b. Series circuit laws were applied to each
    c. branch
    d. Parallel circuit laws reduced the elements to minimum
       All of the above

20. When solving Series-Parallel Networks:
    a. Parallel circuit clusters are reduced with parallel laws
    b. Series laws are used to reduce elements to minimum series elements
    c. The total current is found from the total equivalent series resistance
    d. All of the above

Lesson 10

Voltage, Current, and Power

This lesson introduces the loaded voltage divider as a particular application of series-parallel circuits. The concept of dividing voltage is illustrated with a simple voltage divider circuit and this circuit is used to examine the effect of selecting different ground points in the circuit. More practical voltage dividers with loads are discussed, and then the basic power formulas are reviewed and applied to a voltage divider circuit. The procedures for finding square roots with a calculator and with square root tables are also discussed.

LESSON 10. VOLTAGE DIVIDERS AND POWER

● Objectives

In this lesson your knowledge of series-parallel circuits will be extended to cover the voltage divider circuit configuration. In addition, the concept of power will be reviewed and calculation of power consumption for more complex circuits will be covered. Upon successful completion of this lesson, you should be able to:

1. *Design* a voltage divider circuit using a 100-volt power supply and five 10-kilohm resistors that will provide voltages of −20 V, −40 V, −60 V, +20 V, and +40 V to an external circuit that draws little or no current.

2. *Write* an explanation of the terms shown below, including diagrams where necessary:

    a.   Polarity
    b.   Ground reference
    c.   Load
    d.   Bleeder current

3. *Write* the "rules of thumb" by which bleeder currents may be selected for voltage dividers in simple applications.

4. *Design* a voltage divider that could be used to supply power to two loads requiring 45 volts at 20 milliamps, and 150 volts at 10 milliamps from a 200-volt power supply.

5. Using circle diagram (if necessary), *write* formulas that can be used to calculate power if

    a.   Voltage across and current through a load are known
    b.   Current through and resistance of a load are known
    c.   Voltage across and resistance of a load are known.

6. With what you have learned in previous lessons, *calculate* the voltage across, current through, or resistance of any resistor in a circuit schematic such as the one shown. At the end of this lesson, given the same schematic and using Ohm's law, the power formulas, and circuit reduction techniques, *calculate* the power each resistor dissipates.

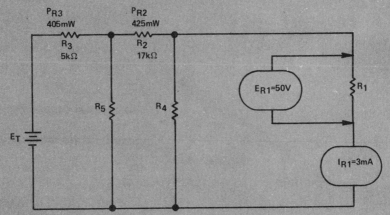

7. When performing square root calculations required in problems such as the above, *use a handheld calculator or square root tables to find the square roots.*

- **Voltage Dividers**

This lesson, Lesson 10, introduces the topic of voltage dividers, and reviews and expands your knowledge of the power formulas used in dc circuits and how to use them. The review and discussion of the power formulas will be presented later on in the lesson, and they will be related to series-parallel circuits of the type that were covered in Lessons 8 and 9.

Voltage Dividers — The first part of this lesson gives you a look at what is called a voltage divider. You will learn what voltage dividers are, and why they are used (Figure 10.1). As you will see, a voltage divider is actually a series-parallel circuits, so in order to understand and work with voltage dividers, you need to know Ohm's law, the series voltage law, and the parallel current law.

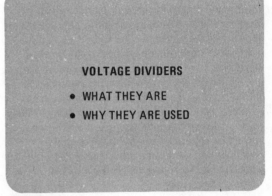

Figure 10.1

Now you may be asking, "What are voltage dividers anyway, and why should I study them?" Often in your study of electricity or electronics, you may have an application or circuit situation that requires a voltage source which can provide several specified voltages and currents, but there is no power supply handy that provides just the voltages you need. (For example, suppose you need to operate devices that require 15, 25, and 150 volts, and maybe only a 200-volt supply is available.) Voltage dividers provide a fairly economical way to obtain one or several lower voltages from a single higher voltage supply. Since this requirement occurs quite often, it is convenient to know about voltage dividers and their use. It is also important to realize the limitations and tradeoffs involved in their use. They do waste some power and in general cannot be used to operate devices whose demand for current is very high or varies greatly.

Sample Voltage Divider — In order to better understand voltage dividers, it will be helpful to review some of the topics related to them that have already been covered. In Lesson 5, it was pointed out how it is possible to get both positive and negative voltages from one series string of resistors, depending on where the reference point is in the circuit. It may seem unusual that a circuit may require negative and positive voltages from a single source; however, circuits and devices requiring more than one polarity of voltage for their operation are quite common in many electronic applications, from your TV to the most advanced computers.

Figure 10.2 shows a simple series circuit with four resistors each having 25 ohms of resistance. This means that in this circuit there is a total of 100 ohms of resistance across a 100-volt supply.

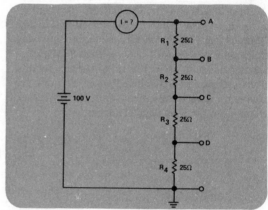

Figure 10.2

- **Calculations for Sample Circuit**
- **Sample Divider with Voltages**
- Voltage Divider Equation

Calculations for Sample Circuit — Using Ohm's law as shown in Figure 10.3, you can calculate that the total current flowing in this circuit is 1 amp. You can use Ohm's law once again in the form E = I times R to determine the voltage across R_4. Since you know the current is the same in all parts of a series circuit, the current through R_4 is 1 amp. Multiplying 1 amp times 25 ohms yields a calculated voltage drop of 25 volts across R_4.

$$I = E/R$$

$$I = \frac{100 \text{ VOLTS}}{100 \text{ OHMS}} \qquad I = 1 \text{ AMP}$$

$$E = I \times R$$

$$E = 1 \text{ AMP} \times 25 \text{ OHMS}$$

$$E = 25 \text{ VOLTS}$$

Figure 10.3

Sample Divider with Voltages — In the circuit of Figure 10.4, 25 volts is measured from ground to point D. If you were to measure the voltage from ground to point C, you would have an additional 25 volts across R_3 which when added to the voltage drop across R_4 would give you a total of 50 volts. If you were to measure the voltage from ground to point B, you would have 75 volts, and from ground to point A, you would measure the total supply voltage of 100 volts. You can see that at points A, B, C, and D, there are four different voltages increasing in 25-volt steps; the voltage has been *divided* by this circuit.

Figure 10.4

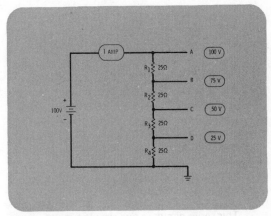

Figure 10.5

Voltage Divider Equation — The voltage output between any two points of a simple series circuit voltage divider such as this can be expressed in terms of a formula often called the *voltage divider* equation. Consider the simple circuit shown in Figure 10.5, where R_1, R_2, R_3, and R_4 can be any resistor values, and E_{supply} is the supply voltage connected in series with them. You know from Ohm's law that the total current flowing in this circuit, I, equals the supply voltage divided by the total series resistance of the circuit:

$$I = \frac{E_{supply}}{R_1 + R_2 + R_3 + R_4}$$

The voltage between any two points on this divider equals the product of this current times the resistance between these two points. For example, $E_{AB} = I \times R_1$. If you substitute for I, its equivalent expression as shown, you find that:

$$E_{AB} = \left(\frac{E_{supply}}{R_1 + R_2 + R_3 + R_4} \right) \times R_1$$

It turns out that for any two points on this divider the voltage output can be related directly to the supply voltage through a simple formula like this. Recognize that $R_1 + R_2 + R_3 + R_4$ is the total resistance of the circuit, R_{total}. Then the output voltage between any two points, E_{out}, can be expressed as

$$E_{out} = \left(\frac{E_{supply}}{R_{total}} \right) \times R_{out}$$

or, just moving these terms around:

$$E_{out} = \left(\frac{R_{out}}{R_{total}} \right) \times E_{supply}$$

This last expression is called the *voltage divider equation*. It states that the voltage output between any two points of a voltage divider equals the supply voltage times the ratio of the resistance between these two points, to the total resistance of the circuit.

This series circuit is one simple type of voltage divider. Suppose that you wanted to obtain a negative 25 volts from this same 100-volt supply. How could this circuit be altered to provide that? All you have to do is move the ground reference to point D, and move point D down to where the ground point was originally.

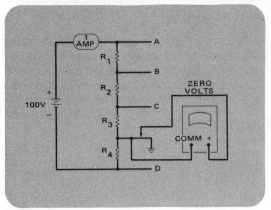

Figure 10.6

Review: Grounds and Voltage Reference — At this point it might be helpful to review the concept of a reference point for voltage measurement and ground. As has been mentioned previously, whenever a voltage is being measured, *two points* are involved. There are two probes on any voltmeter and the meter will measure the potential difference *between* these points. In circuits, voltage values are often stated with respect to one common reference point in the circuit. This reference point is given the general name "ground." Note that as shown in Figure 10.6, once this reference point is established for voltage, it is considered to be the zero voltage point in the circuit. This is because it is at zero volts with respect to *itself* as a reference. Think about this; *any* point is at zero volts with respect to *itself* as a reference. Also, *any* point in the circuit can be picked as a reference point for measuring voltage. If you place the voltmeter's reference probe at the reference point of the circuit, you can then measure all voltages and their polarities with respect to that point by touching the voltmeter's positive probe to other points in the circuit. Note that if you touch the positive probe to the reference point itself, you will read zero volts. The probes are effectively touched together.

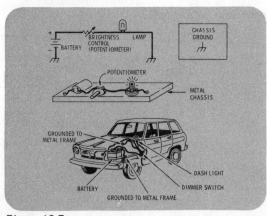

Figure 10.7

Return Path for Current — In addition to being used to specify the reference point from which voltage measurements are taken, the word *ground* is also often used to designate the *return path for current flow in a circuit*. In much electronic circuitry, the metal chassis upon which the circuit is assembled is used as the "return" path. In your car, the body and frame of the car are used as a return path for the current and are usually part of the path completing all circuits as shown in Figure 10.7. The great advantage of the common ground is realized in its contribution to the economy of wiring in circuits. Only one wire need be run to the part, and then the chassis completes the circuit. In addition, schematic diagrams are simplified, and voltage checks in equipment are made easier. Usually the technician is given a table of voltages with respect to the chassis of a piece of equipment. With the meter reference probe connected to the chassis, voltage readings may then be taken easily throughout the circuit with the other probe. The symbol used for a chassis ground is shown in Figure 10.7.

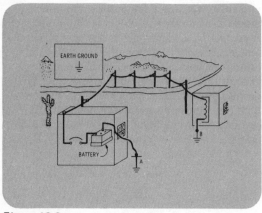

Figure 10.8

Earth Ground — As the use of electricity developed, one of the earliest reference points for voltage measurement and return paths for current flow was the earth itself. This is how the use of the word "ground" got started. In early telegraph systems, for example, one side of the system was connected directly into the earth. (A good long pipe or metal rod running into the earth is often used as a ground — good earth contact must be made.) The earth itself completed the circuit. (Actually, a good earth contact can be considered as a huge neutral reservoir containing both positive and negative charges. In the telegraph circuit shown in Figure 10.8, electrons are pushed into the ground at point A, and pulled out at point B). The use of earth grounding eliminated the need to string *two* telegraph wires over long distances and saved considerable cost.

Figure 10.9

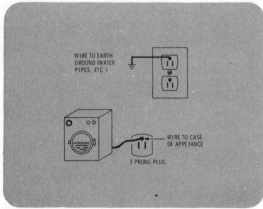

Figure 10.10

Grounding — Earth ground is an important concept to review because in most homes and laboratories the structural metal surfaces are at earth ground potential. Water pipes, gratings, electric conduit boxes and plates should all be connected to earth ground. Since it is easy to touch these things as you move about your home or the lab, it is important that none of the other surfaces you can easily touch have a greatly different potential from ground. If, for example, through faulty wiring, the outside of the refrigerator in your kitchen was raised to 110 volts, look at the possibilities in Figure 10.9. If you touched a faucet with one hand and the refrigerator with the other, you would have a 110-volt potential difference right across your body. This is very often a lethal situation.

Three-Prong Plug and Outlet — For this reason most appliances now come with a special three-prong plug. The third (long) prong is connected to a wire which should be connected to nothing but the outside surfaces and case of the appliance. In your wall outlet, the third socket in the receptacle should be connected directly to a good earth ground (Figure 10.10). In this way, all the appliances and fixtures in your kitchen and the rest of your home have their outside conducting surfaces at ground potential. If through faulty wiring some appliance developed a high potential on its outside case, a large current would flow through the ground wire, usually enough to blow a fuse and alert you of trouble.

Don't Ground Yourself — Electrical chassis are often connected to earth ground for safety reasons. In schematics you may see the earth ground symbol used to indicate an earth grounded point. But often electrical chassis grounds are NOT earth grounded. *This means a metal chassis may be at a much higher (or lower) potential than earth ground*, in which case touching the chassis and touching a good ground could result in an unhealthy shock. Always be careful when handling electrical equipment, and, in general, avoid grounding your body while working in the lab. If the floor and your shoes are wet, for example, you could become well grounded through the water.

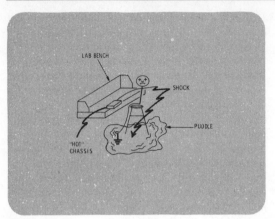

Figure 10.11

Touching a "hot" wire could then cause quite a bit of current flow through your body (Figure 10.11).

In review:

1. Voltages are measured between two points, one of these is usually referred to as a reference point or "ground."

2. A chassis ground (⏚) refers to an electrical chassis or metal frame that is used as part of the current pathway for circuits wired on it. The chassis is usually also used as the reference point from which voltages in these circuits are measured. A chassis ground may or may not be an earth ground.

3. An earth ground (⏚) refers to a point that is at the same potential as the earth itself, and most usually is a point that is electrically well connected to a set of metal water pipes that run for long distances under ground.

Another Similar Voltage Divider — To get back to voltage dividers, consider a circuit similar to the previous voltage divider circuit. This circuit (Figure 10.12) is essentially the same as the first voltage divider shown in Figure 10.2. All that has been done is that the ground reference point has been moved. If you were to measure the voltage from the ground reference to point C, you would measure a positive 25 volts.

If you were to measure from ground to point B, you would get a plus 50 volts, and from ground to point A, you would get a plus 75 volts. However, if you were to measure from ground to point D, you would get a negative voltage, a

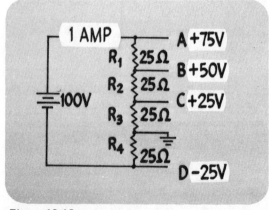

Figure 10.12

negative 25 volts. Remember that the term "polarity" is used when speaking of positive or negative voltage. For instance, in this circuit, the polarity of voltage from points A through C is positive with respect to ground; the polarity of voltage at point D is negative with respect to ground. Notice that this circuit still divides the applied voltage into four equal "chunks," and that the same current will flow as before. The maximum positive voltage available is 75 volts, but note a −25 volts is available from the reference point to point D.

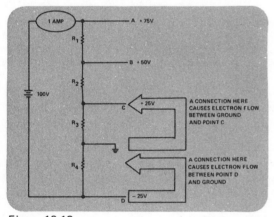

Figure 10.13

Polarity and Ground — Notice that when a voltage is said to be positive with respect to ground, this means that if a circuit were connected between that point and ground, electrons would flow out of ground to that point. If a point is negative with respect to ground, connecting the point and ground would result in a flow of electrons from that point to ground.

This situation is pictured for you in Figure 10.13. If ground and point C were connected, electron current would flow from ground to point C. If ground and point D were connected, electron current would flow from point D to ground.

A Load — Notice that so far in this discussion of voltage dividers, no external circuits that would draw any current have been connected to the voltage divider. If a current carrying circuit were attached to one of the voltage points, the whole operation of the circuit would change. Such an external circuit is called a *"load"*.

Concentrate your attention for a moment on this word, load. *A load is defined as any circuit or device that draws current and/or has resistance, requires voltage, or dissipates power.* As shown in Figure 10.14, when there is a load on a voltage source or power supply, current is drawn. The load may be a simple resistor.

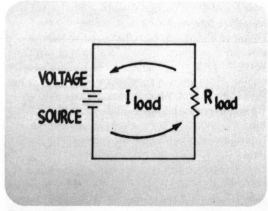

Figure 10.14

- **Large and Small Loads**
- **Voltage Divider Problem**
- **Practical Voltage Divider**

Large and Small Loads — Different devices will create different loading effects when attached to a power supply or circuit. Figure 10.15 shows an important point, a lower resistance draws a greater current and is, therefore, a greater load. A higher resistance draws less current, and is a lighter load. So a larger load causes a large current drain on the power supply, while a small load causes a small current drain. In some voltage divider applications, a voltage reference may be needed that will not have to drive any load. However, in many practical applications, a load drawing significant current will be attached to the divider, and the current drawn must be considered in its design.

A **LOWER RESISTANCE** DRAWS A GREATER CURRENT AND IS THEREFORE A GREATER LOAD.

A **HIGHER RESISTANCE** DRAWS LESS CURRENT AND IS A LIGHTER LOAD.

Figure 10.15

Voltage Divider Problem — Figure 10.16 shows a more typical type of voltage divider problem. Consider that you have to operate a load that draws 20 milliamps of current and requires 100 volts to operate. In this situation, also imagine that all that is available in your lab is a 150-volt power source. The problem is to design a voltage divider circuit to supply the correct voltage and current to the load, using what you have learned about series-parallel circuits in previous lessons.

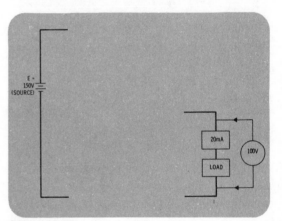

Figure 10.16

Practical Voltage Divider Circuit — Figure 10.17 shows the schematic of a basic voltage divider circuit to do the job, with the specified load connected to points A and B. Notice that this voltage divider is basically just a series-parallel circuit. There are two parallel paths for current to flow through. One branch current flows through R_2 and the other branch current flows through the load. The sum of these two currents equals the total current, which flows through R_1. The dotted lines indicate the paths of current flow.

To make this voltage divider supply the correct voltage and current for the load, you must select the correct resistances for R_1 and R_2. How

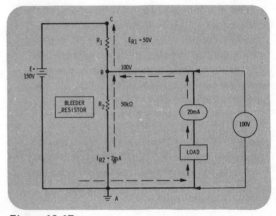

Figure 10.17

do you do this? This question leads to several interesting points concerning voltage dividers. The voltage delivered to the load depends on the relative sizes of R_1 and R_2, their ratio. Notice again that resistor R_1 will carry the total current in the circuit but that resistor R_2 carries a smaller current, called the *bleeder current*. Resistor R_2, through which the bleeder current flows, is called the *bleeder resistor*. The bleeder resistor is what develops the voltage that is delivered to the load, and also will function to stabilize the voltage to the load.

Choosing Bleeder Current — The design of a voltage divider begins by choosing a value of bleeder current. A large bleeder current will tend to keep the load voltage constant, even if the load current should vary for some reason. Variations in load current may occur for a variety of reasons, which depend on the nature of the load. The load attached to this circuit may be a motor or other device whose current demand may be continually varying. A high bleeder current causes a lot of power to be wasted in the voltage divider.

A compromise is made and as a general rule of thumb, shown in Figure 10.18, for simple voltage divider applications, bleeder current is selected to be 10% or one-tenth of the total load current. This conserves power, while allowing some measure of stability for the voltage divider.

"RULE OF THUMB" FOR VOLTAGE DIVIDERS

THE BLEEDER CURRENT EQUALS 10% OR ONE-TENTH OF THE TOTAL LOAD CURRENT

Figure 10.18

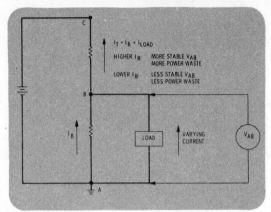

Figure 10.19

Voltage Divider Bleeder Current — This "rule of thumb" for voltage dividers is one that achieves a good compromise for most low-power, constant-load demand situations. To accommodate other loads and other power situations, you may see a variety of "rules of thumb" listed in various textbooks. Any.rule, however, is working around the same compromise. The higher the bleeder current, the more stable the load voltage will be if the load current should vary. This is illustrated in Figure 10.19. However, bleeder current causes wasted power, all of which must be dissipated in the bleeder resistor. So in reality, the 10% rule offers a good compromise for loads drawing a moderate amount of current (generally around 100 milliamps or less) that will not vary drastically. For heavier loads, this rule is sometimes modified to read as follows: For loads from zero to 99 milliamps, select the bleeder current as 10% of the load current. For loads drawing greater than 100 milliamps, choose a bleeder current of 10 milliamps. This modified rule is primarily designed to keep the power dissipated by the bleeder resistor to a level that can be handled by fairly common components.

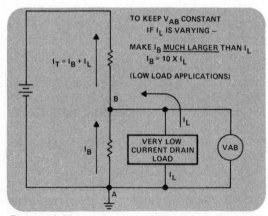

Figure 10.20

Low Power Highly Varying Load — The choice of bleeder current might take another direction in a case where you have a small load drawing very little current but whose current drain is varying wildly. If a load such as this required a constant voltage to operate, you might choose to make the bleeder current much higher than the load current, say ten times the load current. In this case (Figure 10.20), the voltage between points A and B is primarily determined by the bleeder current. Actually, if the bleeder current is very high and the load current is low and varying, the varying load acts as a slight disturbance to the total current. The resulting change in V_{AB} will be quite small. The amount of bleeder current, as mentioned earlier, is limited by how much power loss can be tolerated and whether or not the bleeder resistor can safely dissipate this power.

What about loads that need a lot of current and power and vary as well? For loads of this type, a voltage divider is probably not the best choice of circuitry to provide power. A regulated power supply will be needed to handle a large varying load. The word "regulated" means that the power supply contains special circuitry designed to keep its output voltage constant, even if the current drain on it is changing. Some regulation circuits are quite sophisticated and complex and their design often incorporates circuit components called capacitors, as will be discussed in Lesson 13.

Note again that the 10% rule for bleeder current will work for simple loads and voltage divider applications and that is what has been assumed here. The example voltage dividers you will see in this lesson will be confined to handling load currents of about 100 milliamps or less.

Calculation of Bleeder Current, I_{R2} — As shown in Figure 10.21, the value of the current through R_2 is chosen to be 10% or one-tenth of the total load current, or 0.1 times 20 milliamps, which equals 2 milliamps.

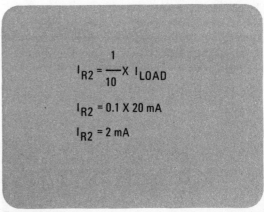

$$I_{R2} = \frac{1}{10} \times I_{LOAD}$$

$$I_{R2} = 0.1 \times 20 \text{ mA}$$

$$I_{R2} = 2 \text{ mA}$$

Figure 10.21

- **Calculation of R$_2$**
- **Partially Completed Voltage Divider**
- **Total Circuit Current**

Calculation of R$_2$ — You know that you want 2 milliamps of current to flow through R$_2$, and you know that the voltage across R$_2$ must equal 100 volts, since it is connected in parallel with the load which requires 100 volts. To find the resistance of R$_2$, you can use Ohm's law as shown in Figure 10.22. When you substitute the values of voltage and current in the formula, you should have 100 volts divided by 2 milliamps, which equals 50 kilohms.

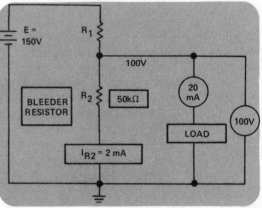

$$R_2 = \frac{E_{R2}}{I_{R2}}$$

$$R_2 = \frac{100\ V}{2\ mA} = \frac{100\ V}{2 \times 10^{-3}\ A}$$

$$R_2 = 50 \times 10^{+3}\ \Omega$$

$$R_2 = 50\ k\Omega$$

Figure 10.22

Partially Completed Voltage Divider — Figure 10.23 shows the voltage divider circuit with the bleeder resistance and bleeder current labeled. You are ready to calculate the value of R$_1$. From the series circuit laws, you know that the voltage across R$_2$ plus the voltage across R$_1$ must equal the total source voltage of 150 volts. Since you know the voltage across R$_2$ is 100 volts, the remainder of 50 volts must be dropped across R$_1$. Note also that the *total circuit current* flows through R$_1$. So before you calculate R$_1$, it will be necessary to calculate the total circuit current.

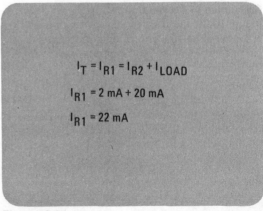

Figure 10.23

Total Circuit Current — As shown in Figure 10.24, this is equal to the current through R$_2$, plus the current through the load, which simply equals 2 milliamps plus 20 milliamps. Thus the current through R$_1$ equals 22 milliamps.

$$I_T = I_{R1} = I_{R2} + I_{LOAD}$$

$$I_{R1} = 2\ mA + 20\ mA$$

$$I_{R1} = 22\ mA$$

Figure 10.24

Calculation of R_1 — Knowing the current flowing through R_1 and the voltage that must appear across it, you can use Ohm's law in the form $R = E/I$ to find the resistance of R_1. As shown in Figure 10.25, R_1 equals E_{R1} divided by I_{R1}. When you substitute the values into the formula, you should have 50 volts divided by 22 milliamps which equals 2.27 kilohms.

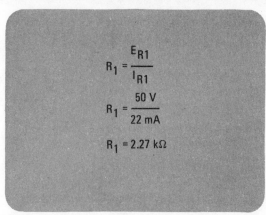

Figure 10.25

Final Circuit — Figure 10.26 shows the completed voltage divider design with all values labeled.

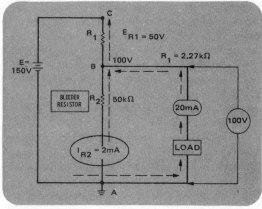

Figure 10.26

VOLTAGE DIVIDER DESIGN BASICS

1) EXAMINE POWER SUPPLY AND LOAD REQUIREMENTS
2) SELECT BLEEDER CURRENT
3) CALCULATE BLEEDER RESISTANCE
4) CALCULATE RESISTANCE OF OTHER DIVIDER RESISTOR(S)

Figure 10.27

Basic Voltage Divider Design — The basics of voltage divider design have been reviewed in this example and are shown in abbreviated form in Figure 10.27. In the rest of this lesson several examples will be used to illustrate and reinforce this procedure. Basically, the procedure is:

1. Examine your available power supply output voltage and the requirements of your load carefully. (Your power supply must provide a higher voltage and current capability than your load in order for a voltage divider to be designed between them.)

2. Select a value of bleeder current for the divider. For most voltage dividers, one tenth or 10% of the load current is selected.

3. Calculate the value needed for the bleeder resistor. (In building a divider, be sure to use a resistor with a high enough *power* rating to handle the bleeder current at the load voltage.)

4. Calculate the value of the other resistor or resistors needed for the circuit by calculating the total current flow through it, and then using Ohm's law in the form $R = E/I$.

Voltage Divider with Two Loads — The next logical step in considering the design of voltage divider circuits is to consider the design of a voltage divider that will supply the voltage and current needed to power two or more loads. This type of circuit basically involves a fairly straightforward extension of what has already been covered and the problem being considered is shown in Figure 10.28.

In this situation there are two loads; one load (load 1) requires 45 volts and draws 20 milliamps of current, while the other load (load 2) requires 150 volts and draws 10 milliamps of current. Suppose that the only power supply readily available is a 200-volt supply.

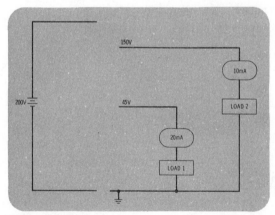

Figure 10.28

Resistor Voltage Divider — In order to deliver the required voltages and currents you will need a voltage divider with three resistors of the type shown in Figure 10.29. The problem boils down to one of calculating the values of R_1, R_2, and the bleeder resistor, R_3.

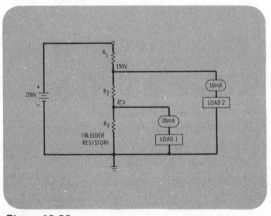

Figure 10.29

- Calculation of Bleeder Current
- Calculation of R_3

Calculation of Bleeder Current – To solve this problem you will follow the same basic steps that were followed previously (Figure 10.30). First of all, assume that the power supply has ample current capability to handle the job of powering the 10-milliamp and 20-milliamp loads, plus providing the bleeder current. Your next step is to select a suitable bleeder current to flow through R_3.

If you follow the rule of thumb for the bleeder current, you will want the current through R_3 to be about 10% of the total load current. In this case, since the load currents are 10 milliamps and 20 milliamps, the total load current is 10 milliamps plus 20 milliamps, which equals 30 milliamps. The current through R_3 then equals 10% of 30 milliamps, which is 3 milliamps.

$$I_{BLEEDER} = I_{R3} = \frac{1}{10} I_{LOAD}$$

$$I_{LOAD} = 10\text{ mA} + 20\text{ mA} = 30\text{ mA}$$

$$I_{R3} = (0.1) \times (30\text{ mA}) = 3\text{ mA}$$

Figure 10.30

Calculation of R_3 – Load 1 must have a voltage of 45 volts across it to operate correctly. Since R_3, the bleeder resistor, is in parallel with load 1, you know that the voltage across R_3 must also equal 45 volts. So at this point you know the current flowing through R_3, the bleeder current, and the voltage across it, 45 volts. Therefore, you can use Ohm's law in the form R_3 equals E_{R3} divided by I_{R3} to find R_3 as shown in Figure 10.31. Substituting the values of voltage and current into the formula, you have 45 volts divided by 3 milliamps, which in scientific notation equals $4.5 \times 10^{+1}$ divided by 3×10^{-3}. When you divide, you get $1.5 \times 10^{+4}$, which is 15 kilohms.

$$R_3 = \frac{E_{R3}}{I_{R3}} = \frac{45\text{ V}}{3\text{ mA}}$$

$$R_3 = \frac{4.5 \times 10^{+1}}{3 \times 10^{-3}}$$

$$R_3 = 1.5 \times 10^{+4} = 15\text{ k}\Omega$$

Figure 10.31

Determination of I_{R2} and R_2 — With R_3 determined, move up the divider to consider the next resistor, R_2. First you should analyze the currents flowing through R_2 as shown in Figure 10.32. From the parallel circuit laws, the current through R_2 equals the sum of the currents flowing through R_3 and load 1. This equals 3 milliamps for the bleeder current plus 20 milliamps from load 1 for a total current through R_2 of 23 milliamps.

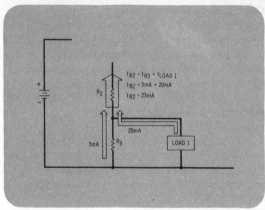

Figure 10.32

Calculation of E_{R2} — You need to determine the voltage across R_2. As shown in Figure 10.33, the voltage between ground and point B equals the voltage required by load 2, which is 150 volts. The voltage between ground and point A is 45 volts. The voltage across R_2 equals the difference between these two voltages, so subtract 45 volts from 150 volts and you get 105 volts. Now that you know the voltage across R_2 is 105 volts, and the current through R_2 is 23 milliamps, you can use Ohm's law to calculate the resistance of R_2.

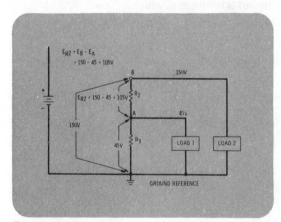

Figure 10.33

Calculation of R_2 — As shown in Figure 10.34, R_2 equals E_{R2} divided by I_{R2}. Substituting the values of voltage and current in the formula yields 105 volts divided by 23 milliamps. In scientific notation that equals $1.05 \times 10^{+2}$ divided by 2.3×10^{-2} which equals about 4.6 kilohms for R_2.

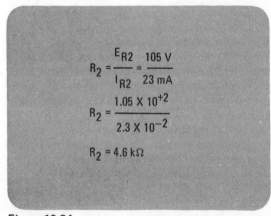

$$R_2 = \frac{E_{R2}}{I_{R2}} = \frac{105\ V}{23\ mA}$$

$$R_2 = \frac{1.05 \times 10^{+2}}{2.3 \times 10^{-2}}$$

$$R_2 = 4.6\ k\Omega$$

Figure 10.34

Determination of I_{R1} — Move up the divider one more time and consider how to calculate the resistance needed for R_1. This procedure is the same as for R_2 and would be the same for a fourth or fifth resistor in this circuit. First determine the current flowing through the resistor, then the voltage across it, and finally use Ohm's law in the form R = E/I to calculate the resistance.

First consider the flow of current as shown in Figure 10.35. The current through R_1 equals the 23 milliamps of current flowing through R_2 plus the 10 milliamps of current flowing through load 2. The sum of these two currents is 33 milliamps.

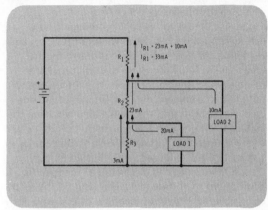

Figure 10.35

Calculation of E_{R1} — You need to calculate the voltage across R_1. As shown in Figure 10.36, the voltage from ground to point C is the full supply voltage of 200 volts. The voltage between ground and point B is 150 volts. The voltage across R_1 is the difference between the two, or 200 volts minus 150 volts which equals 50 volts across R_1.

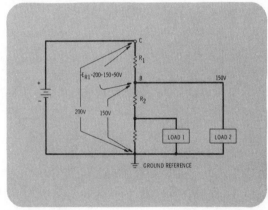

Figure 10.36

Calculation of R_1 — To find R_1 you can use Ohm's law as shown in Figure 10.37. R_1 equals E_{R1} divided by I_{R1}. When you substitute the circuit values in the formula, you have 50 volts divided by 33 milliamps. In scientific notation this equals $5 \times 10^{+1}$ divided by 3.3×10^{-2}. When you divide, you should get $1.515 \times 10^{+3}$ which is about 1.5 kilohms for R_1.

$$R_1 = \frac{E_{R1}}{I_{R1}} = \frac{50 \text{ V}}{33 \text{ mA}}$$

$$R_1 = \frac{5 \times 10^{+1}}{3.3 \times 10^{-2}} = 1.515 \times 10^{+3}$$

$$R_1 = 1.5 \text{ k}\Omega$$

Figure 10.37

● **Completed Voltage Divider**
● Additional Voltage Divider Problem
● Basic Voltage Divider Circuit

Completed Voltage Divider — As shown in Figure 10.38, the voltage divider design is now complete with the resistance values of R_1, R_2, and R_3 found. As long as the current drawn by the load remains fairly constant, this will provide a reliable power source for them. It is interesting to note that in a voltage divider with more than one load, such as this one, one stable load will keep the voltage to an unstable load constant. If load 1 was a very constant load, it would help stabilize the voltage at point B if load 2 should start to vary.

A more advanced discussion of the specific applications of voltage dividers is beyond the scope of this course. However, for those of you who are interested, some reference books on this subject are listed at the end of this lesson.

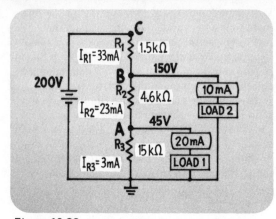

Figure 10.38

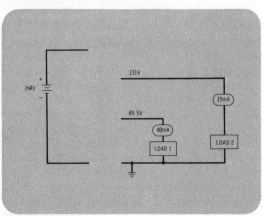

Figure 10.39

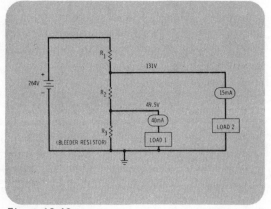

Figure 10.40

Additional Voltage Divider Problem — Consider two additional examples of voltage divider design. Figure 10.39 shows the requirements for the first problem. Load 1 draws 40 milliamps of current and operates at 49.5 volts while load 2 draws 15 milliamps of current and needs 131 volts applied to operate properly. Suppose that the only readily available power supply has an output voltage of 264 volts.

Basic Voltage Divider Circuit — The voltage divider circuit necessary to supply the correct voltages and currents to these two loads is shown in Figure 10.40. As you saw in the previous case, the design of this voltage divider boils down to the calculation of three resistors, R_1, R_2 and the bleeder resistor, R_3.

10-24

- Calculation of I_B
- Calculation of R_3
- Determination of I_{R2} and R_2

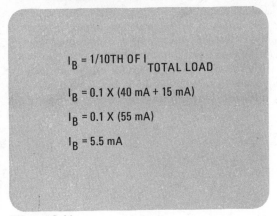

$$I_B = 1/10\text{TH OF } I_{\text{TOTAL LOAD}}$$

$$I_B = 0.1 \times (40\text{ mA} + 15\text{ mA})$$

$$I_B = 0.1 \times (55\text{ mA})$$

$$I_B = 5.5\text{ mA}$$

Figure 10.41

Calculation of I_B — To begin the design of this voltage divider, you need to select a value for the bleeder current, I_B. From the rule of thumb for bleeder current, I_B equals 10% or one-tenth of the total load current. As shown in Figure 10.41, I_B equals one-tenth of 40 milliamps plus 15 milliamps. If you add the two load currents and multiply by 0.1, you get 5.5 milliamps for the bleeder current.

$$R_3 = \frac{E_3}{I_b}$$

$$R_3 = \frac{49.5\text{ V}}{5.5\text{ mA}}$$

$$R_3 = \frac{4.95 \times 10^{+1}}{5.5 \times 10^{-3}}$$

$$R_3 = 0.9 \times 10^{+4} = 9.0\text{ k}\Omega$$

Figure 10.42

Calculation of R_3 — You can use that information to find R_3 by using Ohm's law in the form $R = E/I$. When you substitute the appropriate values in the formula as shown in Figure 10.42, you get 49.5 volts for E_{R3} divided by 5.5 milliamps for I_B. When you divide, you get 9.0 kilohms for R_3.

Here's an interesting point. If you were to look at a chart of preferred resistance values you would not find 9.0 listed. In the actual construction of the circuit you could use two 18-kilohm resistors in parallel in order to obtain the 9 kilohms needed for R_3.

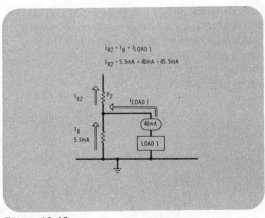

Figure 10.43

Determination of I_{R2} and R_2 — To calculate the value of R_2, you need to know the current flow through R_2 (I_{R2}) and the voltage across R_2 (E_{R2}). As shown in Figure 10.43, I_{R2} is equal to the sum of I_B and the current through load 1. When these are added, you get 45.5 milliamps for I_{R2}.

- Calculation of E_{R2}
- Calculation of R_2
- Determination of I_{R1} and R_1

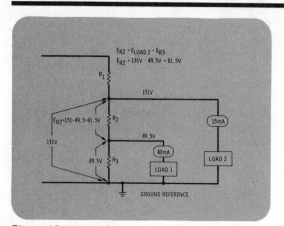

Figure 10.44

Calculation of E_{R2} — Figure 10.44 illustrates the calculation of E_{R2}. The voltage across R_2 equals the difference between the two load voltages since R_2 is essentially connected between the two loads. The voltage required by load 2 is 131 volts, and the voltage required by load 1 is 49.5 volts. The difference between these two is 81.5 volts for E_{R2}.

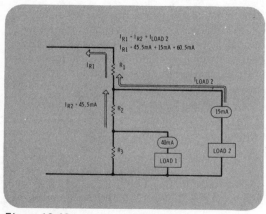

$$R_2 = \frac{E_{R2}}{I_{R2}}$$

$$R_2 = \frac{81.5\ V}{45.5\ mA}$$

$$R_2 = \frac{8.15 \times 10^{+1}}{4.55 \times 10^{-2}}$$

$$R_2 = 1.79 \times 10^{+3} = 1.79\ k\Omega$$

Figure 10.45

Calculation of R_2 — You can use Ohm's law in the form R = E/I to find the value of R_2. As shown in Figure 10.45, when you substitute 81.5 volts for E_{R2} and 45.5 milliamps in the formula and divide, you get 1.79 kilohms for R_2. In actual circuit construction you would use a 1.8-kilohm resistor.

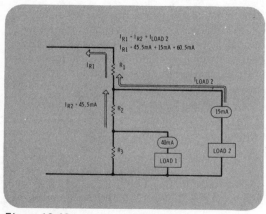

Figure 10.46

Determination of I_{R1} and R_1 — To finish the design of this voltage divider circuit, you need to find the value of R_1. First you can find the current flow through R_1 as illustrated in Figure 10.46 by adding I_{R2} and the current through load 2. Their sum is 60.5 milliamps for I_{R1}.

- Calculation of E_{R1}
- Calculation of R_1
- Completed Voltage Divider

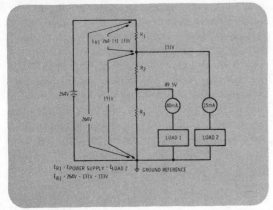

Figure 10.47

Calculation of E_{R1} — You also need to know the voltage across R_1 in order to calculate the resistance value of R_1. As illustrated in Figure 10.47, E_{R1} is the difference between the supply voltage of 264 volts and the voltage required by load 2 of 131 volts. This difference is 133 volts for E_{R1}.

$$R_1 = \frac{E_{R1}}{I_{R1}}$$

$$R_1 = \frac{133\ V}{60.5\ mA}$$

$$R_1 = \frac{1.33 \times 10^{+2}}{6.05 \times 10^{-2}}$$

$$R_1 = 0.2198 \times 10^{+4} = 2.2\ k\Omega$$

Figure 10.48

Calculation of R_1 — Now you can use Ohm's law in the form R = E/I to find R_1. As shown in Figure 10.48, when you substitute the appropriate values in the formula, you get 133 volts over 60.5 milliamps, and when you divide, the result is 2.2 kilohms for R_1.

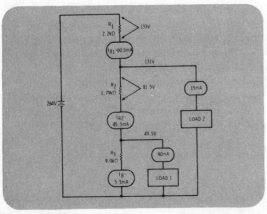

Figure 10.49

Completed Voltage Divider — The design of this voltage divider is complete, the values of R_1, R_2 and R_3 have been calculated and are shown in Figure 10.49 along with the values of voltage and current used to calculate the resistances.

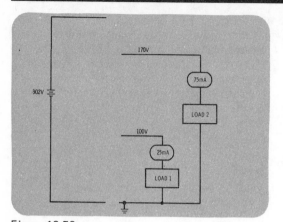

Figure 10.50

Another Voltage Divider Design – In order to become thoroughly familiar with the design of voltage dividers, consider one more example. The requirements for the circuit are shown in Figure 10.50. Load 1 draws 25 milliamps of current and requires 100 volts to operate properly, and load 2 draws 75 milliamps of current and requires 170 volts. Suppose that the only available power supply has an output voltage of 302 volts and assume that it is capable of delivering the required currents.

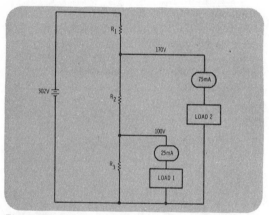

Figure 10.51

Basic Voltage Divider Circuit – As before, the voltage divider circuit necessary to supply these voltages and current to the two loads consists of three resistors, R_1, R_2, and the bleeder resistor, R_3 shown in Figure 10.51. Again, the design of this voltage divider simply involves the calculation of the three resistances.

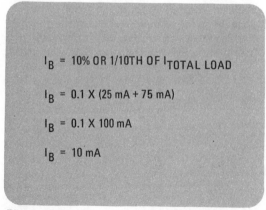

Figure 10.52

Determination of I_B and R_3 – In order to calculate R_3, you need to know the current flowing through it, which is the bleeder current, I_B, and the voltage across it, which is 100 volts. (R_3 is in parallel with load 1, which requires 100 volts.) From your rule of thumb for bleeder current, I_B equals 10% or one-tenth of the total load current, or, as shown in Figure 10.52, I_B equals one-tenth of 25 milliamps plus 75 milliamps, therefore I_B equals one-tenth of 100 milliamps, which is 10 milliamps.

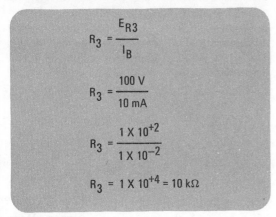

$$R_3 = \frac{E_{R3}}{I_B}$$

$$R_3 = \frac{100\ V}{10\ mA}$$

$$R_3 = \frac{1 \times 10^{+2}}{1 \times 10^{-2}}$$

$$R_3 = 1 \times 10^{+4} = 10\ k\Omega$$

Figure 10.53

Calculation of R_3 — If you substitute the values of E_{R3} and I_B in the Ohm's law formula as shown in Figure 10.53 and divide, you get 10 kilohms for R_3.

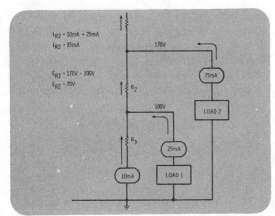

Figure 10.54

Determination of I_{R2} and E_{R2} — Moving up the voltage divider to R_2, you will need to determine I_{R2} and E_{R2} in order to calculate R_2. I_{R2} is simply the sum of I_B and $I_{load\ 1}$, which is 10 milliamps plus 25 milliamps. When you add these two currents, you obtain 35 milliamps for I_{R2}.

To find E_{R2} you need to subtract the voltage across load 1 from the voltage across load 2. Since R_2 is between these loads, E_{R2} is the difference between their two voltage requirements. As shown in Figure 10.54, this is 170 volts minus 100 volts or 70 volts for E_{R2}.

$$R_2 = \frac{E_{R2}}{I_{R2}}$$

$$R_2 = \frac{70\ V}{35\ mA}$$

$$R_2 = \frac{7.0 \times 10^{+1}}{3.5 \times 10^{-2}}$$

$$R_2 = 2 \times 10^{+3} = 2\ k\Omega$$

Figure 10.55

Calculation of R_2 — Now that you know E_{R2}, you can use Ohm's law in the form $R = E/I$ to calculate R_2. As shown in Figure 10.55, when you substitute the values in the formula and divide, the result is 2 kilohms for R_2.

- Determination of I_{R1} and E_{R1}
- Calculation of R_1
- **Power**

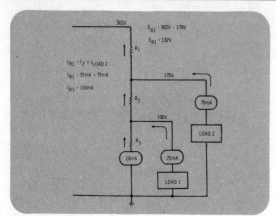

Figure 10.56

$$R_1 = \frac{E_{R1}}{I_{R1}}$$

$$R_1 = \frac{132\ V}{110\ mA}$$

$$R_1 = \frac{1.32 \times 10^{+2}}{1.1 \times 10^{-1}}$$

$$R_1 = 1.2 \times 10^{+3} = 1.2\ k\Omega$$

Figure 10.57

Determination of I_{R1} and E_{R1} — Following the same procedure for R_1, you should find the voltage across R_1 is 132 volts and the current through R_1 is 110 milliamps, as illustrated by Figure 10.56.

Calculation of R_1 — In order to complete the design of this voltage divider all you need to do is to use Ohm's law in the form R = E/I as shown in Figure 10.57. When you substitute the values of voltage and current in the formula, the result is 132 volts divided by 110 milliamps, which equals 1.2 kilohms and the design is complete.

Power — Thus far you have seen how voltage dividers can be used to provide different polarities of voltage, and how to calculate voltages, currents, and resistances in a voltage divider circuit. Loads and how the voltage or current of a load affects a voltage divider were also discussed. There is another factor used as a measure of a load, however, and that is its power or wattage rating. The concept of power was introduced in Lesson 4 along with a discussion of Ohm's law. At this point, it will be helpful to review this important subject and introduce some additional topics of interest that will expand your useful knowledge in this area.

Basic Power Formula in Circle Form — As you may recall from Lesson 4, the basic formula for power states that power equals current times voltage, and remember the unit for power is the watt. This formula may be put into a circle form as shown in Figure 10.58, which can be used in the same way that you used the Ohm's law circle. This gives you a convenient device for handling problems involving power calculations. Simply cover the quantity you want to find with your thumb, and the position of the remaining letters tells you the procedure to follow. Remember, a vertical line means multiply the quantities on either side of the line, and a horizontal line means divide the quantity on the top by the quantity on the bottom. For example, if you cover P, the position of the remaining letters gives you the basic power formula, power equals current times voltage. If you cover up the I, the formula is I = P/E, and covering E yields E = P/I.

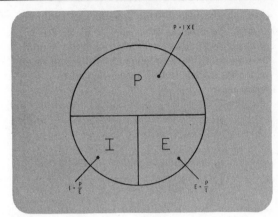

Figure 10.58

Derived Power Formula — In Lesson 4 another formula was derived for power using the first power formula and Ohm's law. That formula was P = I_2R. Figure 10.59 shows that formula in a circle form similar to the one above. This time by covering the P, you can see that power equals the current squared times the resistance. In other words, to find power, multiply current times itself and then multiply by the resistance.

You can also use this circle to find current when you know the power dissipated by a resistor, and the value of resistance. If you cover I^2, you can see that the square of the current equals power

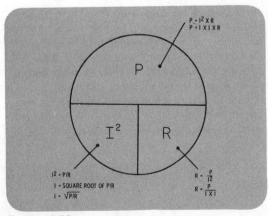

Figure 10.59

divided by resistance. How then do you find the current, if you know the square of the current? As you may recall, you must take the square root of the answer. In this case you can find the current by taking the square root of power divided by resistance.

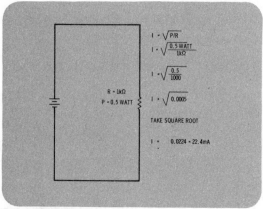

Figure 10.60

Example: $I = \sqrt{P/R}$ — From the circle formula shown in Figure 10.59, covering the I^2 gives P/R so you can easily write $I^2 = P/R$. This means that P/R is the square of I, or equal to I times I, not equal to I itself. You can find I by taking the square root of P/R. In the simple circuit of Figure 10.60, the 1-kilohm resistor is dissipating one-half of a watt. How would you calculate the current flowing through it? Substituting in the formula as shown, I equals the square root of P/R, which is the square root of 0.0005. This square root can be found either using a calculator or square root tables (both methods will be reviewed later in the lesson). When the square root is computed, you find that I = 22 milliamps.

Circle Diagram for Calculating R — The third way you can use this circle is in finding resistance when you know the power dissipated by a resistor and the current flowing through the resistor. By covering the R, you can see that resistance equals power divided by the square of current (Figure 10.61). In this case, you must square the current or multiply it by itself before you divide it into the power, to calculate the resistance.

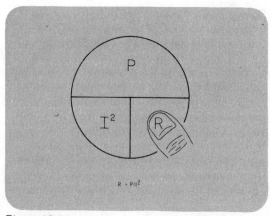

Figure 10.61

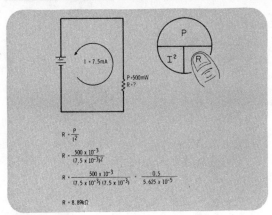

$$R = \frac{P}{I^2}$$

$$R = \frac{500 \times 10^{-3}}{(7.5 \times 10^{-3})^2}$$

$$R = \frac{500 \times 10^{-3}}{(7.5 \times 10^{-3})(7.5 \times 10^{-3})} = \frac{0.5}{5.625 \times 10^{-5}}$$

$$R = 8.89 k\Omega$$

Figure 10.62

Example $R = P/I^2$ — For example, if you know that a resistor in a circuit is dissipating 500 milliwatts and is handling a current of 7.5 milliamps, how would you calculate its resistance? Use the formula $R = P/I^2$ as shown in Figure 10.62 and substitute. Remember that the 7.5 milliamps must be multiplied by itself (squared) before it is divided into the power. When you perform the calculations, you find that $R = 8.89$ kilohms.

Third Power Formula — A third helpful power circle can be developed by using Ohm's law and the first power formula that was introduced. Figure 10.63 shows the first power formula, P equals I times E, and also shows Ohm's law in the form I equals E over R. What you can do is substitute the equivalent of current from Ohm's law into the power formula, that is, you can replace current in the power formula with E over R. This enables you to write power as the product of voltage times voltage all divided by resistance, and this is equivalent to voltage squared divided by resistance.

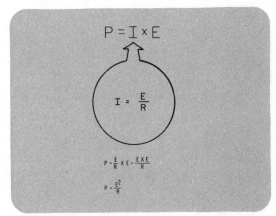

Figure 10.63

Third Circle Diagram — This relationship can now be put in circle form. You should have voltage squared on the top with power and resistance on the bottom as shown in Figure 10.64. This circle diagram can be used to give you three formulas in the same way as all the others. If you cover P, you should find that power equals voltage squared divided by resistance. In order to find the power dissipated by a resistor, when you know the voltage across the resistor and the value of resistance, you must square the voltage, and then divide by the resistance.

A second way this circle can be used is to find resistance when you know the power dissipated by

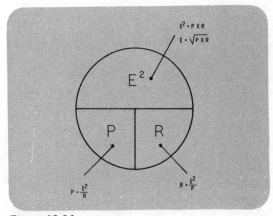

Figure 10.64

- Example $P = E^2/R$
- Example $R = E^2/P$

a resistor and the voltage drop across the resistor. By covering the R, you can see that resistance equals the square of voltage divided by power.

You can also use this circle formula to find voltage when you know the power dissipated by a resistor and the value of resistance. If you cover E squared, all you have to do is multiply power times resistance. However, that does not give you voltage, it gives you the square of voltage. You must take the square root of that to find the voltage. Thus, voltage equals the square root of power times resistance.

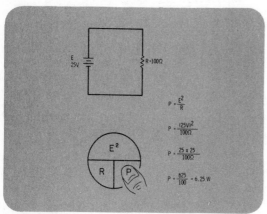

Figure 10.65

Example $P = E^2/R$ — In order for you to become more familiar with this third circle formula for power, consider some examples of its use. The 100-ohm resistor in Figure 10.65 has 25 volts applied to it. How much power is it dissipating? Cover the P in the circle to find that $P = E^2/R$. Then substitute 25 volts in the formula for E and 100 ohms for R. When you square 25 and divide by 100, you get 6.25 watts for the power dissipated by the resistor.

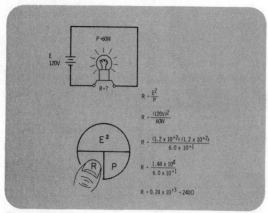

Figure 10.66

Example $R = E^2/P$ — A light bulb is rated at 60 watts and the required voltage is 120 volts. What is the resistance value? In Figure 10.66, cover the R in the circle to get $R = E^2/P$, then substitute 120 volts in the formula for E and 60 watts for P. When you square 120 and divide by 60, you find that the resistance of the bulb is 240 ohms.

- Example $E = \sqrt{P \times R}$
- **Power in Series-Parallel Circuits**

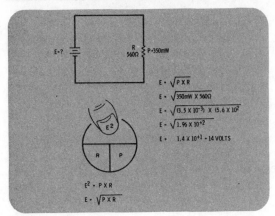

Figure 10.67

Example $E = \sqrt{P \times R}$ — The power dissipated by a 460-ohm resistor is 350 milliwatts. What is the voltage drop across the resistor? Cover the E in the circle as shown in Figure 10.67 to get $E^2 = P \times R$. Remember that this means $E = \sqrt{P \times R}$. Then substitute 560 ohms for R and 350 milliwatts for P, multiply, and take the square root of that to get $1.4 \times 10^{+1}$ which equals 14 volts dropped across the resistor.

Power in Series-Parallel Circuits — Now that three separate circle formulas for power have been introduced and discussed, it will be helpful to show how they all can be applied to the analysis of a series-parallel circuit of the type shown in Figure 10.68.

In this circuit diagram, all the known quantities have been labeled and the unknown quantities have been labeled with question marks. This circuit can be analyzed in a variety of ways by focusing your attention on each component and each unknown, one at a time. You can begin your analysis by using the first power formula to find the power dissipated by R_1. First of all, what do you know about this resistor? You know that the current through R_1 is 3 milliamps, and you know that the voltage across R_1 is 50 volts. You have to calculate the power.

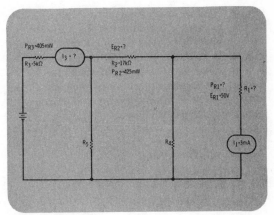

Figure 10.68

Calculation of P_{R1} — The first circle formula that was introduced gave you the relationship between P, I, and E, as shown in Figure 10.69. If you cover the P, you can see that power dissipated in a resistor equals current through it times voltage across it. Substituting the values of voltage and current in the formula gives you 3 milliamps times 50 volts. In powers of ten form, 3 milliamps equals 3×10^{-3} and 50 volts equals $5 \times 10^{+1}$. When you multiply, you should have 15×10^{-2} which equals 150 milliwatts for the power being dissipated by R_1.

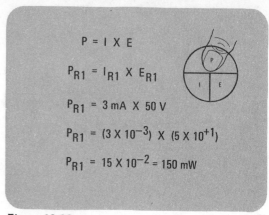

$$P = I \times E$$
$$P_{R1} = I_{R1} \times E_{R1}$$
$$P_{R1} = 3 \text{ mA} \times 50 \text{ V}$$
$$P_{R1} = (3 \times 10^{-3}) \times (5 \times 10^{+1})$$
$$P_{R1} = 15 \times 10^{-2} = 150 \text{ mW}$$

Figure 10.69

Circuit Diagram: Study R_3 — From Figure 10.70 you can see that the resistance of R_3 is 5 kilohms and the power dissipated by R_3 is 405 milliwatts. You know resistance and power dissipated and need to calculate the current flowing in the resistor. The second circle diagram that was introduced relates power, current, and resistance and can be used to help in this calculation.

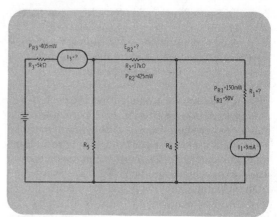

Figure 10.70

Calculation of I_{R3} — If you look at this circle diagram, reproduced in Figure 10.71, and cover I_2, you can see that the square of current equals power divided by resistance. Substituting the values into the formula as shown, you should have 405 milliwatts divided by 5 kilohms. In scientific notation, this equals 4.05×10^{-1} divided by $5 \times 10^{+3}$. When you divide, you can see that the square of the current through R_3 equals 0.81×10^{-4}.

You must take the square root of that to find the current through R_3. In previous lessons it was shown how a calculator such as the TI SR-50 can

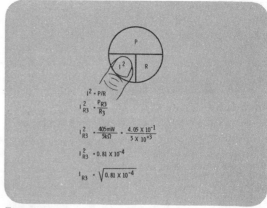

$$I^2 = P/R$$
$$I_{R3}^2 = \frac{P_{R3}}{R_3}$$
$$I_{R3}^2 = \frac{405 \text{mW}}{5\text{k}\Omega} = \frac{4.05 \times 10^{-1}}{5 \times 10^{+3}}$$
$$I_{R3}^2 = 0.81 \times 10^{-4}$$
$$I_{R3} = \sqrt{0.81 \times 10^{-4}}$$

Figure 10.71

be used to help simplify calculations of this sort. You can also use it to find the square root in this example.

Use of Calculator for Square Root — The chart in Figure 10.72 will help you keep track of the steps needed and what the display should read as you go along. First enter 0.81. Then press the $\boxed{EE}$ or enter exponent key. (The $\boxed{EE}$ or enter exponent key is what tells the calculator that the number has an exponent; the exponent is displayed to the right of the number.) Next press the $\boxed{+/-}$ key to make the sign of the exponent negative. Then enter four and the calculator should display 0.81 X 10^{-4}. In order to find the square root of this number, you simply press the square root key. The calculator should display 9 X 10^{-3} which is the current through R$_3$ expressed in scientific notation. In abbreviated form, this is 9 milliamps of current through R$_3$.

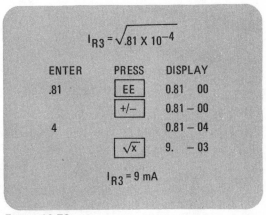

Figure 10.72

Circuit Diagram: Consider R$_1$ — Figure 10.73 shows the circuit diagram with the value of I$_{R3}$ and P$_{R1}$ labeled. You might recall that there are other methods that can be used to determine square roots. The use of tables and a manual calculation method were introduced in Lesson 4. The tabular method will be reviewed later as you proceed to analyze this circuit. Right now, focus your attention on R$_1$. At this point you still need to calculate its resistance value.

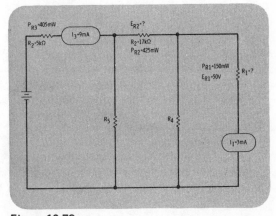

Figure 10.73

Calculation of R_1 — Since you know the voltage across and the current through R_1, you could use Ohm's law to find the resistance. However, from a previous calculation, you know that the power dissipated by R_1 is 150 milliwatts. The last circle diagram for power relates power, voltage, and resistance. In this case you can use this circle to help calculate R_1. As shown in Figure 10.74, if you cover R, you can see that resistance equals voltage squared divided by power. Substituting the values of voltage and power into the formula as shown, you should have 50 volts squared divided by 150 milliwatts. In powers of ten form, this equals $5 \times 10^{+1}$ times $5 \times 10^{+1}$ divided by 1.5×10^{-1}. This works out to be $16.7 \times 10^{+3}$ which equals 16.7 kilohms; thus the resistance of R_1 is 16.7 kilohms.

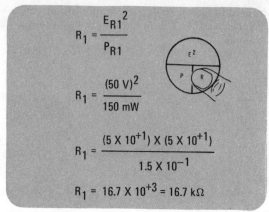

$$R_1 = \frac{E_{R1}^2}{P_{R1}}$$

$$R_1 = \frac{(50\ V)^2}{150\ mW}$$

$$R_1 = \frac{(5 \times 10^{+1}) \times (5 \times 10^{+1})}{1.5 \times 10^{-1}}$$

$$R_1 = 16.7 \times 10^{+3} = 16.7\ k\Omega$$

Figure 10.74

Calculation of E_{R2} — If you look back at the circuit and scan it for additional unknown quantities, you see that E_{R2} needs to be calculated. You can find the voltage across R_2 using the last circle formula. You know the resistance of R_2 is 17 kilohms, and you know that the power dissipated by R_2 is 415 milliwatts. If you look at the third circle formula for power as shown in Figure 10.75 and cover E^2, you can see that the square of voltage equals power times resistance. Substituting the values into the formula as shown, you should have 425 milliwatts times 17 kilohms. In scientific notation, this is

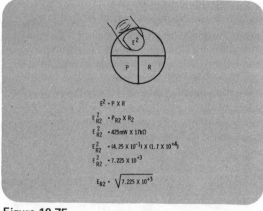

$$E^2 = P \times R$$
$$E_{R2}^2 = P_{R2} \times R_2$$
$$E_{R2}^2 = 425\ mW \times 17 k\Omega$$
$$E_{R2}^2 = (4.25 \times 10^{-1}) \times (1.7 \times 10^{+4})$$
$$E_{R2}^2 = 7.225 \times 10^{+3}$$

$$E_{R2} = \sqrt{7.225 \times 10^{+3}}$$

Figure 10.75

4.25 X 10^{-1} times 1.7 X 10^{+4}. When you multiply, you can see that the square of the voltage across R_2 equals 7.225 X 10^{+3}.

Square Root Tables — You must take the square root of that to get the voltage. Before you do this, however, consider how you can find square roots using square root tables. As shown in Figure 10.76, many of these tables list numbers from one to a thousand, and then across the page to the right are columns listing the squares and square roots. Some tables also list cubes and cube roots, but these will not be discussed here.

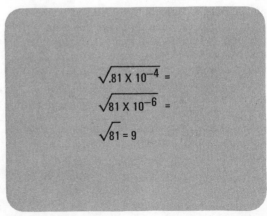

SQUARE ROOT TABLE

n	n^2	$\sqrt{n}$	n^3	$\sqrt[3]{n}$
1	1	1	1	1
1000	1,000,000	31.62278		

Figure 10.76

Square Root Example 1 — As a review of using tables to find square roots, go back to your first example and try to find the square root of 0.81 X 10^{-4}. When using tables, a good way to proceed is to try to alter the number you are working with until it is in a form that is easier to find in the tables. You will find that you can find the square root of this number much more easily by converting it to 81 X 10^{-6} as shown in Figure 10.77. (All this operation does is move the decimal point two places to the right and make the exponent more negative to make up for it.) Looking in the square root table, you see that the square root of 81 is 9.

$$\sqrt{.81 \times 10^{-4}} =$$
$$\sqrt{81 \times 10^{-6}} =$$
$$\sqrt{81} = 9$$

Figure 10.77

- Square Root of Exponent
- Example 1 Complete
- Square Root Example 2

Square Root of Exponent — Here's the key point on taking the square root of the exponent. As stated in Figure 10.78, *to find the square root of the power of ten, simply divide the power or exponent by 2.* You want to avoid powers of ten that are not whole numbers for the results, so you must make sure that the power of ten you are dividing is an even number, or one that is a multiple of 2. If not, the power of ten in your result may come out uneven like $10^{3.91}$ power. Powers such as this are difficult to handle and should be avoided.

TO FIND THE SQUARE ROOT OF A POWER OF TEN, DIVIDE THE POWER OR EXPONENT BY 2.

Figure 10.78

Example 1 Complete — For example, in Figure 10.79, you know that the square root of 81 is 9 from the tables. You must now take the square root of the power of ten which is minus 6. To do this, you just divide the exponent by 2, giving you a minus 3. So, you can see that the square root of 81×10^{-6} equals 9×10^{-3}.

$$\sqrt{81 \times 10^{-6}}$$

$$= \sqrt{81} \times \sqrt{10^{-6}}$$

$$= 9 \times 10^{-3}$$

Figure 10.79

Square Root Example 2 — As a second example, you can finish the circuit problem you were working. To find R_2 you need to take the square root of $7.225 \times 10^{+3}$. As shown in Figure 10.80, you could convert this number to $72.25 \times 10^{+2}$ and then find 71 in the square root tables. However, since the tables list only whole numbers, this would not be very accurate. There is a more accurate method which can be used to find the square roots of numbers that are larger or smaller than those listed in the square root table.

$$E_{R2} = \sqrt{7.225 \times 10^{+3}}$$

$$E_{R2} = \sqrt{72.25 \times 10^{2}}$$

Figure 10.80

Alternate Method — As shown in Figure 10.81, convert the number to decimal form and you should have 7225. Then there is a little mathematical trick you can use to find its square root. Find two numbers that when multiplied together give 7225, both of which are listed in your square root table. You can then take the square root of each of these numbers and multiply them together to get your answer. For example, select some number, say 25, and divide it into 7225. You find that 7225 is equal to 289 times 25. Looking in the tables you can find the square root of each of these numbers. When you look up the square roots, you find that the square root of 289 is 17 and the square root of 25 is 5. Then you multiply these two square roots together, 17 times 5 equals 85. Thus, the square root of 7225 is 85, and this is also the result for E_{R2}.

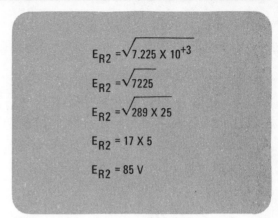

$$E_{R2} = \sqrt{7.225 \times 10^{+3}}$$

$$E_{R2} = \sqrt{7225}$$

$$E_{R2} = \sqrt{289 \times 25}$$

$$E_{R2} = 17 \times 5$$

$$E_{R2} = 85 \text{ V}$$

Figure 10.81

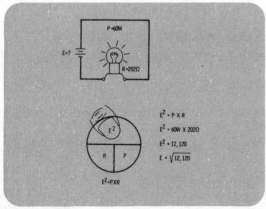

Figure 10.82

Additional Square Root Example — Suppose you wanted to know the proper voltage to apply to a light bulb rated at 60 watts, and you have measured its resistance and found it to be 202 ohms. Here again, you can use the third circle for power as shown in Figure 10.82. First, cover E^2 and the formula is $E^2 = R \times P$. When you substitute the appropriate values in the formula and multiply, you get 12,120 for E^2. You must find the square root of that to get the voltage. As shown in Figure 10.83, you must first find two numbers that when multiplied together equal 12,120. To do this, divide 12,120 by, say 60, and you get 202. Now find the square root of each of

- Additional Square Root Example
- **Additional Reference Material on Voltage Dividers**

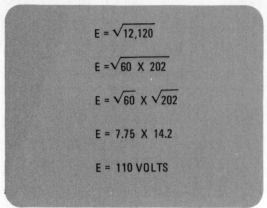

$$E = \sqrt{12{,}120}$$

$$E = \sqrt{60 \times 202}$$

$$E = \sqrt{60} \times \sqrt{202}$$

$$E = 7.75 \times 14.2$$

$$E = 110 \text{ VOLTS}$$

Figure 10.83

these numbers in the square root tables. The square root of 60 is 7.75 and the square root of 202 is 14.2. When you multiply these two square roots together, you find that the voltage required by the 60 watt bulb is 110 volts.

In this lesson, several new concepts have been discussed, along with a review and expansion of some that were covered previously. The voltage divider circuit (both with and without loading) was covered. At this point you should be able to design a voltage divider circuit to power several small loads from a single adequate power supply. The concept of power has been reviewed and expanded, and at this point, you should be able to use the three power circle diagrams as an aid in analyzing complex circuits. You are now ready to discuss multiple source dc circuits and some of the methods used to analyze them.

Additional Reference Material on Voltage Dividers

Grob, B., *Basic Electronics*, 3rd edition (New York: McGraw-Hill, 1971), pp. 61-64, 106-108.

Herrick, Clyde N., *Unified Concepts of Electronics* (Englewood Cliffs, New Jersey: Prentice-Hall, 1970), pp. 173-178.

Korneff, T., *Introduction to Electronics* (New York: Academic Press, 1966), pp. 160-164.

Tocci, R. J., *Introduction to Electric Circuit Analysis* (Columbus, Ohio: Charles E. Merrill Publishing Co., 1974), p. 168 (unloaded), p. 238 (loaded).

Weick, Carl B., *Principles of Electronic Technology* (Toronto, Canada: McGraw-Hill, 1969), pp. 79-82.

- **Worked Through Examples**

In these examples and in the practice problems that follow, you will be designing voltage divider circuits for various loads which operate at specific values of voltage and current. You will find that quite often the resistances you calculate for your voltage divider circuits will not be "preferred values" of resistance. Therefore, if you were to actually build any of these circuits, you would more than likely have to combine various resistors in parallel or series to obtain the value of resistance required for the voltage divider circuit.

1. Design a voltage divider to supply power to a load which draws 30 milliamps of current and requires 50 volts to operate properly. Assume that the only readily available power supply capable of delivering the required current has an output voltage of 80 volts.

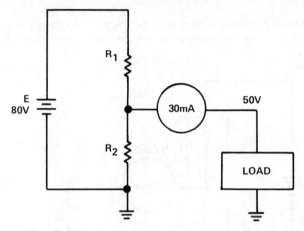

Since there is only one load, this voltage divider requires only two resistors to divide the 80 volts down to the 50 volts required by the load. The design of this voltage divider then simply requires you to calculate the values of R_1 and R_2.

The first step is to find the value of the bleeder current which flows through R_2, the bleeder resistor. The rule of thumb for finding bleeder current says that the bleeder current should be 10% or one-tenth of the total load current.

$$I_b = 1/10\text{th of } I_{total\ load}$$

$$I_b = I_{R2} = 0.1 \times 30 \text{ mA}$$

$$I_b = I_{R2} = 3 \text{ mA}$$

Now, since R_2 is in parallel with the load it will have the same voltage of 50 volts dropped across it.

You now know the current through and the voltage across R_2. and can therefore use Ohm's law in the form $R = E/I$ to find the value of R_2.

$$R_2 = \frac{E}{I}$$

$$R_2 = \frac{50\ V}{3\ mA}$$

$$R_2 = \frac{5 \times 10^{+1}}{3 \times 10^{-3}}$$

$$R_2 = 1.67 \times 10^{+4} = 16.7\ k\Omega$$

Now to find the value of R_1 you first need to know the current through it. As shown in the schematic below, the current through R_1 is the sum of I_b and the current through the load.

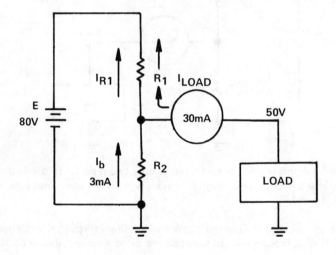

$$I_{R1} = I_b + I_{load}$$

$$I_{R1} = 3\ mA + 30\ mA$$

$$I_{R1} = 33\ mA$$

Next you need to determine the voltage across R_1.

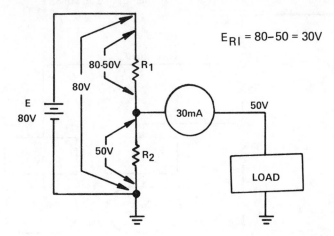

$$E_{RI} = 80-50 = 30V$$

As shown, E_{R1} is the difference between the supply voltage of 80 volts and the load voltage of 50 volts and consequently, E_{R1} is 30 volts.

Now you can use Ohm's law in the form R = E/I to find R_1.

$$R_1 = \frac{E_{R1}}{I_{R1}} = \frac{30 \text{ V}}{33 \text{ mA}}$$

$$R_1 = \frac{3.0 \times 10^{+1}}{3.3 \times 10^{-2}}$$

$$R_1 = 0.909 \times 10^{+3}$$

$$R_1 = 909 \; \Omega$$

This calculation completes your design of the voltage divider for this load.

2. Design a voltage divider circuit for a 250-volt power supply. The loads to be connected to the voltage divider require 40 milliamps at 150 volts and 50 milliamps at 200 volts.

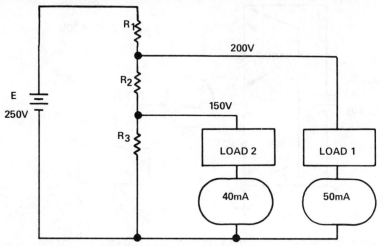

First find the bleeder current through R_3.

$$I_b = 10\% \text{ or } 1/10\text{th } I_{total\ load}$$

$$I_b = 0.1 \times (40\ mA + 50\ mA)$$

$$I_b = 0.1 \times 90\ mA = 9\ mA$$

Since R_3 is in parallel with load 2, E_{R3} equals 150 volts, and you can now use Ohm's law to calculate R_3.

$$R_3 = \frac{E_3}{I_b} = \frac{150\ V}{9\ mA}$$

$$R_3 = \frac{1.5 \times 10^{+2}}{9 \times 10^{-3}} = 0.167 \times 10^{+5} = 16.7\ k\Omega$$

Moving up the voltage divider to R_2, you need to determine the voltage across R_2 and the current through it.

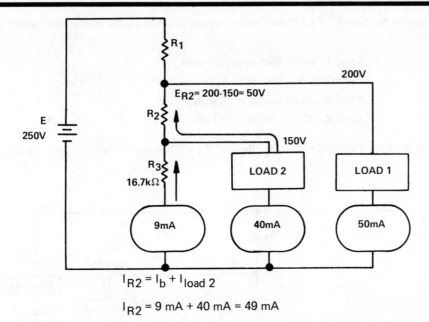

$$I_{R2} = I_b + I_{load\ 2}$$

$$I_{R2} = 9\ mA + 40\ mA = 49\ mA$$

As shown in the above sketch, E_{R2} is the difference between the two load voltages or 50 volts, and I_{R2} is the sum of the bleeder current and the current through load 2, which equals 49 milliamps.

You can use Ohm's law as shown to calculate R_2.

$$R_2 = \frac{E_{R2}}{I_{R2}} = \frac{50\ V}{49\ mA}$$

$$R_2 = \frac{5.0 \times 10^{+1}}{4.9 \times 10^{-2}} = 1.02 \times 10^{+3} = 1.02\ k\Omega$$

In order to calculate R_1 you need to find its voltage and current. E_{R1} is the difference between the supply voltage and the voltage required by load 1, or $250 - 200$, which equals 50 volts. I_{R1} is the total current in the circuit, which equals the sum of I_{R2} and the current through load 1. Here, 49 milliamps plus 50 milliamps equals 99 milliamps for I_{R1}.

You can use Ohm's law to find R_1.

$$R_1 = \frac{E_{R1}}{I_{R1}} = \frac{50\ V}{99\ mA}$$

$$R_1 = \frac{5.0 \times 10^{+1}}{9.9 \times 10^{-2}} = 0.505 \times 10^{+3}$$

$$R_1 = 505\ \Omega$$

and your design is complete.

3. Design a voltage divider circuit for a 125-volt power supply that will supply voltage and current to the following loads.

   Load 1: 0.0 milliamps at −25 volts

   Load 2: 5.0 milliamps at +25 volts

   Load 3: 15 milliamps at 50 volts

   Load 4: 30 milliamps at 100 volts

The voltage divider circuit consists of R_1, R_2, R_3, and R_4 with loads connected as shown in the sketch.

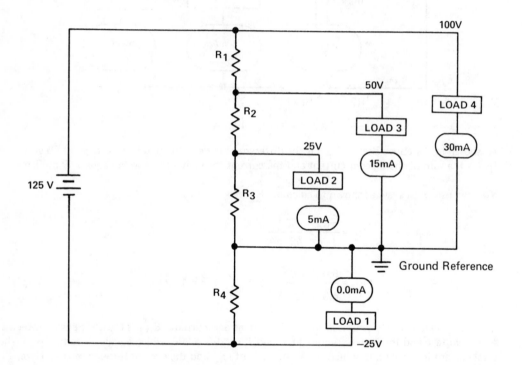

Since load 1 requires a negative voltage, it is connected from ground to the negative side of the source. All that is necessary to complete the design of this voltage divider circuit is to calculate the values of resistors 1 through 4 using the same procedures and techniques for the proceding examples.

In this case, R_3 is the bleeder resistor and R_4 is simply a voltage dropping resistor necessary to produce the −25 volts required by load 1.

To find I_b, take one-tenth of the total load current.

$$I_b = 10\% \text{ or } 1/10\text{th } I_{total\ load}$$

$$I_b = 0.1 \times (5 \text{ mA} + 15 \text{ mA} + 30 \text{ mA})$$

$$I_b = 0.1 \times (50 \text{ mA}) = 5 \text{ mA}$$

E_{R3} equals plus 25 volts since R_3 is in parallel with load 2. Now you can calculate R_3.

$$R_3 = \frac{E_{R3}}{I_b} = \frac{25 \text{ V}}{5 \text{ mA}}$$

$$R_3 = \frac{2.5 \times 10^{+1}}{5 \times 10^{-3}}$$

$$R_3 = 0.5 \times 10^{+4} = 5 \text{ k}\Omega$$

Moving up the divider to R_2, you need to know I_{R2} and E_{R2}. The current through R_2 is simply the sum of I_b and the current through load 2.

$$I_{R2} = I_b + I_{load\ 2}$$

$$I_{R2} = 5 \text{ mA} + 5 \text{ mA} = 10 \text{ mA}.$$

The voltage across R_2 is the difference between the voltages required by load 2 and load 3 since R_2 is connected between these two loads.

$$E_{R2} = E_{load\ 3} - E_{load\ 2}$$

$$E_{R2} = 50 \text{ V} - 25 \text{ V} = 25 \text{ V}$$

Using Ohm's law in the form $R = E/I$, you can calculate the value of R_2.

$$R_2 = \frac{E_{R2}}{I_{R2}} = \frac{25 \text{ V}}{10 \text{ mA}}$$

$$R_2 = \frac{2.5 \times 10^{+1}}{1.0 \times 10^{-2}}$$

$$R_2 = 2.5 \times 10^{+3} = 2.5 \text{ k}\Omega$$

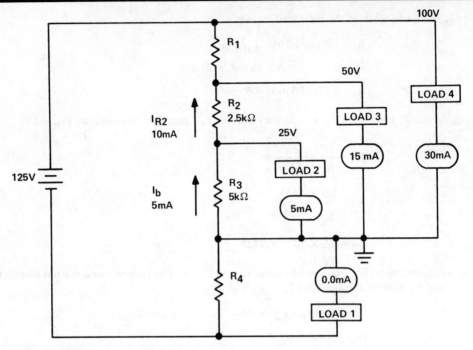

Proceeding up the voltage divider to R_1, you need to determine E_{R1} and I_{R1}. The current through R_1 is simply the sum of I_{R2} and the current through load 3.

$$I_{R1} = I_{R2} + I_{load\ 3}$$
$$I_{R1} = 10\ mA + 15\ mA$$
$$I_{R1} = 25\ mA$$

E_{R1} is the difference between the voltages required by load 3 and load 4 because R_1 is connected between these two loads.

$$E_{R1} = E_{load\ 4} - E_{load\ 3}$$
$$E_{R1} = 100\ V - 50\ V$$
$$E_{R1} = 50\ V$$

Using Ohm's law in the same form as before, you can calculate the value of R_1.

$$R_1 = \frac{E_{R1}}{I_{R1}} = \frac{50\ V}{25\ mA}$$

$$R_1 = \frac{5.0 \times 10^{+1}}{2.5 \times 10^{-2}}$$

$$R_1 = 2 \times 10^{+3} = 2\ k\Omega$$

All that remains to finish the design is to calculate the resistance of R_4. Because it is in parallel with load 1, you know that E_{R4} is 25 volts. You also know that no current flows through load 1 ($I_{load\ 1} = 0.0$ mA), therefore the total circuit current must flow through R_4.

$$I_{R4} = I_b + I_{load\ 1} + I_{load\ 2} + I_{load\ 3}$$

$$I_{R4} = 5\ mA + 5\ mA + 15\ mA + 30\ mA$$

$$I_{R4} = 55\ mA$$

Using Ohm's law in the form $R = E/I$, you can calculate the value of R_4.

$$R_4 = \frac{E_{R4}}{I_{R4}} = \frac{25\ V}{55\ mA}$$

$$R_4 = \frac{2.5 \times 10^{+1}}{5.5 \times 10^{-2}} = 0.455 \times 10^{+3}$$

$$R_4 = 455\ \Omega$$

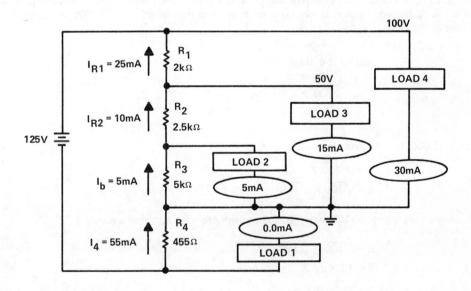

4. An electric iron dissipates 300 watts of power, and its measured resistance is 50 ohms. Using the appropriate power circle memory aid, determine the correct formula for finding the operating voltage of the iron and then solve for the voltage.

Cover E^2 in the $E^2 - R - P$ circle to see that $E^2 = P \times R$, and then take the square root to get:

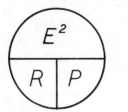

$$E^2 = P \times R$$
$$E = \sqrt{P \times R}$$

Then substitute the appropriate values in the formula and multiply.

$$E = \sqrt{300 \times 50}$$
$$E = \sqrt{15000}$$

In order to find the voltage required by the iron, you must take the square root of 15,000. If you have a calculator with a square root key, simply enter 15,000 and press the square root key to get 122 volts. If you don't have a calculator, you may use the square root tables. Since 15,000 is too large to be listed listed in the tables, you must find two numbers that when multiplied equal 15,000 and both of which are listed in the tables.

```
              150
100  √15000
      100
      ‾‾‾‾‾
       500
       500
       ‾‾‾
```

Dividing 15,000 by 100 gives you 150. Then

$$E = \sqrt{100 \times 150}$$
$$E = \sqrt{100} \times \sqrt{150}$$

Look up the square root of 100 and 150, and multiply to get your final answer.

$$E = \sqrt{100} \times \sqrt{150}$$
$$E = 10 \times 12.2$$
$$E = 122 \text{ volts.}$$

The voltage required by the iron to produce 300 watts of power is 122 volts, which agrees with the previous answer.

LESSON 10. VOLTAGE DIVIDERS AND POWER

● **Practice Problems**

The key objectives of this lesson have been achieved if you can now:
1. Design a simple voltage divider for use in any typical low-power application.
2. Apply the power formulas in analyzing circuit configurations of the type covered up to this point in the course.

The following problems are divided into two sets to enable you to get some practice in these areas. Fold over the page to check your progress and the accuracy of your calculations.

Depending upon the approach you use in solving these problems and how you round off intermediate results, your answers may vary slightly from those given here. However, any differences you encounter should only occur in the third significant digit of your answer. If the first two significant digits of your answers do not agree with those given here, recheck your calculations.

Calculate the following values: **Fold Over**

a.

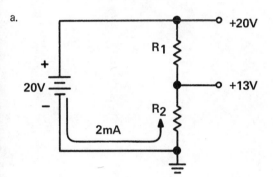

$R_1 =$ _____

$R_2 =$ _____

b.

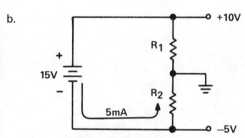

$R_1 =$ _____

$R_2 =$ _____

Hint: (Bleeder current should be one-tenth of the total load current)

c.

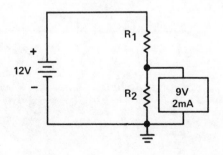

$I_{R1} =$ _____

$I_{R2} =$ _____

$R_1 =$ _____

$R_2 =$ _____

10-53

Answers

1.

a. $R_1 = 3.5$ kΩ

    $R_2 = 6.5$ kΩ

b. $R_1 = 2$ kΩ

    $R_2 = 1$ kΩ

c. $I_{R1} = 2.2$ mA

    $I_{R2} = 0.2$ mA

    $R_1 = 1.36$ kΩ

    $R_2 = 45$ kΩ

Fold Over

d.

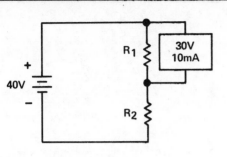

$I_{R1} =$ _____

$I_{R2} =$ _____

$R_1 =$ _____

$R_2 =$ _____

e.

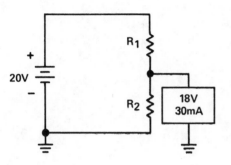

$I_{R1} =$ _____

$I_{R2} =$ _____

$R_1 =$ _____

$R_2 =$ _____

$P_{R1} =$ _____

$P_{R2} =$ _____

f.

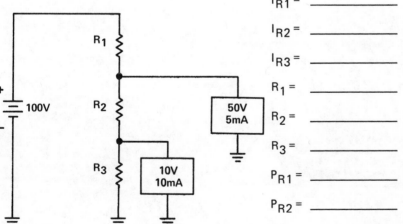

$I_{R1} =$ _____

$I_{R2} =$ _____

$I_{R3} =$ _____

$R_1 =$ _____

$R_2 =$ _____

$R_3 =$ _____

$P_{R1} =$ _____

$P_{R2} =$ _____

$P_{R3} =$ _____

- **Practice Problems**

Answers

d. $I_{R1} = 1$ mA

$I_{R2} = 11$ mA

$R_1 = 30$ kΩ

$R_2 = 909$ Ω

e. $I_{R1} = 33$ mA

$I_{R2} = 3$ mA

$R_1 = 60.6$ Ω

$R_2 = 6$ kΩ

$P_{R1} = 66$ mW

$P_{R2} = 54$ mW

f. $I_{R1} = 16.5$ mA

$I_{R2} = 11.5$ mA

$I_{R3} = 1.5$ mA

$R_1 = 3.03$ kΩ

$R_2 = 3.48$ kΩ

$R_3 = 6.67$ kΩ

$P_{R1} = 8 \ 25$ mW

$P_{R2} = 460$ mW

$P_{R3} = 15$ mW

Fold Over

g.

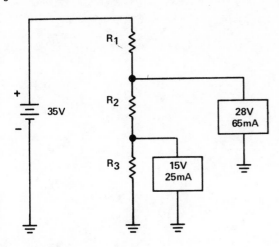

$I_{R1} =$ _____

$I_{R2} =$ _____

$I_{R3} =$ _____

$R_1 =$ _____

$R_2 =$ _____

$R_3 =$ _____

$P_{R1} =$ _____

$P_{R2} =$ _____

$P_{R3} =$ _____

h.

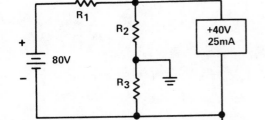

$I_{R1} =$ _____

$I_{R2} =$ _____

$I_{R3} =$ _____

$R_1 =$ _____

$R_2 =$ _____

$R_3 =$ _____

$P_{R1} =$ _____

$P_{R2} =$ _____

$P_{R3} =$ _____

Answers

g. $I_{R1} = 99$ mA

$I_{R2} = 34$ mA

$I_{R3} = 9$ mA

$R_1 = 70.7 \; \Omega$

$R_2 = 382 \; \Omega$

$R_3 = 1.67 \; k\Omega$

$P_{R1} = 693$ mW

$P_{R2} = 442$ mW

$P_{R3} = 135$ mW

h. $I_{R1} = 44$ mA

$I_{R2} = 19$ mA

$I_{R3} = 4$ mA

$R_1 = 909 \; \Omega$

$R_2 = 526 \; \Omega$

$R_3 = 7.5 \; k\Omega$

$P_{R1} = 1.76$ W

$P_{R2} = 190$ mW

$P_{R3} = 120$ mW

Fold Over

i.

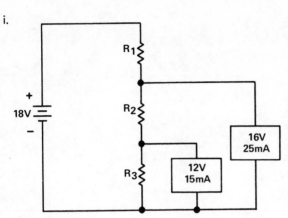

I_{R1} = _____

I_{R2} = _____

I_{R3} = _____

R_1 = _____

R_2 = _____

R_3 = _____

P_{R1} = _____

P_{R2} = _____

P_{R3} = _____

j.

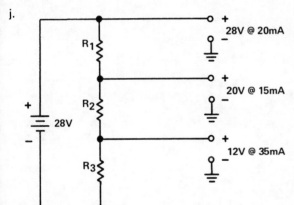

I_{R1} = _____

I_{R2} = _____

I_{R3} = _____

R_1 = _____

R_2 = _____

R_3 = _____

P_{R1} = _____

P_{R2} = _____

P_{R3} = _____

- **Practice Problems**

Answers

i. $I_{R1} = 44$ mA

     $I_{R2} = 19$ mA

     $I_{R3} = 4$ mA

     $R_1 = 45\ \Omega$

     $R_2 = 211\ \Omega$

     $R_3 = 3\ k\Omega$

     $P_{R1} = 88$ mW

     $P_{R2} = 76$ mW

     $P_{R3} = 48$ mW

j. $I_{R1} = 57$ mA

     $I_{R2} = 42$ mA

     $I_{R3} = 7$ mA

     $R_1 = 140\ \Omega$

     $R_2 = 190\ \Omega$

     $R_3 = 1.71\ k\Omega$

     $P_{R1} = 456$ mW

     $P_{R2} = 336$ mW

     $P_{R3} = 84$ mW

Fold Over

k.

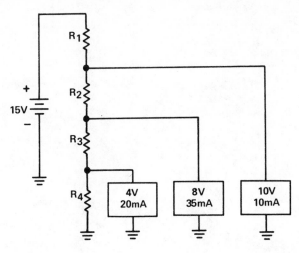

I_{R1} = _____

I_{R2} = _____

I_{R3} = _____

I_{R4} = _____

R_1 = _____

R_2 = _____

R_3 = _____

R_4 = _____

P_{R1} = _____

P_{R2} = _____

P_{R3} = _____

P_{R4} = _____

l.

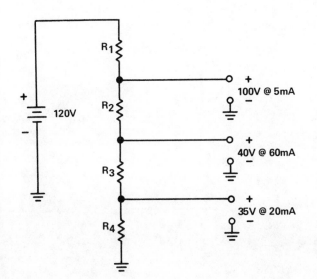

I_{R1} = _____

I_{R2} = _____

I_{R3} = _____

I_{R4} = _____

R_1 = _____

R_2 = _____

R_3 = _____

R_4 = _____

P_{R1} = _____

P_{R2} = _____

P_{R3} = _____

P_{R4} = _____

Answers

k. $I_{R1} = 71.5$ mA

$I_{R2} = 61.5$ mA

$I_{R3} = 26.5$ mA

$I_{R4} = 6.5$ mA

$R_1 = 70\ \Omega$

$R_2 = 32.5\ \Omega$

$R_3 = 151\ \Omega$

$R_4 = 615\ \Omega$

$P_{R1} = 358$ mW

$P_{R2} = 123$ mW

$P_{R3} = 106$ mW

$P_{R4} = 26$ mW

l. $I_{R1} = 93.5$ mA

$I_{R2} = 88.5$ mA

$I_{R3} = 28.5$ mA

$I_{R4} = 8.5$ mA

$R_1 = 214\ \Omega$

$R_2 = 678\ \Omega$

$R_3 = 175\ \Omega$

$R_4 = 4.12$ kΩ

$P_{R1} = 1.87$ W

$P_{R2} = 5.31$ W

$P_{R3} = 143$ mW

$P_{R4} = 298$ mW

Fold Over

m.

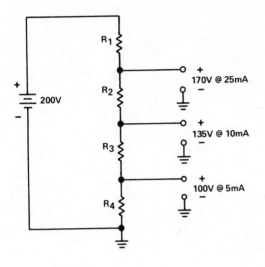

I_{R1} = _____

I_{R2} = _____

I_{R3} = _____

I_{R4} = _____

R_1 = _____

R_2 = _____

R_3 = _____

R_4 = _____

P_{R1} = _____

P_{R2} = _____

P_{R3} = _____

P_{R4} = _____

n.

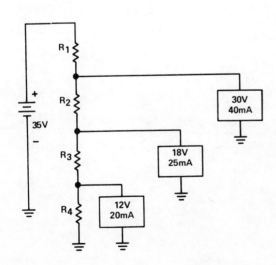

I_{R1} = _____

I_{R2} = _____

I_{R3} = _____

I_{R4} = _____

R_1 = _____

R_2 = _____

R_3 = _____

R_4 = _____

P_{R1} = _____

P_{R2} = _____

P_{R3} = _____

P_{R4} = _____

Answers

m. $I_{R1} = 44$ mA

$I_{R2} = 19$ mA

$I_{R3} = 9$ mA

$I_{R4} = 4$ mA

$R_1 = 682\ \Omega$

$R_2 = 1.84$ kΩ

$R_3 = 3.89$ kΩ

$R_4 = 25$ kΩ

$P_{R1} = 1.32$ W

$P_{R2} = 665$ mW

$P_{R3} = 315$ mW

$P_{R4} = 400$ mW

n. $I_{R1} = 93.5$ mA

$I_{R2} = 53.5$ mA

$I_{R3} = 28.5$ mA

$I_{R4} = 8.5$ mA

$R_1 = 53.5\ \Omega$

$R_2 = 224\ \Omega$

$R_3 = 211\ \Omega$

$R_4 = 1.41$ kΩ

$P_{R1} = 468$ mW

$P_{R2} = 642$ mW

$P_{R3} = 171$ mW

$P_{R4} = 102$ mW

Fold Over

o.

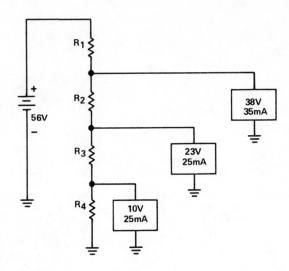

I_{R1} = _____

I_{R2} = _____

I_{R3} = _____

I_{R4} = _____

R_1 = _____

R_2 = _____

R_3 = _____

R_4 = _____

P_{R1} = _____

P_{R2} = _____

P_{R3} = _____

P_{R4} = _____

2.   Calculate the following unknown values using the three power formulas:

     a.   P = 5 W

         I = 25 mA

         E = _____

     b.   P = 1320 W

         I = _____

         E = 12 V

     c.   P = _____

         I = 6 A

         E = 5 V

Answers

o. I_{R1} = 93.5 mA

   I_{R2} = 58.5 mA

   I_{R3} = 33.5 mA

   I_{R4} = 8.5 mA

   R_1 = 193 Ω

   R_2 = 256 Ω

   R_3 = 388 Ω

   R_4 = 1.18 kΩ

   P_{R1} = 1.68 W

   P_{R2} = 878 mW

   P_{R3} = 436 mW

   P_{R4} = 85 mW

2.

a.   E = 200 V

b.   I = 110 A

c.   P = 30 W

Fold Over

2. d.   P = 6 W

         I = 0.39 A

         E = _____

    e.   P = 100 W

         I = _____

         E = 38 V

    f.   P = 30 W

         I = 3 A

         R = _____

    g.   P = 6 W

         I = _____

         R = 500 Ω

    h.   P = _____

         I = 0.036 A

         R = 15 kΩ

    i.   P = 2 W

         I = 0.009 A

         R = _____

    j.   P = 12 W

         I = _____

         R = 320 Ω

Answers

d.   E = 15.4 V

e.   I = 2.63 A

f.   R = 3.33 Ω

g.   I = 110 mA

h.   P = 19.4 W

i.   R = 24.7 kΩ

j.   I = 194 mA

Fold Over

2. k. E = _____

    R = 33 kΩ

    P = 20 W

    l. E = 120 V

    R = 400 kΩ

    P = _____

    m. E = 12 V

    R = _____

    P = 0.5 W

    n. E = _____

    R = 10 kΩ

    P = 0.25 W

    o. E = 1000 V

    R = 5 MΩ

    P = _____

Answers

k. E = 812 V

l. P = 36 mW

m. R = 288 Ω

n. E = 50 V

o. P = 200 mW

1. Any circuit or device that draws current and/ or has resistance, requires voltage, or dissipates power is defined as:

    a. A voltage generator
    b. A load
    c. An alternator
    d. A short circuit

2. A point that is at the same potential as the earth itself is called:

    a. Chassis ground
    b. The minus terminal
    c. An earth ground
    d. The positive terminal

3. A rule of thumb for voltage dividers: _____% of the load current is selected as bleeder current.

    a. 10%
    b. 25%
    c. 50%
    d. 90%

4. The next step in designing a voltage divider after examining the power supply and load requirements is:

    a. To draw a schematic
    b. To select the bleeder current
    c. To turn on the switch
    d. To calculate the current

5. A 100 watt light bulb requires 120 volts; what is its resistance?

    a. 14.4 K
    b. 120 ohms
    c. 1.2 ohms
    d. 144 ohms

Two quantities are given for each of the five resistors drawn below. In each case, calculate the quantity indicated with a question mark.

6.

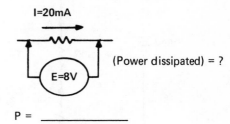

I=20mA

E=8V

(Power dissipated) = ?

P = _____

7.

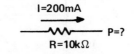

I=200mA

R=10kΩ   P=?

P = _____

8.

I=?

R=3.9kΩ
P=2.44W

I = _____

9.

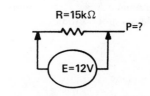

R=15kΩ

P=?

E=12V

P = _____

10.

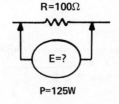

R=100Ω

E=?

P=125W

E = _____

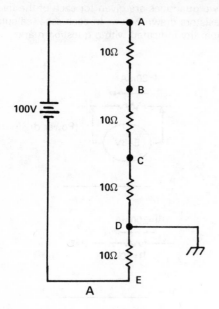

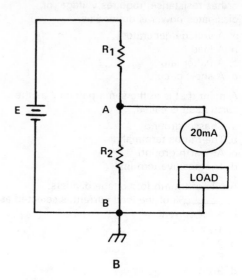

The questions that follow refer to schematics A and B.

11. The series network of resistors from A thru E in schematic A is known as a:
    a. Series-parallel circuit
    b. Voltage divider
    c. Parallel - series circuit
    d. Open circuit

12. Point E in schematic A is_____with respect to chassis ground (point D).
    a. Negative
    b. Positive
    c. Neutral
    d. The same voltage

13. Point A in Schematic A is_____with respect to chassis ground (Point D).
    a. Negative
    b. Positive
    c. Neutral
    d. The same voltage

14. Point C of Schematic A has a voltage with respect to point E that is_____of the applied voltage from A to E.
    a. 10%
    b. 20%
    c. 60%
    d. 50%

15. R_2 of Schematic B is called:
    a. The load
    b. A needless bypass
    c. A bleeder resistor
    d. A power saver

16. R_1 of Schematic B has a current through it that should be at least_____of the load current:
    a. 5%
    b. 50%
    c. 110%
    c. 90%

17. Increasing the current through R_2 of Schematic B will make V_{AB} more stable:
    a. But wastes more power
    b. But doesn't help the circuit.
    c. And requires changing R_1
    d. All of above
    e. a and c above

18. If the load of Schematic B is changed to a smaller resistor the current drain from the power supply:
    a. Decreases
    b. Increases
    c. Remains the same
    d. Goes negative

Lesson 11

Introduction to Kirchhoff's Laws

This lesson introduces *Kirchhoff's Current Law* and *Kirchhoff's Voltage Law* and explains all new terminology relating to these two laws. Discussion includes an examination of how to *write* and *solve loop equations* for the unknown current or currents. This includes all algebraic manipulations necessary to solve the loop equations for *multiple source* circuits.

● **Objectives**

This lesson introduces two new and powerful laws that you will find useful in analyzing dc circuits where you cannot use Ohm's law alone. This lesson and the next explore Kirchhoff's laws and several advanced methods of circuit analysis. At the end of this lesson, you should be able to:

1. *Write* Kirchhoff's current law, using diagrams to explain it.

2. In any circuit of the type illustrated in the schematic diagram below

   a. *Identify* and label the loops and nodes (or junctions)

   b. *Identify* three typical circuit paths that are not loops.

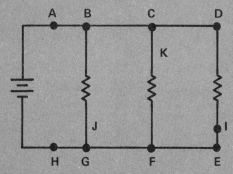

3. At any node of the type illustrated below, *use Kirchhoff's current law to calculate* the unknown current labeled with a question mark.

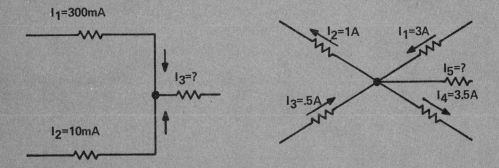

4. *Write* Kirchhoff's voltage law, using diagrams to explain it.

5. *Write* the six rules governing series circuit and parallel circuit operation. *Explain* which of these rules are related to Kirchhoff's voltage law, which to Kirchhoff's current law, and why.

6. *Write* an explanation of the significance of a negative current value solution in a Kirchhoff's law problem.

- Objectives

7. In any loop, such as the type represented in the schematic below, *write* a Kirchhoff's voltage law or "loop" equation, being careful to observe the correct rules with respect to the signs of the voltages. *Write* one equation using electron current and another equation using conventional current.

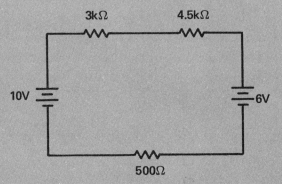

8. *Solve* any loop equation of the type shown for a single unknown quantity such as the current, *correctly using the procedures of*:

   a. Transposing

   b. Combining "like" terms

   c. Multiplying or dividing both sides of the equation by the same quantity

   d. Adding or subtracting the same quantity on both sides of an equation

   e. Changing the signs of all parts of an equation.

   $$10\,V - 3\,kI - 4.5\,kI - 6\,V - 500\,kI = 0$$

9. In a multiple source circuit of the type shown, using Kirchhoff's laws, *solve* for all unknown currents (including direction) and voltages (including polarity). You should be able to write loop equations for this circuit using either conventional or electron current.

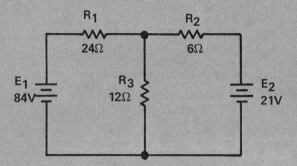

LESSON 11. INTRODUCTION TO KIRCHHOFF'S LAWS

● **Gustav Kirchhoff**

An important objective of this course on dc circuits is to provide you with the tools you will need to make electricity work for you, or to predict how it will behave in any given circuit situation. Up to this point, you have been using Ohm's law, the power formulas, and some basic circuit rules as tools for analyzing dc circuits (Figure 11.1).

Figure 11.1

In this lesson and the next, you will be introduced to some new tools you can use to help simplify and analyze more complex circuits (Figure 11.2). The key difference between the methods that will be covered in this lesson and methods you have seen earlier is that the methods introduced here will allow you to analyze dc circuits which cannot be solved using Ohm's law alone. This includes certain types of single power supply circuits, as well as those with more than one voltage source. You will find that in certain circuits, the solution is not possible using Ohm's law alone.

Figure 11.2

Gustav Kirchhoff — Some of the basic and general methods for analyzing circuits that will be introduced and analyzed in this lesson, were developed in 1874 by the German physicist, Gustav Kirchhoff (pronounced Kirk'hawf). A photo of Kirchhoff is shown as Figure 11.3.

Figure 11.3

- **Lesson Objectives**
- **Basic Circuit Rules: Series Circuit**
- **Basic Circuit Rules: Parallel Circuit**

Lesson Objectives — The key objective of this lesson and the next is to enable you to write down and use what are called Kirchhoff's laws to completely analyze a complex, multiple source dc circuit, such as the one in Figure 11.4. At the end of Lessons 11 and 12, you should be able to calculate any voltage drop and any current flowing in a multiple source complex circuit, such as this.

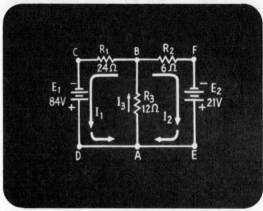

Figure 11.4

Basic Circuit Rules: Series Circuit — You have already seen Kirchhoff's laws at work in some specific cases, such as when the rules describing the operation of series and parallel circuits were introduced. Take a minute to briefly review these rules. As listed in Figure 11.5 for series circuits, you have seen that:

1. The current is the same in all parts of a series circuit.
2. The sum of the individual voltage drops in a series circuit equals the total applied voltage.
3. The total resistance of a series circuit is equal to the sum of the individual resistances.

SERIES CIRCUIT RULES

1. CURRENT IS THE SAME IN ALL PARTS OF A SERIES CIRCUIT.

2. THE SUM OF THE INDIVIDUAL VOLTAGE DROPS IN A SERIES CIRCUIT EQUALS THE TOTAL APPLIED VOLTAGE.

3. THE TOTAL RESISTANCE OF A SERIES CIRCUIT EQUALS THE SUM OF THE INDIVIDUAL RESISTANCES.

Figure 11.5

Basic Circuit Rules: Parallel Circuit — For parallel circuits (Figure 11.6) you have seen that:

1. The total or main line current is the sum of the individual branch currents.
2. The voltage is the same across all branches.
3. The total resistance is always less than, or approximately equal to, the smallest branch resistance.

As you proceed through this lesson, you will see how Kirchhoff's laws really are just more general statements of these circuit rules you have been using.

PARALLEL CIRCUIT RULES

1. TOTAL CURRENT IS THE SUM OF THE INDIVIDUAL BRANCH CURRENTS.

2. VOLTAGE IS THE SAME ACROSS ALL BRANCHES.

3. TOTAL RESISTANCE IS ALWAYS LESS THAN OR APPROXIMATELY EQUAL TO THE SMALLEST BRANCH RESISTANCE.

Figure 11.6

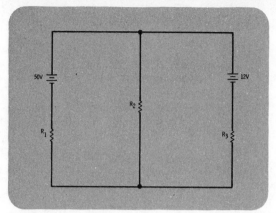

Figure 11.7

Why Do You Need Kirchhoff's Laws? — You may be wondering just why these new laws are needed. The reason is that the laws you already know won't always work with complex circuits such as the one shown in Figure 11.7.

Why? Suppose that you need to find the voltage dropped across R_2. There are two voltage sources in the circuit, and as you see, each one acting on R_2.

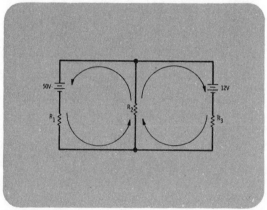

Figure 11.8

Which Way Does Current Flow Through R_2 — There are several possibilities for this question. Will the currents flow as shown in Figure 11.8, where electron current from both sources combines and flows through R_2?

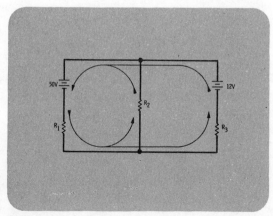

Figure 11.9

Or, will the larger battery "overpower" the smaller battery and push current backwards through the smaller source as shown in Figure 11.9?

If this is the case, what effect does the 12-volt battery have on the circuit? Should it be treated as a resistance, an open circuit, a short circuit, or something else?

These are all good questions. Unfortunately, they cannot be answered by applying Ohm's law and the series and parallel circuit laws you already know. For this reason, some other circuit analysis methods, including methods such as Kirchhoff's laws must be studied. There are *two* of these laws, and they will be discussed one at a time.

- Kirchhoff's Current Law
- Junctions or Nodes
- Kirchhoff's Current Law at a Junction

Kirchhoff's Current Law — Kirchhoff's first law, sometimes called *Kirchhoff's current law*, simply states that the sum of the currents *arriving* at any point in a circuit must equal the sum of the currents *leaving* that point (Figure 11.10). You may see this law stated several different ways, and you will be shown several alternate statements of this law. But, basically, any statement of Kirchhoff's current law means the same thing: whatever current arrives at any point in a circuit must equal the total current that leaves.

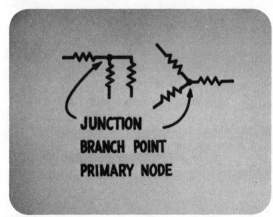

KIRCHHOFF'S FIRST LAW OR KIRCHHOFF'S CURRENT LAW

THE SUM OF THE CURRENTS ARRIVING AT ANY POINT IN A CIRCUIT MUST EQUAL THE SUM OF THE CURRENTS LEAVING THAT POINT.

Figure 11.10

Junctions or Nodes — This law applies to any point in a circuit but is most frequently used to analyze points in circuits where three or more components are joined together. As shown in Figure 11.11, points with three or more connections are called "junction points" or *junctions*. They may also be called *branch points* or *nodes* as well.

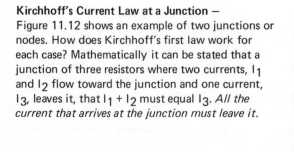

JUNCTION

BRANCH POINT

PRIMARY NODE

Figure 11.11

Kirchhoff's Current Law at a Junction — Figure 11.12 shows an example of two junctions or nodes. How does Kirchhoff's first law work for each case? Mathematically it can be stated that a junction of three resistors where two currents, I_1 and I_2 flow toward the junction and one current, I_3, leaves it, that $I_1 + I_2$ must equal I_3. *All the current that arrives at the junction must leave it.*

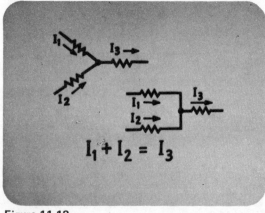

$$I_1 + I_2 = I_3$$

Figure 11.12

- Kirchhoff's Current Law at a Junction
- If Kirchhoff's Current Law Were Not Followed
- If More Electrons Leave Than Arrive

Kirchhoff's Current Law at a Junction —
Figure 11.13 shows another example set of two
junctions. In each case there is one current, I_1,
entering the junction and two currents, I_2 and I_3,
leaving the junction. By Kirchhoff's first law, I_1
must equal $I_2 + I_3$. For example, suppose you
know that I_1 equals 7 amps, and I_2 equals 5 amps.
How would you determine I_3? Recall again that
the current leaving the junction must be equal to
the current entering. In order for this to be true, I_3
must be 2 amps.

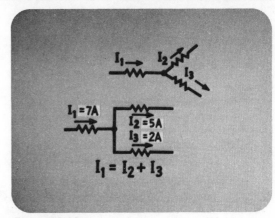

Figure 11.13

If Kirchhoff's Current Law Were Not Followed —
Consider for a second what would happen if
Kirchhoff's current law were not followed.
Suppose, as shown in Figure 11.14, that more
current arrives at a point in a circuit than leaves it.
Remember that electron current is a flow of
electrons, and if there is more electron current
arriving at a point than leaving, what would the
result be? Electrons would have to be building up
somehow at a point since more negative charges are
coming in than are leaving. This type of circuit
behavior — with a wire blowing up like a balloon
just doesn't happen anywhere in nature.

Figure 11.14

If More Electrons Leave Than Arrive — In the
opposite vein, as shown in Figure 11.15, suppose
more electrons were leaving a circuit point than
arrived. If this is the case, electrons have to be
magically created somehow, or secretly "snuck"
into the circuit and this doesn't happen either.
Kirchhoff's first law states that all the electrons
that enter any point in a circuit, leave it, no more,
no less. The total current arriving at any point,
must leave that point.

Figure 11.15

11-9

- Example: Kirchhoff's First Law
- **Kirchhoff's Current Law in Parallel Circuits**
- **Kirchhoff's Current Law in Series Circuits**

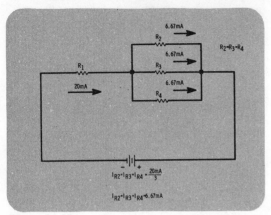

Figure 11.16

Example: Kirchhoff's First Law — Say that you have the circuit pictured in Figure 11.16. The current flowing through R_1 is 20 milliamps. Resistors 2, 3, and 4 are of equal size. Kirchhoff's current law says that the current leaving a junction must equal the current flowing into that junction. The 20 milliamps flowing into the junction will be divided three ways by the three equal-sized resistors. You could then calculate that the current flowing through each resistor will be 6.67 milliamps, for a total of 20 milliamps.

Kirchhoff's Current Law in Parallel Circuits — You have already seen Kirchhoff's first law at work in parallel and series circuits. In parallel circuits, recall that "the total or main line current equals the sum of the branch currents." Basically, you have seen this law expressed as the formula $I_T = I_1 + I_2 + I_3$, for parallel circuits. If you focus your attention on the points where the circuit branches in Figure 11.17, you will see that the law for currents in a parallel circuit is actually just a specific statement of Kirchhoff's current law that applies to parallel circuits.

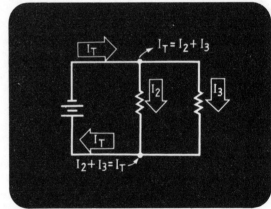

Figure 11.17

Kirchhoff's Current Law in Series Circuits — In series circuits you have seen that the "current is the same in all parts of the circuit." This just means that if you closely examine any point in the circuit, as shown in Figure 11.18, the current entering that point always equals the current leaving it. This is, again, just a specific statement of Kirchhoff's first law or Kirchhoff's current law that applies to series circuits.

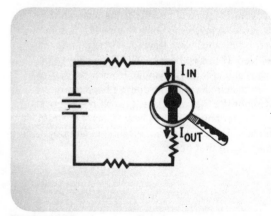

Figure 11.18

11-10

- Kirchhoff's Voltage Law
- Closed Circuit Path
- Other Loops in this Circuit

Kirchhoff's Voltage Law — Moving on, Kirchhoff's second law, sometimes called Kirchhoff's voltage law will be discussed. Then the discussion will proceed to how Kirchhoff's current and voltage laws may be used together to analyze complex dc circuits. Figure 11.19 shows one way that Kirchhoff's voltage law can be stated: the total *voltage applied* to any *closed circuit path* is always equal to the sum of the *voltage drops* across the individual parts of the path. To really understand the meaning of this law and how to use it, you will have to concentrate your attention on all the parts of the law one at a time. First, consider the concept of a *"closed circuit path"* for a minute.

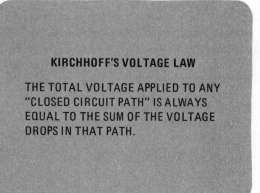

KIRCHHOFF'S VOLTAGE LAW

THE TOTAL VOLTAGE APPLIED TO ANY "CLOSED CIRCUIT PATH" IS ALWAYS EQUAL TO THE SUM OF THE VOLTAGE DROPS IN THAT PATH.

Figure 11.19

Closed Circuit Path — A "closed circuit path" simply means any continuous path you trace in a circuit that starts and ends at the same point. In electricity, these closed circuit pathways are usually called *loops*, as they will be referred to from now on in this course. In Figure 11.20, the pathway ABCD and back to A is a loop.

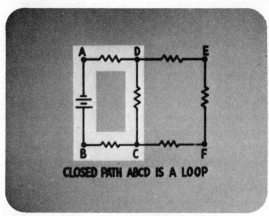

CLOSED PATH ABCD IS A LOOP

Figure 11.20

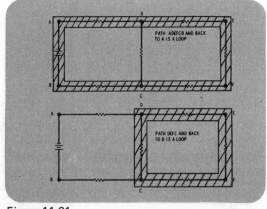

Figure 11.21

Other Loops in this Circuit — Actually in most any circuit, it is possible to trace out several loops. A loop is any closed circuit pathway, regardless of what kinds of components it may contain. Since one of the objectives of this lesson requires that you be able to identify loops in a circuit, it is important that you spend a little time familiarizing yourself with loops. For example, in Figure 11.21, two other simple loops in the circuit are shown. To trace a loop in your mind, start at any point and mentally move around (or *traverse*) a path that returns to the same point. In doing this, you will have traversed a closed path, or loop.

- Paths That Are Not Loops
- Kirchhoff's Voltage Law in Series Circuits
- Loops in Parallel Circuits

Paths That Are Not Loops — Circuit pathways that are *not closed* are *not loops*. This means that if a path in a circuit doesn't start and end at the same point, it is not a loop. In Figure 11.22, paths going through points BAD and CFE are not loops. Now remember that Kirchhoff's voltage law holds for *loops* only, and again states that the total voltage applied to a loop equals the sum or all the voltage drops in the loop.

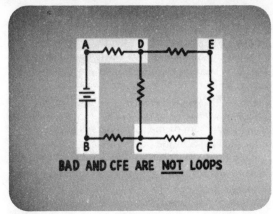

Figure 11.22

Kirchhoff's Voltage Law in Series Circuits — You have already seen Kirchhoff's voltage law in operation in series circuits. Series circuits are circuits with only one closed circuit path, or only one loop, as shown in Figure 11.23. You have seen that in any series circuit such as this, the sum of the voltage drops across the circuit resistors must equal the applied voltage. This is just another way of stating Kirchhoff's second law. This law tells us that in any loop the algebraic sum of the voltage applied by generators, batteries, etc., must always equal the sum of the voltage drops across all resistances.

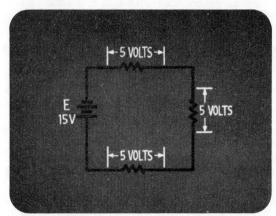

Figure 11.23

Loops in Parallel Circuits — The really *new* thing about Kirchhoff's second law is that it applies to loops anywhere in any type of circuit. For example, Figure 11.24 shows a simple parallel circuit. In this circuit you can "move around" or "traverse" several loops, starting at any point. You can start at point A and find several possible loops in this circuit. There is one loop around the outer path (points ABCDHGFE and back to A); there is another loop through the central branch (points ABCGFE and back to A); and there is a third loop through points ABFE and back to A. Note in Figure 11.24(D) that loop CDHG is also a loop; this particular loop contains only resistors, no

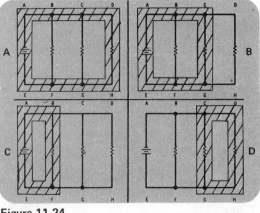

Figure 11.24

11-12

voltage sources. Kirchhoff's laws hold in loops such as this, also.

Kirchhoff's Voltage Law: Alternate Statement — In each of these loops, and in any closed circuit path, Kirchhoff's voltage law holds true. As this lesson proceeds, this law will be stated for you in several different ways to help clarify its meaning. One alternate way it may be stated is: *for any loop the sum of all the voltages that aid current flow in the loop, must equal the sum of all those voltages that oppose it* (Figure 11.25).

**KIRCHHOFF'S SECOND LAW
IN ANY LOOP**

SUM OF VOLTAGES   SUM OF VOLTAGES
AIDING CURRENT   =   OPPOSING CURRENT
FLOW   FLOW

Figure 11.25

Voltages Aiding and Opposing Current — As you study Kirchhoff's law, you will be asked to keep track of several facts concerning loops. Normally, as you analyze a loop you will start at one point in the loop and mentally "walk around" or *traverse* the loop. As you traverse the loop you will be writing down each voltage you come across along with its correct sign. That is, you will write down all the positive and negative voltages you come to as you go around the loop. Anytime you come to a battery or voltage source, you will write down its voltage, and any time you come to a resistor, you will write down a voltage expressed as a current times a resistance (IR drop). Now a key point. The *sign* (positive or negative) that you put in front of

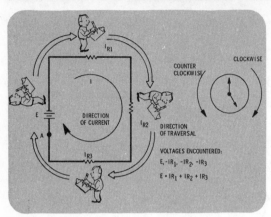

Figure 11.26

these voltages will be important. How do you determine these signs? Basically, it is a matter of considering what effect each voltage you come to has on the current flow in the circuit. Consider Figure 11.26; you see a single loop with electron current flowing clockwise as shown. If you traverse this circuit in the same direction as the current, then you mark all voltage sources *positive* that *push current in that same direction*. When you come to a *resistor* and traverse it in the same direction as current flow through it, you write down a negative voltage, $-IR$. This is because the resistors act to *oppose* current flow; a voltage *drop* develops across them. So starting at point A in this simple loop and going around the circuit, you would encounter voltages $+E$, $-IR_1$, $-IR_2$ and $-IR_3$. Kirchhoff's second law states that the applied voltage E, equals IR_1 plus IR_2 plus IR_3 or $E = IR_1 + IR_2 + IR_3$.

To use Kirchhoff's second law in more complex circuit situations, you need to be careful just how you add up the applied voltages and the voltage drops in circuit loops. In some more complex cases, it might not be obvious which voltages aid current flow and which voltages oppose it, or even in what direction the currents are flowing.

Kirchhoff's Voltage Law: Alternate Form — In cases such as this, it is often more convenient to rewrite Kirchhoff's second law in another form. If you label all the voltages aiding current flow in a loop with a plus sign and all voltages hindering or opposing current flow in the same loop with a minus sign, then Kirchhoff's second law says that their *algebraic sum* must equal zero (Figure 11.27).

KIRCHHOFF'S VOLTAGE LAW

SUM OF VOLTAGES	VOLTAGES OPPOSING
+ AIDING CURRENT	− CURRENT FLOW = 0
FLOW	

Figure 11.27

Kirchhoff's Voltage Law Example — The voltage law tells you that the sum of these voltages aiding current flow minus those that oppose it equals zero. This is an alternate (but equivalent) statement of Kirchhoff's voltage law. You will find that writing this law in this second way may make it easier to simplify solutions of more complex circuits.

To use Kirchhoff's second law, what you really need to do is go around or traverse the loop and focus on the voltage sources and resistors you encounter. Voltages which aid current flow in the direction you are moving get a plus sign. Voltages which are opposing current flow in the direction you are moving get a minus sign. Put all these plus and minus voltages on one side of an equal sign. Kirchhoff's voltage law tells you there must be a zero on the other side. This then gives you a Kirchhoff's voltage law equation.

Consider the expression containing all the voltages and their signs on the left-hand side of the equal sign in Figure 11.28. This is called the *algebraic sum* of these voltages. To take the algebraic sum of these voltages, you add all of the positive voltages together, and subtract each negative voltage from that result. Kirchhoff's second law states that for any loop you have as many positive as negative volts; so that when you finish adding and subtracting, the result will be exactly zero.

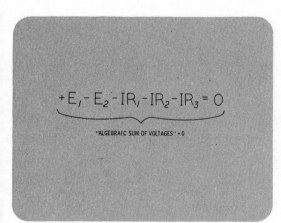

$$+E_1 - E_2 - IR_1 - IR_2 - IR_3 = 0$$

"ALGEBRAIC SUM OF VOLTAGES" = 0

Figure 11.28

Kirchhoff's Voltage Law: Third Form — If you keep careful track of the signs of all the voltages in the circuit, you can rewrite Kirchhoff's voltage law once again, this time in a simpler form as shown in Figure 11.29. The algebraic sum of all the voltages encountered in any loop equals zero.

Again, algebraic sum means the sum of the voltages taking into account whether each is positive or negative. Positive voltages are simply added, and negative voltages are subtracted to get the total.

KIRCHHOFF'S VOLTAGE LAW

THE ALGEBRAIC SUM OF ALL THE VOLTAGES ENCOUNTERED IN ANY LOOP EQUALS ZERO.

Figure 11.29

Loop Equation — When the algebraic sum of all the voltages in a loop is set to equal zero, the result is called a loop equation. A loop equation (Figure 11.30) is simply a mathematical expression of Kirchhoff's voltage law. As you will see, loop equations can be used to help solve for unknown currents and voltages in circuits, where Ohm's law and basic circuit rules can't always be used.

LOOP EQUATION

THE ALGEBRAIC SUM OF THE VOLTAGES IN A LOOP EQUALS ZERO.

$$+ \begin{matrix} \text{SUM OF} \\ \text{APPLIED} \\ \text{VOLTAGES} \end{matrix} - \begin{matrix} \text{SUM OF} \\ \text{VOLTAGE} \\ \text{DROPS} \end{matrix} = 0$$

Figure 11.30

Example: Kirchhoff's Voltage Law — As an example, examine the single-loop circuit shown in Figure 11.31, and go through the steps that you would need in writing a loop equation for it. In this circuit, a loop equation could be used to allow you to solve for the total current. (Note that you could solve this circuit using series circuit rules, but this type of example will be a good place for you to begin learning the use of Kirchhoff's laws.)

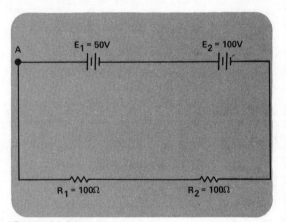

Figure 11.31

Assign Current Directions — The first step in writing a loop equation is to mark all the current directions. In some circumstances, you may not know the direction of the current flow. Here's a trick. In those *cases where the current flow is unknown, simply guess a direction.*

A key point to remember is that if you happen to guess the current direction incorrectly, the current you calculate using Kirchhoff's laws will turn out to be negative. That's a key to using Kirchhoff's laws. *If any current you calculate using Kirchhoff's laws turns out to be negative, you then know it's flowing opposite to the direction you've guessed* (Figure 11.32).

DON'T KNOW CURRENT DIRECTION?

GUESS A DIRECTION!

IF ANY CURRENT YOU CALCULATE IS **NEGATIVE**, IT IS FLOWING IN THE OPPOSITE DIRECTION.

Figure 11.32

Selected Clockwise Electron Current Flow — In this loop you could just blindly assume that electron current is flowing clockwise. An arrow has been inserted in Figure 11.33 to help you keep this in mind. Remember that if you calculate a negative current, this means that this assumed current direction is incorrect. If that's the case, you will know that electron current is actually flowing in the opposite direction in this circuit.

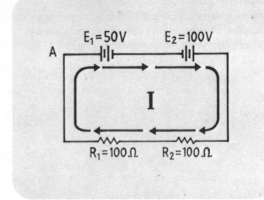

Figure 11.33

Step 2: Traverse the Circuit — The second step in writing a loop equation is to mentally get inside your circuit and walk around or "traverse" it. Start at one point and write down all the voltages you encounter along the way, with their correct signs.

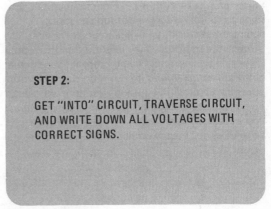

Figure 11.34

Determining Signs: Voltage Sources — How do you determine the correct signs? The trick is to pay careful attention to the direction in which you are going through or traversing your circuit. Source voltages (like batteries) are considered *positive* if you go through (or traverse) them in the *same* direction that they normally push current (Figure 11.35).

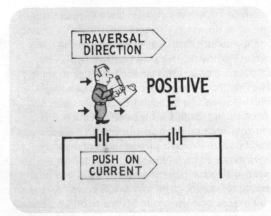

Figure 11.35

- **Negative Voltage Sources**
- **Signs of Source Voltages**
- **Example**

Negative Voltage Sources — Correspondingly, source voltages are considered *negative* in the loop equation if the source is pushing current *against* you as you traverse it, as shown in Figure 11.36.

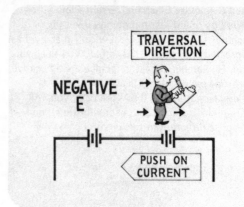

Figure 11.36

Signs of Source Voltages — To determine the right sign for a voltage source in a loop equation, compare the direction in which you are going through the source, to the direction that the source is pushing on current. If you go through the source in the *same direction* as it pushes on current, write down the voltage in your loop equation with a *plus sign*. If the source is pushing current *against you* as you traverse it, write down the voltage with a *negative sign*. These two rules are illustrated in Figure 11.37.

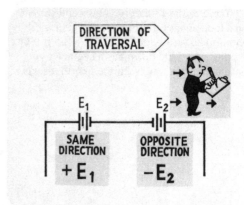

Figure 11.37

Example — Mentally traverse the example circuit and write down the two source voltages according to these rules. Starting at point A, traverse the circuit clockwise. This way you will be moving through the top of this circuit from left to right. The first thing you come to is a voltage source which you will go through from plus to minus. Now notice that this is the same direction this source pushes on electron current. This gives you a plus 50 volts. Proceed through a second source from minus to plus. Notice that this source is pushing electron current against you as you go through it, so you get a minus 100 volts. Next as you move clockwise around this circuit, you come to resistor R_2. So now consider how to handle the

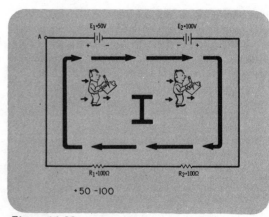

Figure 11.38

voltage across a resistor when writing loop
equations.

Size of Voltage Across Resistors — First of all,
from Ohm's law you know that the *size* of the
voltage across any resistor equals the product of
the current through it times its resistance. The
voltage across a resistor equals I times R, and, as
you know by now, is called an IR drop, as shown
in Figure 11.39.

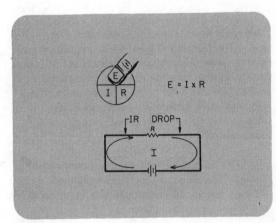

Figure 11.39

Sign of Voltage Across Resistors — How do you
determine the correct sign (positive or negative) for
an IR voltage in your loop equation? To do this,
concentrate on the direction you are moving
through or traversing the resistor and how current
is flowing through it.

As shown in Figure 11.40, if you go through a
resistor *in the direction of assumed current flow*,
you write down its voltage with a *negative* sign.

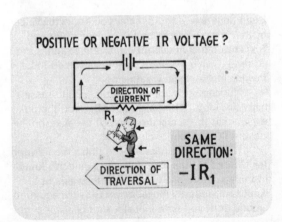

Figure 11.40

Sign of Voltage Across Resistors — If you go through a resistor *opposite to the direction of current* through it, the IR voltage across it is considered *positive*, as shown in Figure 11.41.

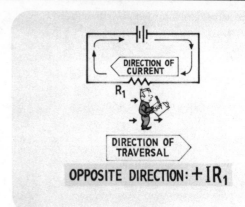

Figure 11.41

Back in the example circuit as you move through R_2 and R_1, you will get voltages of $-IR_2$ and $-IR_1$. Notice in Figure 11.42 that the minus signs are there because you traversed both of these resistors in the same direction as the electron current flowed through them. To complete the loop equation, algebraically add all of these voltages with their correct signs, set the result equal to zero.

$$+50 - 100 - IR_2 - IR_1 = 0$$

This is, in equation form, the statement of Kirchhoff's second law for this simple loop. As you will see, you can use equations like this to solve for unknown quantities in circuits.

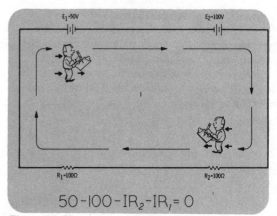

Figure 11.42

Loop Equation — In this case, you know the value of the source voltages, and the values of R_1 and R_2. The unknown quantity in this equation is the current, I, which as you recall was assumed to be flowing in the clockwise direction.

Notice that if you use a little "circuit sense" here, since E_2 is twice as large as E_1, you should expect that the actual direction of the electron current flow is counterclockwise.

What steps are necessary to finish the solution for I? Since I is the only quantity you don't know in this equation, one way to find the value of I would be to simply move the parts of the equation around until you have I all alone on one side of the equal sign. Then the current will simply equal all the known quantities on the other side of the equal sign as shown in Figure 11.43.

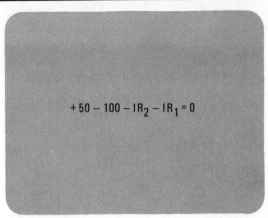

$$+50 - 100 - IR_2 - IR_1 = 0$$

Figure 11.43

SOLVING EQUATIONS

OBJECTIVE: GET UNKNOWN QUANTITY ALL ALONE ON ONE SIDE OF EQUAL SIGN WITH ONLY KNOWN QUANTITIES ON THE OTHER.

Figure 11.44

Solution of Equations — Quite often in electronic problems you may encounter situations where you must "solve" an equation (a mathematical statement with an equal sign). In this equation may be several known quantities and an unknown quantity that you need to find. To "solve the equation" means to rearrange it using correct procedures, until the unknown quantity is all by itself on one side of the equal sign, and only known quantities are on the other (Figure 11.44). When that has been accomplished, you know that your unknown quantity is equal to a combination of known quantities, and you have your answer.

Whenever you are manipulating equations in solving for unknowns, you must follow the correct procedures which will allow you to rearrange an equation without actually changing its equality. These procedures are fairly easy to learn, and will be reviewed for you.

- Basic Principle
- One Equation for Each Unknown

BASIC PRINCIPLE IN SOLVING EQUATIONS

ANY MATHEMATICAL MANIPULATION PERFORMED ON ONE SIDE OF THE EQUAL SIGN **MUST** BE PERFORMED ON THE OTHER SIDE OF THE EQUAL SIGN.

Figure 11.45

EQUATIONS AND UNKNOWNS

YOU NEED **ONE** EQUATION FOR EVERY UNKNOWN FOR WHICH YOU MUST SOLVE.

Figure 11.46

Basic Principle – The basic principle to follow when solving any equation is this: Any mathematical operation that's performed on one side of an equal sign must be performed on the other. If this principle is not followed, as you work with an equation, the equation will no longer be an equation and you will start getting wrong answers. The operations you are allowed to perform on an equation to solve it are listed below. You can apply these to an equation as many times as you need to; and in any order until the unknown is alone on one side of the equal sign. That is always your objective as you work on an equation to solve it: Get the unknown all by itself on one side of the equal sign with known quantities on the other side of the equal sign (Figure 11.45).

One Equation for Each Unknown – Also, note one more point, before the procedures are reviewed. One equation can be solved for only one unknown. You will need one equation for each unknown quantity that shows up in any problem (Figure 11.46). This is why Kirchhoff's laws come in handy in circuits where there are several unknowns. For example, if there are three unknown currents, you can use Kirchhoff's laws to write three equations and then solve these equations together for the three unknowns.

Solving several equations together will be discussed in a moment. For now, consider the rules you can use to solve one equation for one unknown quantity. In the example equations that are discussed for you, the letter "X" will be used to mean "the unknown quantity." In your work, the "X" might be an "I" for an unknown current or an "E" for an unknown voltage.

RULE: YOU CAN **ADD** OR **SUBTRACT** THE SAME QUANTITY FROM BOTH SIDES OF THE EQUAL SIGN.

EXAMPLE: YOU HAVE X − 300 AND NEED TO FIND X

ADD 30 TO BOTH SIDES

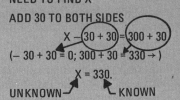

$$X - (30 + 30) = (300 + 30)$$

$$(-30 + 30 = 0; 300 + 30 = 330 \rightarrow)$$

$$X = 330.$$

UNKNOWN —↗   ↖— KNOWN

Figure 11.47

First Rule — What are the procedures you can use with equations in solving them? First of all, you can add or subtract the same quantity from both sides of the equal sign in any equation, as shown in Figure 11.47. For example, if you have an equation such as X − 30 = 300 and need to calculate X, you can add 30 to both sides. Here's where some plain old common sense comes into play. Why would you add 30 to both sides? Because you know that you want X all alone on one side of the equal sign. If you add 30 to both sides of this equation, you get

$$X - 30 + 30 = 300 + 30.$$

The −30 and +30 on the left-hand side of the equal sign will then cancel and you will have

$$X = 300 + 30$$

or

$$X = 330$$

and the equation is solved.

$$X + 150 = 400$$

SUBTRACT 150 FROM BOTH SIDES

$$X + 150 - 150 = 400 - 150$$

$$X = 400 - 150$$

$$X = 250$$

Figure 11.48

Example — Suppose you had an equation like X + 150 = 400, as shown in Figure 11.48. How would you solve this? Subtracting 150 from both sides will put X all alone on the left-hand side of the equal sign, and 250 on the right-hand side.

RULE: YOU CAN **MOVE** A QUANTITY FROM ONE SIDE OF THE EQUAL SIGN TO THE OTHER; **IF YOU CHANGE ITS SIGN** (THIS IS CALLED TRANSPOSING).

EXAMPLE: YOU HAVE +50 +X −30 = 300 AND NEED TO FIND X
TRANSPOSE +50 AND −30 − (CHANGE SIGNS AND MOVE TO RIGHT OF =)
X = 300 + 30 − 50
(300 + 30 − 50 = 280)
X = 280

UNKNOWN ⤴ ⤴ KNOWN

Figure 11.49

Rule 2 — Another rule you can use (that arises directly from the previous rule) states that you can move any quantity from one side of the equal sign to the other, *if you change its sign*. This procedure is called *transposing*. Transposing is really just the same as adding or subtracting the same quantity from both sides of the equation. However, transposing saves you some steps. For example, as shown in Figure 11.49, if you have

$$+50 + X − 30 = 300$$

and you want to find X, you can transpose the −30 and the +50 to the right-hand side. Remember when you do, to *change the signs of the terms you transpose*. This will give you

$$X = 300 + 30 − 50$$

or

$$X = 280$$

RULE: YOU CAN **MULTIPLY OR DIVIDE** BOTH SIDES OF THE EQUAL SIGN BY THE SAME QUANTITY.

EXAMPLE: YOU HAVE: 300X = 30 AND NEED X
DIVIDE BOTH SIDES BY 300

$$\frac{300X}{300} = \frac{30}{300}$$

SINCE 300/300 =1

X = 30/300

UNKNOWN ⤴ KNOWN

Figure 11.50

Rule 3 — Following the basic principle of "whatever you do to one side of an equation you must also do to the other" leads to an additional rule you can use in solving equations. As stated in Figure 11.50, you can multiply or divide the quantities on both sides of the equal sign by the same quantity. This is the rule you use when your unknown in an equation is multiplied by or divided by some number and you want to get the unknown all by itself.

For example, if you have the equation 300X = 30, how would get X all by itself? If you divide this equation (that means all of the terms in it) by 300, you would have (Figure 11.50):

$$\frac{300X}{300} = \frac{30}{300}$$

Now 300/330 equals 1, and 1 times X equals X, so you would then have

$$X = \frac{30}{300}$$

or

$$X = 0.1$$

The trick in cases such as this is to divide both sides of the equation by whatever is multiplying X. This will give you X all by itself.

$$\frac{X}{6000} = .003$$

MULTIPLY BOTH SIDES BY 6000

$$6000 \; \frac{X}{6000} = .003 \,(6000)$$

$$X = 18$$

Figure 11.51

Example — Suppose the unknown is divided by some quantity as in Figure 11.51. How would you get X all by itself in this situation? In cases like this you can multiply both sides of the equation by the quantity by which X is divided. In this case you would get X = 0.003 times 6000 or X = 18.

RULE: YOU CAN CHANGE THE SIGN OF EVERY TERM IN AN EQUATION, AS LONG AS YOU CHANGE THEM ALL AT THE SAME TIME.

EXAMPLE: YOU HAVE $-X = 30 + 400 - 10$ AND NEED X. CHANGE **ALL** SIGNS

$$X = -30 -400 +10$$
$$X = -420$$

Figure 11.52

Rule 4 — Growing out of the last rule is an additional one. In any equation you can change the signs of all of the terms if you need to. (This is actually equivalent to multiplying the entire equation by -1). The thing to remember when doing this is that *all* the terms' signs must be changed. As an example, if you have $-X = 30 + 400 - 10$, as shown in Figure 11.52, you could change all the signs to give you X (actually $+X$) all by itself.

RULE: IN ANY EQUATION YOU CAN COMBINE
LIKE TERMS.

EXAMPLE: YOU HAVE 30X + 60X = 90 AND NEED X
COMBINE   30X
          +60X
          ─────
TO GET   90X

90X = 90
DIVIDE BY 90
X = 1

Figure 11.53

Rule 5 — One additional and useful rule concerns equations where the unknown appears more than once, as shown in Figure 11.53. If you have a situation such as

$$30X + 60X = 90$$

you can *combine the terms that each contain the unknown*, the "like" terms. Then $30X + 60X$ equals $90X$, and your equation reads $90X = 90$.

Now you could use an earlier rule and divide both sides of this equation by 90 to get $X = 1$.

With these rules in mind, you can get back to the solution of basic loop equations.

Solution for the Current, I — How do you proceed to solve the equation underlined at the top of Figure 11.54 for the current? One thing you can do is to move the $50 - 100$ to the right side of the equation. Remember this process is called *transposing* and when you do this you must change the sign of *each* quantity.

Algebraically add -50 and $+100$ to get $+50$. Then, since you know that the values of R_1 and R_2 are each 100 ohms, you can substitute that into the equation.

You can combine like terms: $-100\ I$ combined with $-100\ I$ gives you a $-200\ I$.

Next you can multiply both sides of the equation by -1, remembering that when two minus numbers are multiplied, they yield a plus number. This reduces the equation further to: $200\ I = -50$.

You want I, your unknown, all by itself. Since it is multiplied by 200, you can divide both sides of the equation by 200. When you do, you will find that the current, I, equals -0.25 amp. Notice that this answer is *negative*, which as expected tells you that the *current is actually flowing in the opposite direction*.

$$50 - 100 - IR_1 - IR_2 = 0$$
$$-IR_1 - IR_2 = -50 + 100$$
$$-IR_1 - IR_2 = 50$$
$$-100\ I - 100\ I = 50$$
$$-200\ I = 50$$
$$(-1)(-200\ I) = (50)(-1)$$
$$200\ I = -50$$
$$200\ I\ /200 = -50/200$$
$$I = -.25\ A$$

Figure 11.54

Kirchhoff's Laws in More Complex Circuts — At this point you have seen how to use Kirchhoff's laws and some basic tools to solve a simple type of circuit problem, one which you really know how to solve with simpler techniques. As mentioned, however, this problem was presented as an introduction to Kirchhoff's laws. Their real power comes into play when you are faced with the analysis of a more complex circuit, which may contain several voltage sources in a configuration like that shown in Figure 11.55.

In circuits such as this where more than one branch contains a voltage source, you cannot use Ohm's law and basic circuit rules all by themselves, since they are designed to take into accout only one source at a time. Here is where you must use more powerful tools such as Kirchhoff's laws. All the procedures involved in using these tools will be outlined. To keep things simple, electron current examples will be used at first. Keep in mind, however, that all of these procedures will be applicable, whether you are considering conventional or electron current. Examples using each will be worked through for you.

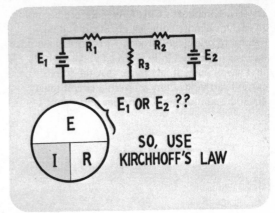

Figure 11.55

Electron and Conventional Current — Remember that all of the effects of electron and conventional current are the same as shown in Figure 11.56. They just flow in opposite directions.

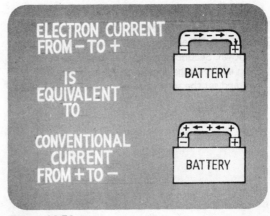

Figure 11.56

- Review: Kirchhoff's First Law
- Review: Kirchhoff's Second Law
- Steps in Using Kirchhoff's Voltage Law

Review: Kirchhoff's First Law — Before beginning to analyze a more complex circuit, it will be helpful to briefly go through Kirchhoff's laws once again as illustrated in Figure 11.57. Kirchhoff's first law or current law states that the sum of the currents arriving at any point in a circuit must equal the sum of the currents leaving.

KIRCHHOFF'S FIRST LAW OR KIRCHHOFF'S CURRENT LAW

THE SUM OF THE CURRENTS ARRIVING AT ANY POINT IN A CIRCUIT MUST EQUAL THE SUM OF THE CURRENTS LEAVING THAT POINT.

Figure 11.57

Review: Kirchhoff's Second Law — Kirchhoff's second law or voltage law states that the algebraic sum of the voltages around any closed loop must be zero (Figure 11.58). Again, when writing loop equations, the following steps must be kept in mind.

KIRCHHOFF'S VOLTAGE LAW

THE TOTAL VOLTAGE APPLIED TO ANY "CLOSED CIRCUIT PATH" IS ALWAYS EQUAL TO THE SUM OF THE VOLTAGE DROPS IN THAT PATH.

Figure 11.58

Steps in Using Kirchhoff's Voltage Law — First, label all of the current directions in the circuit, *assuming* a current direction if one happens to be unknown. Second, traverse the loop and write down each voltage encountered with the correct sign, and set the sum equal to zero (Figure 11.59).

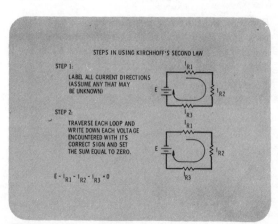

Figure 11.59

- Rules for Voltage Signs
- Rules
- Rules

Rules for Voltage Signs — If you traverse a voltage source in the *same direction* that it pushes on the type of current you are using, write down its voltage with a *plus* sign (Figure 11.60).

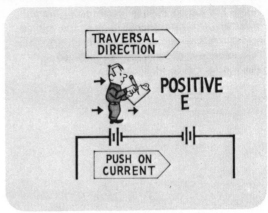

Figure 11.60

Rules — If you traverse a voltage source *opposite* to the direction it pushes the type of current you are using, write down its voltage with a *negative sign* (Figure 11.61).

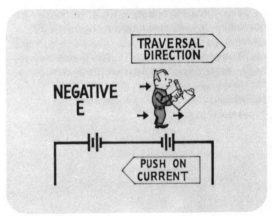

Figure 11.61

Rules — If you traverse a resistor *in the direction of current* flow through it, the voltage across it gets a *negative* sign in the loop equation (Figure 11.62).

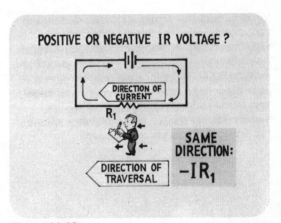

Figure 11.62

Rules — If you go through a resistor *against the direction of current* flow through it, the voltage across it gets a *positive* sign (Figure 11.63). This rule holds true whether you are considering electron or conventional current.

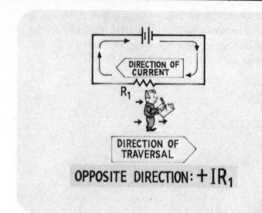

OPPOSITE DIRECTION: $+IR_1$

Figure 11.63

Complex Circuit Example — All of the facts covered in this lesson will be put together by carrying out the analysis of a complex circuit such as the one shown in Figure 11.64. A good way to begin analyzing circuits such as this is to first solve for the *current* in all parts of the circuit. Remember, the currents are your first "unknown" quantities.

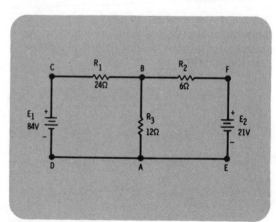

Figure 11.64

Voltage Solution — Once you know the currents, you can then solve for all the voltages in the circuit with Ohm's law. So the first thing to do is label all the different currents with a direction. As has been mentioned, if you don't know a current direction, just assign one arbitrarily. If, in your final answer, any current ends up with a negative sign, this means that the actual current is flowing opposite to the original direction you assumed.

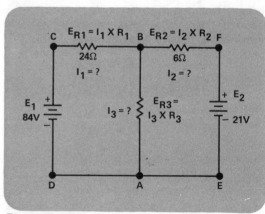

Figure 11.65

Circuit Solution: Step 1 — Label all the currents with their directions. In the same problem the current flowing in the left-hand branch will be labeled I_1, the current in the right-hand branch I_2, and the current through the central resistor I_3, as shown in Figure 11.66.

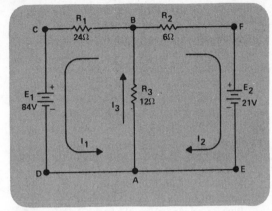

Figure 11.66

Kirchhoff's Current Law Equation — Your "circuit sense" should begin "tingling" a little as soon as you set up the problem. Right away you can see in Figure 11.67 that at junction point A that I_1 and I_2 enter the junction and I_3 leaves. You immediately see that according to Kirchhoff's current law: $I_3 = I_1 + I_2$.

You have three unknown quantities to find: I_1, I_2, and I_3. An important mathematical rule states that you need one equation for each unknown quantity you are trying to find. Since you already have one equation, you now need to find two more. Then these three equations can be solved altogether (simultaneously) for the unknown quantities I_1, I_2, and I_3. The methods you will need will be outlined for you; however, you need two more equations.

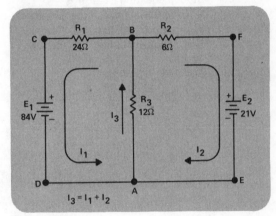

Figure 11.67

Kirchhoff's Voltage Law Equation 1 — The two other equations you need are where Kirchhoff's voltage law applies. Now you simply pick two loops and write a loop equation for each. In the example circuit (Figure 11.68), you can write equations for the left-hand and right-hand loops.

If you go around the left-hand loop counterclockwise starting at point A, and write down all the IR voltages and the source voltage, you will get:

Minus I_3R_3 (since you go through R_3 in the direction of the current I_3)

Minus I_1R_1 (since you go through R_1 in the direction of I_1)

Plus E_1 (since you go through E_1 in the direction that it is pushing current)

Your first loop equation is: $-I_3R_3 - I_1R_1 + E_1 = 0$. On the schematic all the resistances and the source voltages are labeled so you can put them into this equation where they belong. You know that $R_3 = 12\ \Omega$, $R_1 = 24\ \Omega$, and $E_1 = 84$ V. Substituting these values gives you:

$$-12\ I_3 - 24\ I_1 + 84 = 0.$$

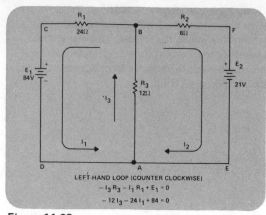

Figure 11.68

Right-Hand Loop Equation — Follow the same procedure in the right-hand loop. Going around the circuit counterclockwise starting at point A, you get (Figure 11.69):

$-E_2$ (since E_2 is pushing current against the direction in which you go through it).

$+I_2R_2$ (since you go through R_2 against the current direction).

$+I_3R_3$ (since you go through R_3 against the current direction).

So for this loop, you have $-E_2 + I_2R_2 + I_3R_3 = 0$. Again, putting in all of the known values labeled on the circuit diagram you have:

$$-21 + 6\ I_2 + 12\ I_3 = 0.$$

This is your second loop equation.

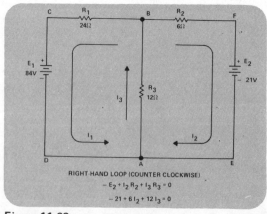

Figure 11.69

Three Equations to Solve — Figure 11.70 shows the current equation and two loop equations together. Now you want to solve for I_1, I_2, and I_3. Your aim in using three equations like this with three unknown quantities is to solve for one unknown quantity at a time.

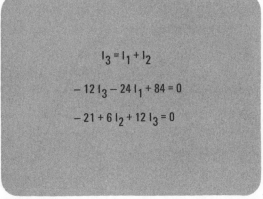

$$I_3 = I_1 + I_2$$

$$-12\,I_3 - 24\,I_1 + 84 = 0$$

$$-21 + 6\,I_2 + 12\,I_3 = 0$$

Figure 11.70

METHODS USED IN SOLVING SIMULTANEOUS EQUATIONS WHICH ALLOW YOU TO ELIMINATE UNKNOWNS FROM ONE OR MORE OF THESE EQUATIONS:

1) ADDITION METHOD
2) SUBSTITUTION METHOD

Figure 11.71

Solving Simultaneous Equations — At this point you encounter the need for another technique for analyzing complex circuits. You now have three equations to solve for three unknown quantities, in this case I_1, and I_2, and I_3. Your goal is the same as before. You want to get each unknown all by itself alone on one side of the equals sign, and only known quantities on the other side. Since each of the three equations contains more than one unknown at this point, the procedures that were described earlier won't enable you to solve these equations. You need some methods that allow you to eliminate some of the unknowns from these equations (Figure 11.71). If you could do this, you could manipulate your three equations so that each equation contained only one unknown quantity.

Addition Method — What methods can you use to eliminate some of the unknowns from these equations? The first is simple addition; any two equations can be added together (Figure 11.72).

ADDITION METHOD

ANY TWO EQUATIONS CAN BE ADDED TOGETHER

Figure 11.72

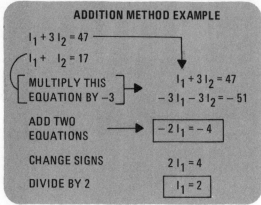

ADDITION METHOD EXAMPLE

$$I_1 + 3 I_2 = 47$$
$$I_1 + I_2 = 17$$

MULTIPLY THIS EQUATION BY -3

$$I_1 + 3 I_2 = 47$$
$$-3 I_1 - 3 I_2 = -51$$

ADD TWO EQUATIONS
$$-2 I_1 = -4$$

CHANGE SIGNS
$$2 I_1 = 4$$

DIVIDE BY 2
$$I_1 = 2$$

Figure 11.73

Addition Method Example — To see how this works, consider the example shown in Figure 11.73. Suppose you have two equations, each of which contains the two unknowns I_1 and I_2, and you need to solve for I_1:

$$I_1 + 3 I_2 = 47$$
$$I_1 + I_2 = 17$$

Notice that each of these equations contains *both* unknowns I_1 and I_2. You can't solve for I_1 until you have an equation whose only unknown quantity is I_1.

Focus your attention on these two equations and consider this point. Any of the procedures outlined in the rules you were given earlier can be performed on either one of the equations. You now know that these two equations can be added together. The secret to getting rid of I_2 in these two equations is to make the I_2 terms equal in value but opposite in sign. For example, if you take the second equation in Figure 11.73 and multiply both sides by -3, it will become:

$$(I_1 + I_2) \times (-3) = (17) \times (-3)$$
$$-3 I_1 - 3 I_2 = -51.$$

Add this equation and your first equation together. See what happens? The $+3 I_2$ in the upper equation and $-3 I_2$ in the lower equation cancel when you add them, and the resulting equation is now

$$-2 I_1 = -4$$

You can now solve this easily for I_1. If you change the signs of both terms in this equation and then divide by 2 you get $I_1 = 2$ and the equation is solved for I_1.

Steps in Using Addition Method — One method you can use in solving simultaneous equations is to eliminate unknowns using addition. To do this, follow these steps, as reviewed in Figure 11.74:

1. Decide which unknown you want to eliminate, say X.
2. Make the terms containing this unknown equal in value but opposite in sign.
3. Add the equations together: X is eliminated.
4. Solve for the other unknown.

STEPS IN USING ADDITION METHOD

DECIDE WHICH UNKNOWN TO ELIMINATE

MAKE THE TERMS CONTAINING THIS UNKNOWN EQUAL IN VALUE BUT OPPOSITE IN SIGN

ADD THE EQUATIONS TOGETHER; ONE UNKNOWN IS ELIMINATED

SOLVE FOR REMAINING UNKNOWN QUANTITY

Figure 11.74

SUBSTITUTION METHOD

SUBSTITUTE ONE EQUATION INTO THE OTHER EQUATION TO ELIMINATE AN UNKNOWN.

Figure 11.75

Substitution Method — Another method exists that will be helpful in solving several equations together. This is called the *substitution* method. In this situation you take one equation and actually substitute it into the other to eliminate an unknown quantity (Figure 11.75).

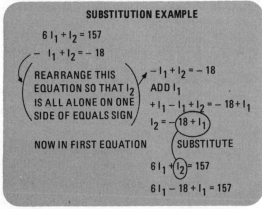

SUBSTITUTION EXAMPLE

$6 I_1 + I_2 = 157$

$- I_1 + I_2 = -18$

REARRANGE THIS EQUATION SO THAT I_2 IS ALL ALONE ON ONE SIDE OF EQUALS SIGN

$-I_1 + I_2 = -18$

ADD I_1

$+I_1 - I_1 + I_2 = -18 + I_1$

$I_2 = -18 + I_1$

NOW IN FIRST EQUATION   SUBSTITUTE

$6 I_1 + I_2 = 157$

$6 I_1 - 18 + I_1 = 157$

Figure 11.76

Substitution Example — Consider the two equations shown in Figure 11.76:

$$6 I_1 + I_2 = 157$$
$$-I_1 + I_2 = -18$$

and you need to calculate I_1. Here is another way to proceed that will allow you to eliminate one unknown in one of these equations. First, rearrange one equation, the second one, so that I_2 is all alone on one side of the equals sign. In this case, if you add I_1 to both sides, you will get

$$+I_1 - I_1 + I_2 = -18 + I_1$$

or

$$I_2 = -18 + I_1.$$

You know that I_2 equals, or is exactly the same as, the expression, $-18 + I_1$. You can go back to your first equation and substitute or replace I_2 by the expression $-18 + I_1$. Therefore your first equation

$$6 I_1 + I_2 = 157$$

becomes

$$6 I_1 - 18 + I_1 = 157.$$

This equation now has only one unknown, I_1.

___

SUBSTITUTION EXAMPLE (CONTINUED)

$$6I_1 - 18 + I_1 = 157$$

COMBINE TERMS

$$7I_1 - 18 = 157$$

ADD 18 TO BOTH SIDES

$$7I_1 - 18 + 18 = 157 + 18$$
$$7I_1 = 175$$

DIVIDE BY 7

$$\frac{7I_1}{7} = \frac{175}{7} \; ; \; I_1 = 25$$

Figure 11.77

Substitution Example — To finish solving for I_1 combine terms

$$7I_1 - 18 = 157$$

Then add 18 to both sides

$$+18 + 7I_1 - 18 = 157 + 18$$

which gives you $7I_1 = 175$. Next, divide both sides by 7 to get

$$\frac{7I_1}{7} = \frac{175}{7}$$

or

$$I_1 = 25$$

These two methods, addition and substitution may be used together and repetitively to solve for any number of unknown quantities. Remember though, when using Kirchhoff's laws that you must have one equation for each unknown. Now you can return to your previous circuit problem.

Circuit Example — Your first goal is to get I_1 on one side of an equals sign, and only things you know on the other side. Examine your equations again carefully. Notice that the second and third equations contain I_1, I_2, and I_3. You know from your first equation that $I_3 = I_1 + I_2$, so now you can substitute the expression $I_1 + I_2$ wherever you see I_3 in your last two equations. Then your last two equations will only contain the two unknowns I_1 and I_2. This will reduce the number of unknowns in the last two equations and bring you a little closer to your goal.

$$I_3 = I_1 + I_2$$
$$-12I_3 - 24I_1 + 84 = 0$$
$$-21 + 6I_2 + 12I_3 = 0$$

Figure 11.78

- Substitution in First Loop Equation
- Substitution in Second Loop Equation
- Two Loop Equations

Substitution in First Loop Equation — The first loop equation is shown in Figure 11.79. When you substitute $I_1 + I_2$ for I_3, as shown, you get
$$-12(I_1 + I_2) - 24 I_1 + 84 = 0.$$
Now notice that when $I_1 + I_2$ are each multiplied by -12, you have $-12 I_1 - 12 I_2 - 24 I_1 + 84 = 0$. You can algebraically add all the terms in this equation that contain the same unknown. (Again, this is called *combining like terms*.) You have a $-12 I_1$ and $-24 I_1$ on the same side of the equation, so add them to get $-36 I_1 - 12 I_2 + 84 = 0$.

FIRST LOOP EQUATION
$$-12 I_3 - 24 I_1 + 84 = 0$$
$$I_3 = I_1 + I_2$$
$$-12(I_1 + I_2) - 24 I_1 + 84 = 0$$
$$-12 I_1 - 12 I_2 - 24 I_1 + 84 = 0$$
$$-36 I_1 - 12 I_2 + 84 = 0$$

Figure 11.79

Substitution in Second Loop Equation — Examine your second loop equation, which is underlined in Figure 11.80. You can follow a similar procedure to eliminate one unknown in this equation. First, substitute $I_1 + I_2$ for I_3 as shown, and this gives you
$$-21 + 6 I_2 + 12(I_1 + I_2) = 0.$$
Multiply the 12 times each of the terms in parentheses to get
$$-21 + 6 I_2 + 12 I_1 + 12 I_2 = 0.$$
Now combine like terms, and you get
$$-21 + 18 I_2 + 12 I_1 = 0.$$

SECOND LOOP EQUATION
$$-21 + 6 I_2 + 12 I_3 = 0$$
$$I_3 = I_1 + I_2$$
$$-21 + 6 I_2 + 12 (I_1 + I_2) = 0$$
$$-21 + 6 I_2 + 12 I_1 + 12 I_2 = 0$$
$$-21 + 18 I_2 + 12 I_1 = 0$$

Figure 11.80

Two Loop Equations — Now that both loop equations have been simplified, you want to manipulate them to eliminate one of the unknown loop currents so that you can solve for the other. You can solve for either unknown first. The analysis will be aimed at solving for I_2, and then I_1.

In Figure 11.81 both simplified loop equations are written one right under the other, and the terms have been moved around a little so that all of the terms of the same kind (that is, containing the same unknown) are aligned one under another. A rule of mathematics says that any two equations can be added together to help eliminate unknowns. The idea is to do this in such

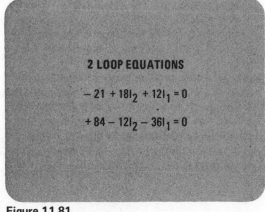

2 LOOP EQUATIONS
$$-21 + 18 I_2 + 12 I_1 = 0$$
$$+84 - 12 I_2 - 36 I_1 = 0$$

Figure 11.81

a way that the sum of the two equations contains only one loop current. So how do you do this?

Manipulation of First Equation — Focus your attention on the first equation. If this equation is multiplied by 3 you get $-63 + 54\,I_2 + 36\,I_1 = 0$, as shown in Figure 11.82. Now, with this change, rewrite the equation above the second equation.

$$-21 + 18I_2 + 12I_1 = 0$$

$$\underline{\qquad\qquad \times 3 \qquad \times 3 \qquad}$$

$$-63 + 54I_2 + 36I_1 = 0$$

Figure 11.82

Solution by Addition — If this equation is added to the second equation, term by term, you will have $21 + 42\,I_2 = 0$. Notice that the two I_1 terms have canceled out. You now have an equation with only one unknown current. Transpose and divide as shown in Figure 11.83 to get $I_2 = -21/42$ which equals -0.5 amp. Notice that this answer came out negative; that means that the wrong direction was originally assumed for I_2. So you now know that I_2 (electron current) is actually flowing in the opposite direction in the right-hand loop.

$$-63 + 54I_2 + 36I_1 = 0$$

$$\underline{+84 - 12I_2 - 36I_1 = 0}$$

$$21 + 42I_2 \qquad\quad = 0$$

$$42I_2 = -21$$

$$I_2 = -21/42 = -.5\ A$$

Figure 11.83

- Solution for I_1
- Solution for I_3
- Solution for Voltages

Solution for I_1 — Now that you know I_2, you can substitute its value in either of the two loop equations to solve for I_1. For example, if you take the second loop equation and replace I_2 with -0.5 amp, as shown in Figure 11.84, you now get $84 + 6 - 36\,I_1 = 0$, or $90 - 36\,I_1 = 0$. Transposing and dividing by -36, you have $I_1 = -90/-36$ or 2.5 amps. Notice that this current came out positive which means the initially assumed direction of flow in this loop was correct.

$$84 - 12I_2 - 36I_1 = 0$$
$$84 - 12(-.5) - 36I_1 = 0$$
$$84 + 6 - 36I_1 = 0$$
$$90 - 36I_1 = 0$$
$$-36I_1 = -90$$
$$I_1 = -90/-36 = 2.5\ A$$

Figure 11.84

Solution for I_3 — Now that you know I_1 and I_2, you can go back to the current equation and solve for I_3 as shown in Figure 11.85. You simply substitute your known values of I_1 and I_2 in the equation, and you get $I_3 = 2.5 - 0.5$ or 2 amps, which is positive, so it's in the correct direction. Now that all of the currents have been calculated, you can use Ohm's law to find the voltage across each resistor.

$$I_3 = I_1 + I_2$$
$$I_3 = 2.5 - .5$$
$$I_3 = 2\ AMPS$$

Figure 11.85

Solution for Voltages — Simply multiply the appropriate currents by the appropriate resistances as shown in Figure 11.86.

$$E_1 = 60\text{ volts}$$
$$E_2 = 3\text{ volts}$$
$$E_3 = 24\text{ volts}$$

and the problem is completely solved.

$$E_1 = I_1 \times R_1 = 2.5 \times 24 = 60\ VOLTS$$
$$E_2 = I_2 \times R_2 = .5 \times 6 = 3\ VOLTS$$
$$E_3 = I_3 \times R_3 = 2.0 \times 12 = 24\ VOLTS$$

Figure 11.86

Complete Solution — Figure 11.87 shows the circuit schematic with all of the answers labeled. Notice also that the voltage polarities have been labeled. Recall that if you wanted to solve this problem using conventional currents, you would follow exactly the same steps and you would get the same answers, except all the current directions would be opposite.

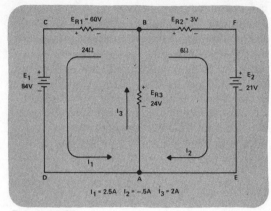

Figure 11.87

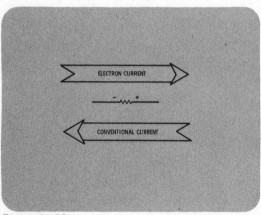

Figure 11.88

How to Determine Voltage Polarities — In simple circuits your rule for determining the polarity of a resistor's voltage drop simply states that the side of a resistor closest to the positive terminal of the battery or voltage source is positive and the side closest to the negative terminal is negative. This is understood when you only have one voltage source or battery, but what do you do when you are working with more complex circuits which contain more than one source?

You use this simple rule (Figure 11.88):

1. First determine the correct direction for the current (either electron or conventional current)
2. Electron current flows through resistors from minus (−) to plus (+)
3. Conventional current flows through resistors from plus (+) to minus (−).

Then you can label your voltage drops accordingly.

•   Example

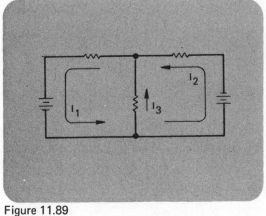

Figure 11.89

Example — Suppose you have determined the correct directions for all the electron currents in a circuit and they are as shown in Figure 11.89. What then are the correct polarities for the voltage drops? Following the above rule you should find that the polarities are as shown in Figure 11.90.

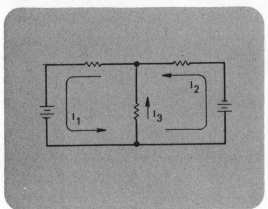

Figure 11.90

This has been a busy lesson. The next lesson will continue to give you some practice using some of what has been covered here; and more importantly, you will be introduced to some shortcuts to make using these laws easier. In the meanwhile, it is suggested that you carefully go through the worked examples set out on the next few pages. These will help you in understanding the techniques involved in using Kirchhoff's laws.

● **Worked Through Examples**

1. Write a node equation for the diagram shown below, substitute the appropriate currents and solve the equation for I_5. Also indicate the direction of I_5.

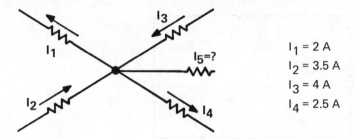

$I_1 = 2$ A
$I_2 = 3.5$ A
$I_3 = 4$ A
$I_4 = 2.5$ A

From Kirchhoff's current law you know that whatever current arrives at a junction must equal the current that leaves the junction. Write down the currents entering the junction on one side of an equals sign, and then write down the currents that leave the junction on the other side of the equals sign.

$$\text{Leaving} = \text{Entering}$$
$$I_1 + I_4 = I_2 + I_3$$

On which side of the equals sign does I_5 belong? If you substitute the values for I_1 through I_4 in the equation, you will see.

$$\text{Leaving} = \text{Entering}$$
$$2\text{ A} + 2.5\text{ A} = 3.5\text{ A} + 4\text{ A}$$
$$4.5\text{ A} = 7.5\text{ A}$$

Obviously, 4.5 amps does not equal 7.5 amps, so I_5 must belong with the 4.5 amp leaving the junction.

$$\text{Leaving} = \text{Entering}$$
$$4.5\text{ A} + I_5 = 7.5\text{ A}$$

In order for the currents leaving to equal the currents entering, I_5 must be the right value so that there will be 7.5 amps leaving *and* entering the junction. I_5 should be 3 amps *leaving* the junction. You can prove this by subtracting 4.5 amps from each side of the equation.

$$
\begin{array}{rcl}
4.5\text{ A} + I_5 & = & 7.5\text{ A} \\
-4.5\text{ A} & & -4.5\text{ A} \\
\hline
I_5 & = & 3\text{ A}
\end{array}
$$

Thus, I_5 does equal 3 amps and it must leave the junction.

2. Write a loop equation for the circuit shown below using electron current, and write another loop equation using conventional current.

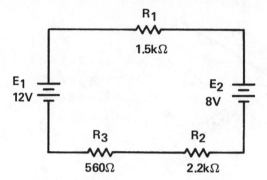

Step One: Assign a current direction. Any direction is fine but more than likely the actual direction of electron current is counterclockwise since E_1 is larger than E_2. Assume that the electron current is flowing in the counterclockwise direction and label it accordingly.

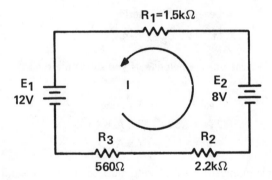

Step Two: Traverse the circuit and write down all the source voltages and IR voltages according to the rules presented in this lesson. If you start at the positive terminal of E_1 and move through the circuit counterclockwise, you should get:

$+E_1$ (since you go through E_1 in the *same* direction it pushes electron current)

$-IR_3$ (since you traverse R_3 *in* the direction of electron current)

$-IR_2$ (since you traverse R_2 *in* the direction of electron current)

$-E_2$ (since you go through E_2 *against* the direction it is pushing electron current)

$-IR_1$ (since you traverse R_1 *in* the direction of electron current).

When you set this equal to zero, the loop equation for this circuit, considering electron current, is:

$$E_1 - IR_3 - IR_2 - E_2 - IR_1 = 0.$$

To write a loop equation for conventional current, traverse the loop again and write down the voltages according to your rules. Assume the same direction for current as before. If you start at the same point (the positive terminal of E_1) and move through the circuit counterclockwise, you should get:

$-E_1$ (since you go through E_1 *against* the direction it pushes conventional current)

$-IR_3$ (since you traverse R_3 *in* the assumed direction for conventional current)

$-IR_2$ (since you traverse R_3 *in* the assumed direction for conventional current)

$+E_2$ (since you go through E_2 in the *same* direction it pushes conventional current)

$-IR_1$ (since you traverse R_1 *in* the assumed direction for conventional current).

The loop equation for this circuit, considering conventional current, is:

$$-E_1 - IR_3 - IR_2 + E_2 - IR_1 = 0.$$

3. Solve each of the equations from the previous example for the current.

Electron Current Equation

$$E_1 - IR_3 - IR_2 - E_2 - IR_1 = 0$$

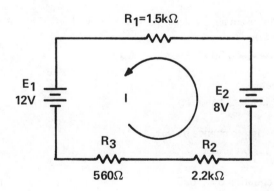

First, substitute the appropriate values from the circuit into the equation.

$$12 - 0.56 \text{ kI} - 2.2 \text{ kI} - 8 - 1.5 \text{ kI} = 0$$

When the two source voltages are added algebraically, they yield 4.

$$4 - 0.56 \text{ kI} - 2.2 \text{ kI} - 1.5 \text{ kI} = 0$$

You can combine the I terms to get:

$$4 - 4.26 \text{ kI} = 0$$

Transpose the 4, remembering to change its sign.

$$-4.26 \text{ kI} = -4$$

Divide both sides of the equation by -4.26 k.

$$\frac{-4.26 \text{ kI}}{-4.26 \text{ k}} = \frac{-4}{-4.26 \text{ k}}$$

$$I = 0.939 \text{ mA or } 939 \text{ } \mu\text{A}$$

Since this answer is positive, the assumed direction for the electron current (counterclockwise) is correct.

Conventional Current Equation

$$-E_1 - IR_3 - IR_2 + E_2 - IR_1 = 0$$

First, substitute the appropriate values from the circuit into the equation.

$$- 12 - 0.56 \text{ kI} - 2.2 \text{ kI} + 8 - 1.5 \text{ kI} = 0$$

When the two source voltages are added algebraically, they yield -4. This, as you will see, will make a difference in your answer.

$$- 4 - 0.56 \text{ kI} - 2.2 \text{ kI} - 1.5 \text{ kI} = 0$$

Combine the I terms to get:

$$- 4 - 4.26 \text{ kI} = 0$$

Transpose the 4, remembering to change its sign.

$$-4.26 \text{ kI} = 4$$

Divide both sides of this equation by -4.26 k.

$$\frac{-4.26 \text{ kI}}{-4.26 \text{ k}} = \frac{4}{-4.26 \text{ k}}$$

$$I = -0.939 \text{ mA or } -939 \text{ } \mu\text{A}$$

Since this answer is *negative* the assumed direction for the conventional current was wrong, and so you know that the conventional current is actually flowing *clockwise*.

You know, if you thought about this answer for a minute, it makes a great deal of sense. The solution to the electron current equation told you that the electron current was flowing *counter-clockwise*. Recall that electron and conventional current have the *same* effect in a circuit; they just flow in *opposite* directions. Thus, you know that conventional current for this circuit must flow in the *clockwise* direction.

4. Write the loop and node equations for the following circuit using electron current. Then solve the equations for the branch currents, including their directions, and use these currents to find the voltage drop across each resistor. Also indicate the polarity of each voltage drop.

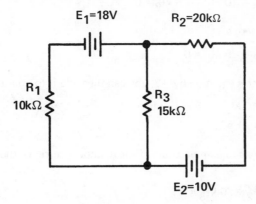

First Step: Assign a direction for each current and label it accordingly.

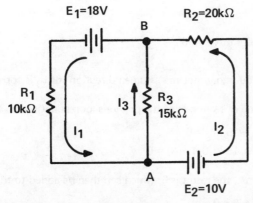

Immediately, you can see from Kirchhoff's current law that at junction point A:

$$I_1 = I_3 + I_2$$

Second Step: Traverse each loop and write down all the voltages you encounter with their correct signs.

Loop 1 $18 - 10 \, kI_1 - 15 \, kI_3 = 0$ (counterclockwise from point B)

Loop 2 $10 - 20 \, kI_2 + 15 \, kI_3 = 0$ (counterclockwise from point A)

Third Step: Simplify the equations. If you substitute $I_3 + I_2$ for I_1 in the first equation, you will then have only two unknowns, and you will have two equations with which to find the two unknowns.

$$18 - 10 \, k \, (I_3 + I_2) - 15 \, kI_3 = 0$$
$$10 - 20 \, k \, I_2 + 15 \, k \, I_3 = 0$$

In the first equation, multiply I_3 and I_2 by $-10k$.

$$18 - 10 \, kI_3 - 10 \, kI_2 - 15 \, kI_3 = 0$$

You can now combine the I_3 terms.

$$18 - 10 \, kI_2 - 25 \, kI_3 = 0.$$

If you multiply both sides of this equation by -2, you can then add it to your equation for loop 2.

$$(-2) \, (18 - 10 \, kI_2 - 25 \, kI_3) = (0) \, (-2)$$
$$-36 + 20 \, kI_2 + 50 \, kI_3 = 0$$

Fourth Step: Add the equations to eliminate one of the unknown currents, thus enabling you to calculate the other current.

$$-36 + 20 \, \cancel{kI_2} + 50 \, kI_3 = 0$$
$$\underline{10 - \cancel{20 \, kI_2} + 15 \, kI_3 = 0}$$
$$-26 \qquad\qquad + 65 \, kI_3 = 0$$

$$65 \, kI_3 = 26$$

$$I_3 = \frac{26}{65 \, k} = 0.4 \text{ mA} = 400 \, \mu A$$

Since this answer is positive, you know that the assumed direction for I_3 is correct.

Fifth Step: Substitute the value of I_3 in one of the previous loop equations to find I_1 or I_2.

Loop 2 $10 - 20 \, kI_2 + 15 \, kI_3 = 0$

$10 - 20 \, kI_2 + 15 \, k \, (0.4 \text{ mA}) = 0$

When 15 k is multiplied by 4 mA, the result is 6, which can then be added to the 10.

$$10 - 20 \, kI_2 + 6 = 0$$
$$16 - 20 \, kI_2 = 0$$

Transpose and divide.

$$-20\,k I_2 = -16$$

$$\frac{-20\,k I_2}{-20\,k} = \frac{-16}{-20\,k}$$

$$I_2 = 0.8\text{ mA} = 800\,\mu\text{A}$$

This answer is also positive, so the assumed direction for I_2 is correct.

Sixth Step: Substitute I_2 and I_3 in the node current equation to find I_1.

$$I_1 = I_3 + I_2$$
$$I_1 = 0.4\text{ mA} + 0.8\text{ mA}$$
$$I_1 = 1.2\text{ mA}$$

The answer is again positive, so its assumed direction is also correct. If any of the answers for the branch currents were negative, you would know that the assumed direction for the current was wrong and that the actual direction was *opposite* to the assumed direction for that current.

Seventh Step: Use Ohm's law to calculate the voltage drops across the resistors.

$$E_{R1} = I_1 \times R_1$$
$$E_{R1} = 1.2\text{ mA} \times 10\text{ k}\Omega$$
$$E_{R1} = 12\text{ V}$$

$$E_{R2} = I_2 \times R_2$$
$$E_{R2} = 0.8\text{ mA} \times 20\text{ k}\Omega$$
$$E_{R2} = 16\text{ V}$$

$$E_{R3} = I_3 \times R_3$$
$$E_{R3} = 0.4\text{ mA} \times 15\text{ k}\Omega$$
$$E_{R3} = 6\text{ V}$$

Recall the rule for determining the polarity of the voltage across a resistor, which states that electron current flows through a resistor from minus to plus or from the negative side to the positive side. Thus, the voltage drops and their polarities are as shown below.

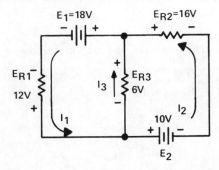

5. Write the loop and node equations for the circuit shown in example 4 using *conventional* current. Then solve the equations for the branch currents, including their directions. Also indicate the polarities of the voltage drops produced by these conventional currents.

    First Step: Assign a direction for each current and lable it accordingly.

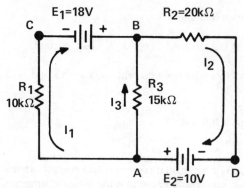

    Then, from Kirchhoff's current law, the node current equation for node A is:

    $$I_2 = I_3 + I_1$$

    Second Step: Traverse each loop and write down all the voltages you encounter with their correct signs.

    Loop 1 $18 + 15\,kI_3 - 10\,kI_1 = 0$ (clockwise from point C)
    Loop 2 $10 - 15\,kI_3 - 20\,kI_2 = 0$ (clockwise from point D)

    Third Step: Simplify the equations. If you substitute $I_3 + I_1$ for I_2 in the second equation, you will have two equations with two unknowns. You can then easily solve the equations for the unknown currents.

    $$10 - 15\,kI_3 - 20\,kI_2 = 0$$
    $$10 - 15\,kI_3 - 20\,k\,(I_3 + I_1) = 0$$

Multiply I_3 and I_1 by $-20\,k$.

    $$10 - 15\,kI_3 - 20\,kI_3 - 20\,kI_1 = 0$$

You can combine the I_3 terms.

    $$10 - 35\,kI_3 - 20\,kI_1 = 0$$

If you divide both sides of this equation by -2, you can add it to the equation for loop 1.

    $$(10 - 35\,kI_3 - 20\,kI_1) \div (-2) = (0) \div (-2)$$
    $$-5 + 17.5\,kI_3 + 10\,kI_1 = 0$$

Fourth Step: Add the equations to eliminate one of the unknown currents, thus enabling you to find the other current.

Loop 1 $18 + 15 \text{ k}I_3 - 10 \text{ k}I_1 = 0$

Loop 2 $-5 + 17.5 \text{ k}I_3 + 10 \text{ k}I_1 = 0$

$$13 + 32.5 \text{ k}I_3 \qquad\qquad = 0$$

$$32.5 \text{ k}I_3 = -13$$

$$I_3 = \frac{-13}{32.5 \text{ k}}$$

$$I_3 = -0.4 \text{ mA} = -400 \text{ }\mu\text{A}$$

Since this answer is negative, you know that the assumed direction for I_3 is wrong and that the conventional current I_3 actually flows down through R_3.

Fifth Step: Substitute the value of I_3 in one of the previous loop equations to find I_1 or I_2.

Loop 1 $18 + 15 \text{ k}I_3 - 10 \text{ k}I_1 = 0$

              $18 + 15 \text{ k} (-0.4 \text{ mA}) - 10 \text{ k}I_1 = 0$

When 15 k is multiplied by −0.4 mA, the result is −6, which can then be added algebraically to the 18.

              $18 - 6 - 10 \text{ k}I_1 = 0$

              $12 - 10 \text{ k}I_1 = 0$

Transpose and divide.

$$-10 \text{ k}I_1 = -12$$

$$\frac{-10 \text{ k}I_1}{-10 \text{ k}} = \frac{-12}{-10 \text{ k}}$$

$$I_1 = 1.2 \text{ mA}$$

This answer is positive, so you know that the assumed direction for I_1 is correct.

Sixth Step: Substitute I_1 and I_3 in the node current equation to find I_2;

$$I_2 = I_3 + I_1$$

$$I_2 = -0.4 \text{ mA} + 1.2 \text{ mA}$$

$$I_2 = 0.8 \text{ mA or } 800 \text{ }\mu\text{A}$$

The answer is positive so the assumed direction for I_2 is correct.

Seventh Step: Use Ohm's law to find the voltage drops across the resistors. Since the answers for the currents have the same numerical value as in the previous example, the voltage drops will be the same as they were before, or:

$$E_{R1} = 12 \text{ V}$$
$$E_{R2} = 16 \text{ V}$$
$$E_{R3} = 6 \text{ V}$$

In determining the correct polarities of these voltage drops, remember two things:

1.   Conventional current flows through resistors from plus to minus.

2. I_3 is actually flowing down through R_3.

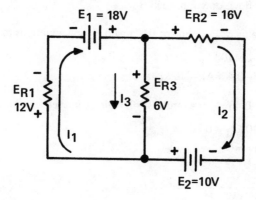

● **Practice Problems**

Depending upon the approach you use in solving these problems and how you round off intermediate results, your answers may vary slightly from those given here. However, any differences you encounter should only occur in the third significant digit of your answer. If the first two significant digits of your answers do not agree with those given here, recheck your calculations. Fold over the page to check your answers.

Fold Over

1. Write the node equations for the following diagrams.

a.
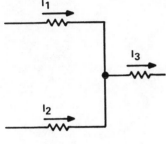

b.
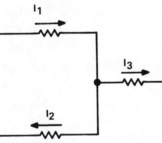

c.
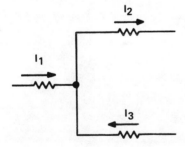

d.
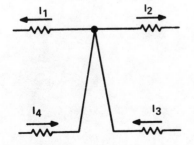

Answers

1.a. $I_1 + I_2 = I_3$

1.b. $I_1 = I_2 + I_3$

1.c. $I_1 + I_3 = I_2$

1.d. $I_4 + I_3 = I_1 + I_2$

e.

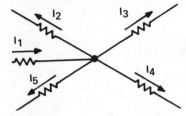

2. Write the loop equations for the following diagrams.

a.

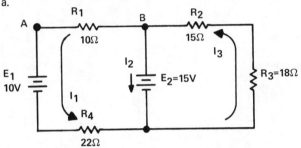

b.

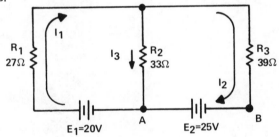

c.

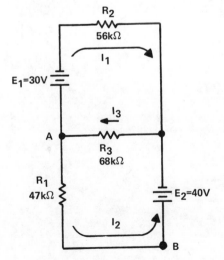

Answers

1.e. $I_1 = I_2 + I_3 + I_4 + I_5$

2.a. Loop 1 — Start at point A and trace the loop ccw.
$$10 - 22I_1 - 15 - 10I_1 = 0$$
Loop 2 — Start at point B and trace the loop ccw.
$$15 - 18I_3 - 15I_3 = 0$$

2.b. Loop 1 — Start at point A and trace the loop cw.
$$20 - 27I_1 - 33I_3 = 0$$
Loop 2 — Start at point B and trace the loop cw.
$$25 + 33I_3 - 39I_2 = 0$$

2.c. Loop 1 — Start at point A and trace the loop cw.
$$30 - 56 kI_1 - 68 kI_3$$
Loop 2 — Start at point B and trace the loop ccw.
$$40 - 68 kI_3 - 47 kI_2$$

d.

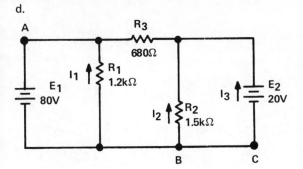

e.

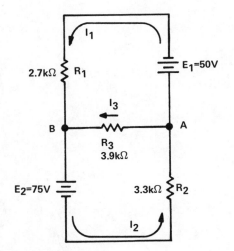

3. Solve the following circuits for all currents and voltage drops. Indicate the polarity of the voltage drops and the direction of the currents.

a.

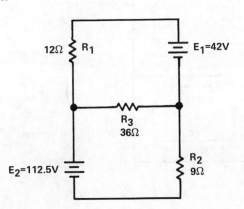

Answers

2.d. Loop 1 – Start at point A and trace the loop ccw.
$$80 - 1.2 \text{ k} I_1 = 0$$
Loop 2 – Start at point B and trace the loop ccw.
$$-1.5 \text{ k} I_2 - .68 \text{ k} (I_2 + I_3) + 1.2 \text{ k} I_1 = 0$$
Loop 3 – Start at point C and trace the loop ccw.
$$-20 + 1.5 \text{ k} I_2 = 0$$

2.e. Loop 1 – Start at point A and trace the loop ccw.
$$50 - 2.7 \text{ k} I_1 + 3.9 \text{ k} I_3 = 0$$
Loop 2 – Start at point B and trace the loop ccw.
$$75 - 3.3 \text{ k} I_2 - 3.9 \text{ k} I_3 = 0$$

3.a.

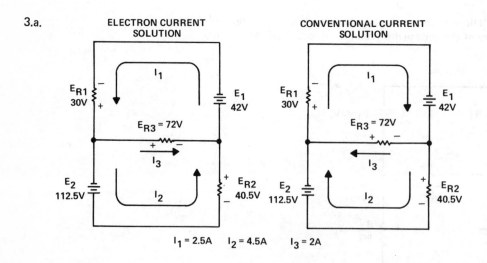

ELECTRON CURRENT SOLUTION   CONVENTIONAL CURRENT SOLUTION

$I_1 = 2.5A$ $I_2 = 4.5A$ $I_3 = 2A$

Fold Over

b.

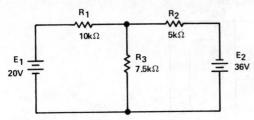

c.

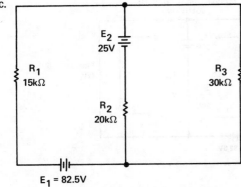

d.

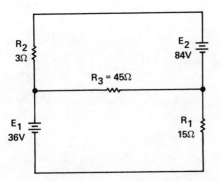

Practice Problems

Answers

3.b.

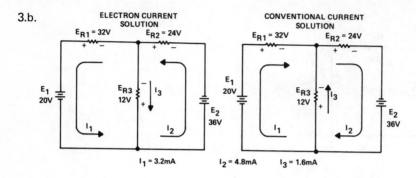

$I_1 = 3.2mA$ $I_2 = 4.8mA$ $I_3 = 1.6mA$

3.c.

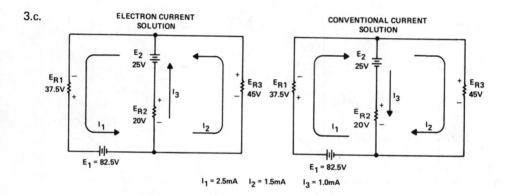

$I_1 = 2.5mA$ $I_2 = 1.5mA$ $I_3 = 1.0mA$

3.d.

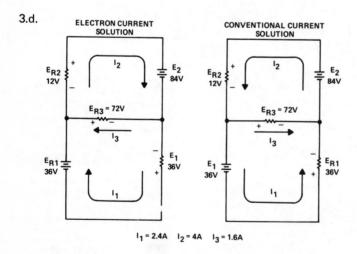

$I_1 = 2.4A$ $I_2 = 4A$ $I_3 = 1.6A$

Fold Over

e.

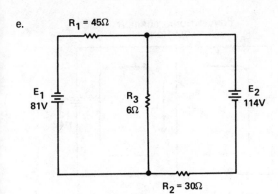

f.

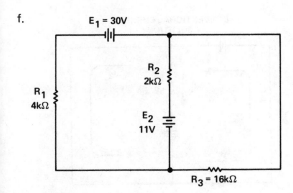

g.

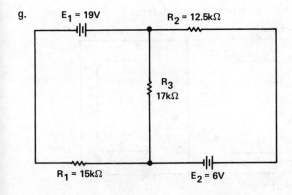

Answers

3.e.

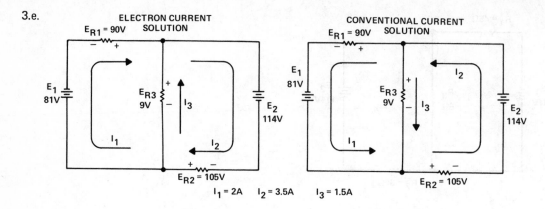

$I_1 = 2A$ $I_2 = 3.5A$ $I_3 = 1.5A$

3.f.

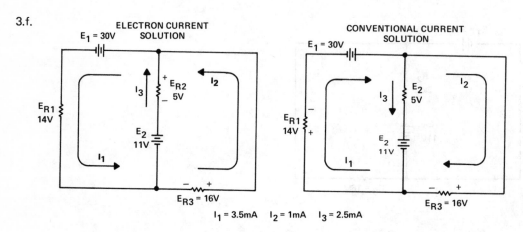

$I_1 = 3.5mA$ $I_2 = 1mA$ $I_3 = 2.5mA$

3.g.

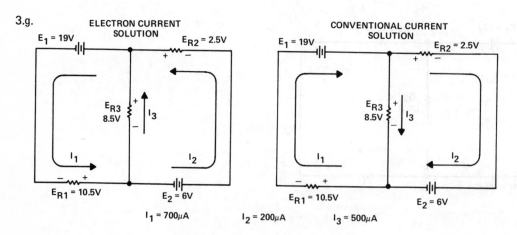

$I_1 = 700\mu A$ $I_2 = 200\mu A$ $I_3 = 500\mu A$

Fold Over

h.

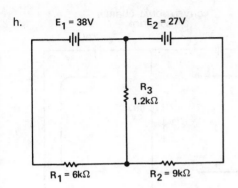

i.

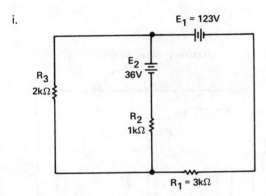

Answers

3.h.

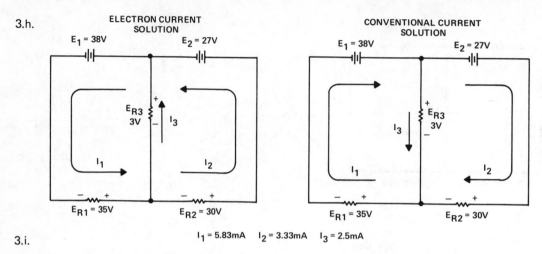

ELECTRON CURRENT SOLUTION

$E_1 = 38V$ $E_2 = 27V$

E_{R3} 3V I_3

I_1 I_2

$E_{R1} = 35V$ $E_{R2} = 30V$

CONVENTIONAL CURRENT SOLUTION

$E_1 = 38V$ $E_2 = 27V$

E_{R3} 3V I_3

I_1 I_2

$E_{R1} = 35V$ $E_{R2} = 30V$

$I_1 = 5.83mA$ $I_2 = 3.33mA$ $I_3 = 2.5mA$

3.i.

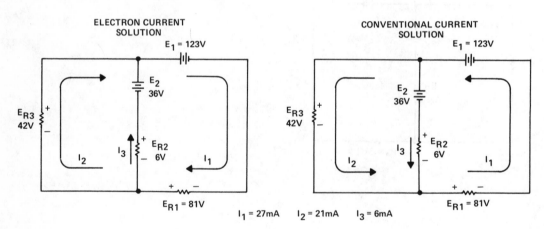

ELECTRON CURRENT SOLUTION

$E_1 = 123V$

E_2 36V

E_{R3} 42V

I_3 E_{R2} 6V

I_2 I_1

$E_{R1} = 81V$

CONVENTIONAL CURRENT SOLUTION

$E_1 = 123V$

E_2 36V

E_{R3} 42V

I_3 E_{R2} 6V

I_2 I_1

$E_{R1} = 81V$

$I_1 = 27mA$ $I_2 = 21mA$ $I_3 = 6mA$

Fold Over

j.

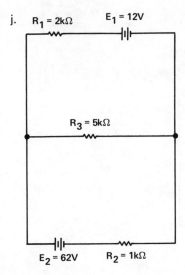

Answers

3.j.

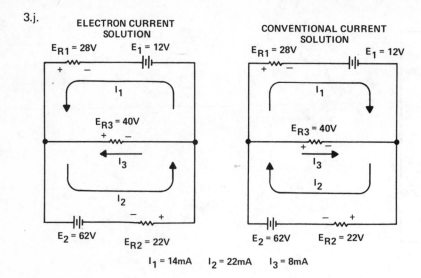

ELECTRON CURRENT
SOLUTION

$E_{R1} = 28V$ $E_1 = 12V$

I_1

$E_{R3} = 40V$

I_3

I_2

$E_2 = 62V$ $E_{R2} = 22V$

CONVENTIONAL CURRENT
SOLUTION

$E_{R1} = 28V$ $E_1 = 12V$

I_1

$E_{R3} = 40V$

I_3

I_2

$E_2 = 62V$ $E_{R2} = 22V$

$I_1 = 14mA$ $I_2 = 22mA$ $I_3 = 8mA$

1. "The sum of currents arriving at any point in a circuit must be equal to the sum of the currents leaving the point" is called:

   a. The law of Electrostatics
   b. Kirchhoff's current law
   c. The product over sum law
   d. The loop equation

2. Junctions or branch points in a circuit are commonly called:

   a. High points
   b. Terminals
   c. Extra paths
   d. Nodes

3. "The total circuit current equals the sum of the branch currents" is:

   a. The first law of electrostatics
   b. Coulomb's law
   c. Kirchhoff's current law for parallel circuits
   d. A series circuit law

4. "The current is the same at any point in the circuit" is:

   a. The first law of electrostatics
   b. A parallel circuit law
   c. Coulomb's law
   d. Kirchhoff's current law for series circuits

5. Kirchhoff's second law is:

   a. For series circuits
   b. For parallel circuits
   c. Kirchhoff's voltage law
   d. For a closed circuit path
   e. All of the above
   f. None of the above

6. "The total voltage applied to any closed circuit path is always equal to the sum of the voltage drops in that path" is:

   a. To be used with series-parallel circuits
   b. To be used with parallel-series circuits
   c. Kirchhoff's voltage law
   d. a, b, c above
   e. a only

7. A continuous path that is traced in a circuit that starts and ends at the same point is called:

   a. A junction
   b. A loop
   c. A closed path
   d. A branch
   e. b and c above
   f. All of above

8. Kirchhoff's voltage law _____ hold for circuit loops that have no voltage sources.

   a. Does
   b. Doesn't
   c. May
   d. May not

9. "For any loop, the sum of all the voltages that aid current flow in the loop, must equal the sum of all those voltages that oppose it" is:

   a. Kirchhoff's current law
   b. An alternate statement of Kirchhoff's voltage law
   c. Applies only to series circuits
   d. Applies only to parallel circuits

10. "The algebraic sum of the voltages aiding current and the voltages opposing current in any circuit loop is equal to zero" is:

    a. To be used only for series circuits
    b. To be used only for parallel circuits
    c. An alternate of Kirchhoff's current law
    d. An alternate statement of Kirchhoff's voltage law.

11. "The algebraic sum of all voltages in a loop equals zero" is:

    a. To be used only for series circuits
    b. To be used only for parallel circuits
    c. An alternate of Kirchhoff's current law
    d. An alternate of Kirchhoff's voltage law

12. When the algebraic sum of all voltages in a loop is set equal to zero the result is called:

    a. A series circuit
    b. A loop equation
    c. The total current
    d. A branch

13. When analyzing circuits, using Kirchhoff's laws for circuit branches where the current direction is unknown, _____ a direction.

    a. Guess
    b. The current dictates
    c. The voltage dictates
    d. All of the above

14. When calculating currents in a circuit using Kirchhoff's laws, if the current is negative it:

    a. Must not be flowing
    b. Is too great in value
    c. Is flowing opposite to the direction chosen
    d. Is very small in value

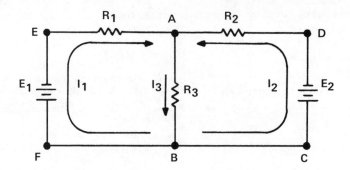

The questions that follow use the schematic above.

15. Point A and Point B are:
    a. Junctions
    b. Nodes
    c. Form a branch
    d. All of above
    e. b only

16. Circuit paths A B F E A and A B C D A are called:
    a. Circuit loops
    b. Nodes
    c. Junctions
    d. Voltage sources

17. The direction of I_1 and I_2 shown is for _____ flow.
    a. Electron
    b. Conventional current
    c. Branch current
    d. Load current

18. If E_1 and E_2 and R_1, R_2 and R_3 are known, solving for I_1, I_2, and I_3 requires _____ equations.
    a. One
    b. Two
    c. Three
    d. Four

19. Kirchhoff's current law can be used to write an equation for:
    a. The loop A B F E A
    b. Point A
    c. Node B
    d. a and b above
    e. b and c above
    f. c only

20. Kirchhoff's voltage law can be used to write equations around:
    a. Loop A B F E A
    b. Loop A B C D A
    c. Loop B F E A D C B
    d. All of the above
    e. a and b only

Lesson 12

Advanced Methods of DC Circuit Analysis

In this lesson, Kirchhoff's laws and the procedures for using them will be reviewed, and a new circuit analysis technique called the superposition theorem will be introduced. The use of the superposition theorem in analyzing multiple source dc circuits will be covered. Several additional advanced methods of dc circuit analysis will also be introduced. A brief synopsis of the use of these methods will be covered at the end of this lesson.

LESSON 12. ADVANCED METHODS OF DC CIRCUIT ANALYSIS

• Objectives

1. Using Kirchhoff's voltage and current laws correctly, *write* the loop and junction equations for any dc circuit such as the bridge circuit shown below, using either electron or conventional current to analyze the circuit.

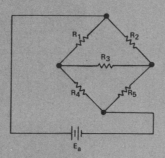

2. *Write* the superposition theorem, including a statement of its limitations.

3. Using the superposition theorem, *solve* for the unknown voltages and currents in multiple source dc circuits of the type illustrated in the schematic diagram below.

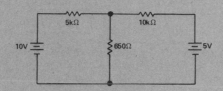

4. With the aid of this lesson summary and other reference material, *state* how any of the following circuit analysis techniques may be used in analyzing dc circuits:
   a. Method of mesh currents
   b. Node voltage analysis
   c. Thevenin's theorem
   d. Norton's theorem
   e. Millman's theorem

-
- Kirchhoff's Voltage Law
- Series Circuit as a Closed Loop

In the previous lesson, Kirchhoff's laws were introduced and you were shown how to apply them in analyzing multiple source dc circuits. This lesson goes on to examine the use of Kirchhoff's laws to analyze a complex series-parallel circuit, and also discusses what is called the *superposition theorem*. You will see that the superposition theorem is a very important tool, because you can use it to greatly simplify the analysis of multiple source circuits. This lesson then goes on to briefly familiarize you with some more methods used in circuit analysis. These advanced methods will not be discussed at great length but they will be concisely outlined for you at the end of the lesson for your later reference.

Kirchhoff's Voltage Law — In the last lesson Kirchhoff's laws were first introduced to you. Before covering any new material in this lesson, it will be helpful to review these laws and the rules you were given on how to use them. Remember there are two laws: Kirchhoff's current law and Kirchhoff's voltage law. It will be helpful to review Kirchhoff's voltage law which is stated as shown in Figure 12.1; *the algebraic sum of the voltages around any closed loop in a circuit must equal zero.*

Since quite a few new terms and concepts are involved in using this law, a brief review of some of its basic elements will be helpful.

KIRCHHOFF'S VOLTAGE LAW

THE ALGEBRAIC SUM OF THE VOLTAGES AROUND ANY CLOSED LOOP MUST EQUAL ZERO.

Figure 12.1

Series Circuit as a Closed Loop — A closed path, or *loop* as it was called in the preceding lesson, is determined by traversing a path through a circuit in a particular direction until the starting point of the path is reached. As you can see in the simple series circuit of Figure 12.2, if you start at the starting point labeled in this circuit and proceed in a counterclockwise direction, you must pass through R_1, R_2, R_3 and the voltage source before you return to the starting point. This path through the circuit is a closed path or loop.

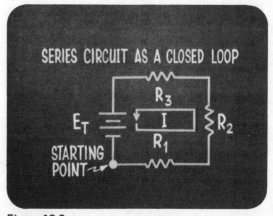

Figure 12.2

- Use of Kirchhoff's Laws
- Positive Source Voltage
- Negative Source Voltage

Use of Kirchhoff's Laws — You must remember the steps involved in using Kirchhoff's second law. In order to write down a loop equation as shown in Figure 12.3, the first step is to label all the currents flowing in the circuit and assign them a direction. Then traverse the loop you are analyzing, adding the voltages algebraically, and set the algebraic sum of the voltages equal to zero. In the loop equation, a voltage source gets a positive sign if you traverse it in the same direction as it normally pushes current.

TO USE KIRCHHOFF'S LAWS

1. LABEL ALL CURRENTS AND ASSIGN THEM A DIRECTION.
2. TRAVERSE THE LOOP, ADD ALL VOLTAGES ALGEBRAICALLY, AND SET THE SUM EQUAL TO ZERO.
3. A VOLTAGE SOURCE RECEIVES A POSITIVE SIGN, IF YOU TRAVERSE IT IN THE SAME DIRECTION, IT NORMALLY PUSHES CURRENT.
4. A VOLTAGE SOURCE RECEIVES A NEGATIVE SIGN, IF YOU TRAVERSE IT OPPOSITE TO THE DIRECTION IT NORMALLY PUSHES CURRENT.

Figure 12.3

Positive Source Voltage — Stop and consider for a moment what that means. If you are considering *electron current* (Figure 12.4), a *source voltage* is considered *positive* if you traverse it from *plus to minus*. If you are considering *conventional current*, a *source voltage* is considered *positive* if you traverse it from *minus to plus*. In either convention, a *voltage source* gets a *positive* sign in the loop equation if the direction you traverse it is the *same* as the direction it pushes current.

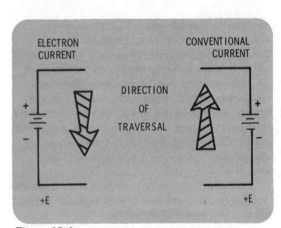

Figure 12.4

Negative Source Voltage — Conversely, a voltage source gets a *negative sign* (Figure 12.5) if you traverse it *opposite* to the direction it normally pushes current. In other words, if you are considering *electron current*, a source voltage receives a *negative sign* when you traverse the source from negative to positive. For *conventional current*, the source voltage is *negative* when you traverse the source from *positive to negative*. In either current convention, a *voltage source* gets a *negative sign* in the loop equation if you traverse it *opposite* to the direction it normally carries current.

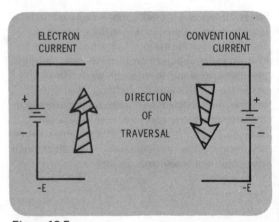

Figure 12.5

- **Signs of Voltages Across Resistors**
- **Voltages Around a Closed Loop**
- **Series Circuit Rule**

Signs of Voltages Across Resistors — Two rules governing the signs of voltage terms across resistors were also covered in Lesson 11 (Figure 12.6). If you traverse a *resistor in the direction of current flow through it*, the *voltage across it* is considered *negative*. If you go through a *resistor against the current direction*, the *voltage across it* is considered *positive*.

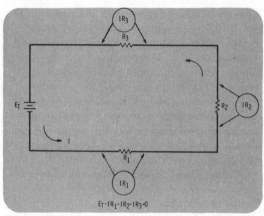

TO USE KIRCHHOFF'S LAWS (CONTINUED)

5. IF YOU TRAVERSE A RESISTOR IN THE DIRECTION OF ASSUMED CURRENT FLOW, THE VOLTAGE ACROSS IT IS CONSIDERED **NEGATIVE.**
6. IF YOU TRAVERSE A RESISTOR **AGAINST** THE DIRECTION OF ASSUMED CURRENT FLOW, THE VOLTAGE ACROSS IT IS CONSIDERED POSITIVE.

Figure 12.6

Voltages Around a Closed Loop — In the single loop shown in Figure 12.7, consider that electron current is flowing counterclockwise as labeled. To write the loop equation for this circuit, begin with the voltage source and traverse the loop, writing down all the voltages you encounter along the way. It is normally convenient in loops such as this to traverse in the same direction as the current flowing in the circuit. If you were traversing counterclockwise, beginning with the voltage source, you would get $E_T - IR_1 - IR_2 - IR_3 = 0$. Remember that the voltages across each resistor are equal to I times R, from Ohm's law.

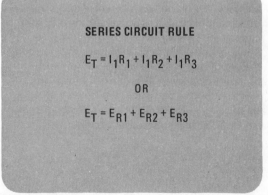

Figure 12.7

Series Circuit Rule — As mentioned in Lesson 11, the loop equation above is simply another way of stating an earlier rule about voltages in a series circuit. If the resistor's IR drops are transposed to the other side of the equation (remember to change the signs), the result is a mathematical expression for the series circuit rule. As shown in Figure 12.8, the total applied voltage must be equal to the sum of the individual drops. Here E_T equals the sum of the voltage across the resistors or E_{R1} plus E_{R2} plus E_{R3}.

SERIES CIRCUIT RULE

$$E_T = I_1R_1 + I_1R_2 + I_1R_3$$

OR

$$E_T = E_{R1} + E_{R2} + E_{R3}$$

Figure 12.8

Kirchhoff's Current Law — Go back a moment to consider Kirchhoff's first law or Kirchhoff's *current* law, which states that the sum of the currents *into* any point of a circuit must equal the sum of the currents *out* of that point (Figure 12.9). This law is generally applied where there is a branch in a circuit, where the current will either divide or recombine. Recall that such circuit points are called *nodes*.

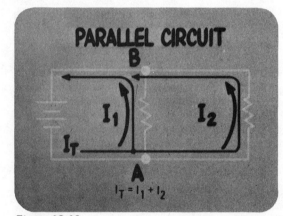

KIRCHHOFF'S CURRENT LAW

THE SUM OF THE CURRENTS INTO ANY POINT OF A CIRCUIT, MUST EQUAL THE SUM OF THE CURRENTS OUT OF THAT POINT.

Figure 12.9

Example Circuit — For example, in the circuit of Figure 12.10, you can see that the current will divide at point A and combine at point B. So, if there is a total of, say, 5 milliamps coming into point A, there must be a total of 5 milliamps leaving that point and dividing into I_1 and I_2. Thus, you can see that this is just another way of saying that the total or main line current in a parallel circuit is equal to the sum of the individual branch currents, or $I_T = I_1 + I_2$. This, you recall, is the rule for currents in parallel circuits.

Remember, Kirchhoff's laws are really just another more general way of stating the series and parallel circuit rules.

In the last lesson it was shown how these laws can be applied to the solution of *multiple source* dc circuits, in configurations where Ohm's law alone would not be enough to complete the circuit analysis. This lesson will help you expand the use of Kirchhoff's two laws and apply them to another class of complex series-parallel circuits called bridge circuits. Although the bridge circuits to be discussed have only one voltage source, they cannot be analyzed using Ohm's law methods alone. After this discussion, the lesson will move on to cover several additional new methods that are useful in solving complex circuits.

PARALLEL CIRCUIT

$I_T = I_1 + I_2$

Figure 12.10

Lesson Objectives — So, at the end of this lesson you should:

1. Know and be able to use Kirchhoff's laws to write the loop and node equations for a bridge circuit
2. Know the superposition theorem, its limitations, and how to use it to analyze multiple source dc circuits
3. Be familiar with more advanced circuit analysis methods, and know where to look for reference material necessary to implement them (Figure 12.11).

- KIRCHHOFF'S LAWS
- SUPERPOSITION THEOREM
- ADVANCED CIRCUIT ANALYSIS METHODS

Figure 12.11

Bridge Circuit — In the previous lesson you saw how to use Kirchhoff's laws to analyze multiple source circuits. This lesson first considers a complex series-parallel circuit which (although it has only one voltage source) cannot be analyzed by ordinary means; that is, with Ohm's law and simple circuit rules.

A circuit of the type shown in Figure 12.12 is called a *bridge* circuit. As you will see in the laboratory portion of this course, a specialized version of this circuit called a *Wheatstone bridge* can be used in making very accurate resistance measurements. At this point in this lesson, Kirchhoff's laws will be used to *begin* the analysis of this circuit. That is, all the loop equations and node equations necessary to find all currents and voltages in the circuit will be written down, going through all procedures step by step. At this point, if you feel ready to write down these equations and solve them on your own, please do so. This would be a good point to see how far you can go on your own in handling Kirchhoff's laws. If you have any difficulty, the complete analysis of this circuit will be worked out step by step for you right here.

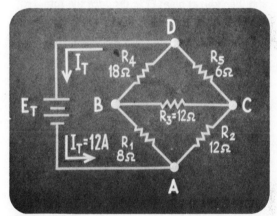

Figure 12.12

Label Current Direction — The first step in analysing this circuit is to label all the electron currents and assign them a direction, as shown in Figure 12.13. (Note, at this point if you do not know the direction of current flow, just guess a direction. Remember that, if any current you solve for turns out *negative*, the current is flowing *opposite* to the direction you guessed.) Notice in the circuit that the total main line electron current is 12 amps, and that it flows from the negative terminal of the source to point A. At point A, the total current divides into two parts which you can label I_1 and I_2, which flow up through R_1 and R_2 respectively. Assume that I_3, the current flowing through R_3, is flowing from left to right. Now I_4 and I_5 flow up through R_4 and R_5 respectively, and then join at point D to produce the total current, which flows back to the voltage source.

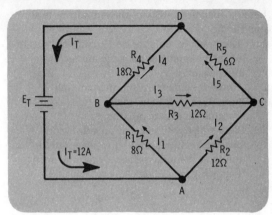

Figure 12.13

Node Current Equations: Node A — Now that all the currents flowing in the circuit have been labeled and a direction assigned to them, you can use Kirchhoff's current law to write the *node* current equations at points A, B, C, and D.

At point A in Figure 12.14, the sum of I_1 and I_2 must equal the total current. Since you know the total current is 12 amps, you can say that I_1 plus I_2 equals 12 amps.

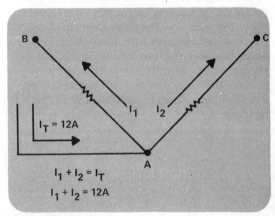

Figure 12.14

- Node B
- Node C
- Node D

Node B — At point B in the circuit, as shown in Figure 12.15, I_1 must equal I_3 plus I_4. This gives you another node equation to use in analyzing this circuit.

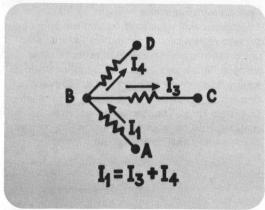

Figure 12.15

Node C — Likewise, at point C in Figure 12.16, I_5 must equal I_3 plus I_2.

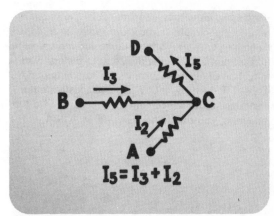

Figure 12.16

Node D — At point D in Figure 12.17, I_4 plus I_5 equals I_T or 12 amps.

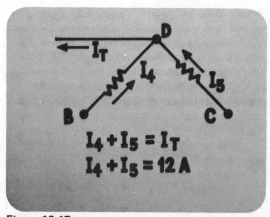

Figure 12.17

12-11

- **Node Current Equations**
- **First Loop Equation**
- **Second Loop Equation**

Node Current Equations — Figure 12.18 shows all the node current equations. As you will be seeing, these equations can be manipulated so that any one current can be expressed in terms of other currents. This is usually done to simplify the loop equations which are developed next. To carry the circuit analysis further, three loop equations will be written for it. The loop equations when analyzed with the node equations, will allow you to completely analyze this circuit.

$$I_1 + I_2 = 12$$
$$I_1 = I_3 + I_4$$
$$I_5 = I_3 + I_2$$
$$I_4 + I_5 = 12$$

Figure 12.18

First Loop Equation — Figure 12.19 shows one loop of the circuit. If you traverse the loop beginning with the voltage source and move around in the counterclockwise direction in the assumed direction of electron current, the loop equation is $E_T - I_1R_1 - I_4R_4 = 0$. When you substitute the resistance values written on the schematic into the equation, you should have $E_T - 8I_1 - 18I_4 = 0$.

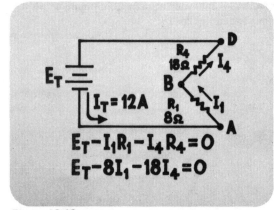

Figure 12.19

Second Loop Equation — Figure 12.20 shows a second loop in the circuit. If you traverse this loop in the clockwise direction starting at point A, the loop equation is $-I_1R_1 - I_3R_3 + I_2R_2 = 0$. Note that since you traversed R_2 *against* the direction of current flowing through it, the last term in the equation has a *plus* sign. When you substitute the resistance values in the equation, you should have $-8I_1 - 12I_3 + 12I_2 = 0$.

Now consider one more loop and write the equation for it.

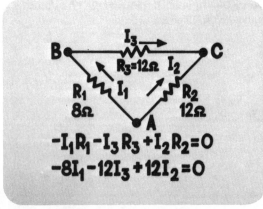

Figure 12.20

12-12

Third Loop Equation — If you traverse the loop in Figure 12.21 in the counterclockwise direction, starting at point B, the equation is $-I_3R_3 - I_5R_5 + I_4R_4 = 0$. Again, substitute the resistance values in the equation, and you should have $-12\,I_3 - 6\,I_5 + 18\,I_4 = 0$. The last term in this equation also has a plus sign since you traverse R_4 against the direction of current flowing through it. (Note, any three loops could be used in arriving at the loop equations you need for this problem.)

As you will see, the remainder of this problem involves manipulations and substitutions with the node current equations and the loop equations to find the individual branch currents. Once all the branch currents are known, you simply multiply them by the appropriate resistances to find the individual voltages in the circuit.

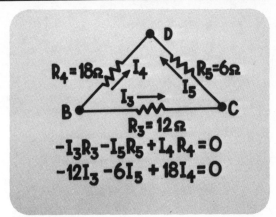

Figure 12.21

For those of you who want to follow the analysis of this circuit, its step-by-step solution is included here.

To start, write all of the node current equations in simplified form:

$$I_1 + I_2 = 12 \rightarrow I_1 = 12 - I_2$$
$$I_1 = I_3 + I_4 \rightarrow I_4 = I_1 - I_3 = 12 - I_2 - I_3$$
$$I_5 = I_3 + I_2 \rightarrow I_3 = I_5 - I_2$$
$$I_4 + I_5 = 12 \rightarrow I_4 = 12 - I_5 = 12 - I_2 - I_3$$

Note that in writing a simplified expression for I_4 in the second equation, the simplified value of I_1 from the first equation was used. This is also done in the fourth equation. By having several alternate expressions for I_4, the problem can be solved more easily.

Write the three loop equations.

1. $E_T - 8\,I_1 - 18\,I_4 = 0$
2. $-8\,I_1 - 12\,I_3 + 12\,I_2 = 0$
3. $-12\,I_3 - 6\,I_5 + 18\,I_4 = 0$

Pick two equations that share a common term so that that term may be canceled out. In this case, equations 2 and 3 are used, because they both contain the term "I_3". The two equations may now be simplified. Equation 2 is divisible by 4, and equation 3 is divisible by 6.

$$\frac{-8\,I_1 - 12\,I_3 + 12\,I_2 = 0}{4} = 2\,I_1 - 3\,I_3 + 3\,I_2 = 0\,^{(*)}$$

$$\frac{-12\,I_3 - 6\,I_5 + 18\,I_4 = 0}{6} = -2\,I_3 - I_5 + 3\,I_4 = 0$$

In order to simplify the problem further, the equations may be reduced to two unknowns. This may be done by substituting a node current equivalent value into the loop equations. For example, I_1 may also be expressed as $12 - I_2$. If this value is substituted into the simplified loop equation (* above) you have:

$$-2 I_1 - 3 I_3 + 3 I_2 = 0$$
$$-2(12 - I_2) - 3 I_3 + 3 I_2 = 0$$
$$-24 + 2 I_2 - 3 I_3 + 3 I_2 = 0$$

or

$$5 I_2 - 3 I_3 \, 24$$

Next, reduce the other equation to two unknowns (I_2 and I_3)

$$-2 I_3 - I_5 + 3 I_4 = 0$$

From the node current equations you know that I_5 is equal to $I_2 + I_3$. I_4 is equal to $12 - I_2 - I_3$. When these values are substituted into the loop equation, the equation will contain only the unknowns I_2 and I_3, and can then be solved.

$$-2 I_3 - I_5 + 3 I_4 = 0$$
$$-2 I_3 - (I_2 + I_3) + 3(12 - I_2 - I_3) = 0$$
$$-2 I_3 - I_2 - I_3 + 36 - 3 I_2 - 3 I_3 = 0$$
$$+36 - 4 I_2 - 6 I_3 = 0$$
$$-4 I_2 - 6 I_3 = -36 \text{ or}$$
$$4 I_2 + 6 I_3 = 36$$

Now the loop equations have been reduced to two unknowns, I_2 and I_3. One of the currents may now be found.

$$5 I_2 - 3 I_3 = 24$$
$$4 I_2 + 6 I_3 = 36$$

In order to cancel the I_3 term, the first equation above should be multiplied by 2, and then the equations can be added.

$$2 (5 I_2 - 3 I_3) = (24)2$$

$$10 I_2 - 6 I_3 = 48$$

$$\underline{4 I_2 + 6 I_3 = 48}$$

$$14 I_2 \qquad = 84$$

$$\frac{14 I_2}{14} \qquad = \frac{84}{14}$$

$$I_2 \qquad = 6 \text{ A}$$

Now that one of the currents is known, this value may be substituted into the node current and loop equations to solve for the remainder of the circuit currents.

Node current equation:

$$I_1 = 12 - I_2$$
$$I_1 = 12 - 6$$
$$I_1 = 6 \text{ A}$$

Loop equation:

$$-3 I_3 + 5 I_2 = 24$$
$$-3 I_3 + 5(6) = 24$$
$$-3 I_3 + 30 = 24$$
$$-3 I_3 = 24 - 30$$
$$-3 I_3 = -6$$
$$I_3 = 2 \text{ A}$$

Node current equation:

$$I_4 = I_1 - I_3$$
$$I_4 = 6 \text{ A} - 2 \text{ A}$$
$$I_4 = 4 \text{ A}$$
$$I_5 = I_2 + I_3$$
$$I_5 = 6 \text{ A} + 2 \text{ A}$$
$$I_5 = 8 \text{ A}$$

To find the voltages across all resistors in the circuit, Ohm's law may be used.

$$E_{R1} = I_1 \times R_1 = 6 \text{ A} \times 8 \, \Omega = 48 \text{ V}$$
$$E_{R2} = I_2 \times R_2 = 6 \text{ A} \times 12 \, \Omega = 72 \text{ V}$$
$$E_{R3} = I_3 \times R_3 = 2 \text{ A} \times 12 \, \Omega = 24 \text{ V}$$
$$E_{R4} = I_4 \times R_4 = 4 \text{ A} \times 18 \, \Omega = 72 \text{ V}$$
$$E_{R5} = I_5 \times R_5 = 8 \text{ A} \times 6 \, \Omega = 48 \text{ V}$$

To determine E_T, go back to the loop equation in Figure 12.19 and substitute the appropriate current values in the equation.

$$E_T - 8 I_1 - 18 I_4 = 0$$
$$E_T - 8(6) - 18(4) = 0$$
$$E_T - 48 - 72 = 0$$
$$E_T - 120 = 0$$
$$E_T = 120 \text{ V}$$

Superposition Theorem — At this point you have
seen how to use Kirchhoff's laws to analyze several
different types of circuits. Several examples have
now been worked through for you to show you
how Kirchhoff's laws may be used in analyzing
multiple source dc circuits and bridge circuits,
which cannot be worked if Ohm's law methods
alone are used. This lesson now goes on to examine
another powerful method which simplifies the
analysis of circuits with more than one voltage
source. This method essentially involves carefully
examining the effect that each source has on the
circuit *by itself*. For example, consider the simple
circuit of Figure 12.22. The basic circuit consists
of a 10-ohm resistor connected to a 10-volt source.
The current produced in the resistor is 10 volts
divided by 10 ohms or 1 amp.

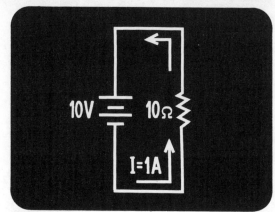

Figure 12.22

Second Source — Figure 12.23 shows this same
10-ohm resistor connected to another 10-volt
source. The current produced in this resistor by
this second source acting alone is again 1 amp.

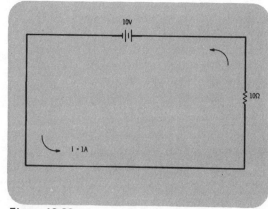

Figure 12.23

- Circuit with Both Sources Acting
- Statement of Superposition Theorem
- Limitations of the Superposition Theorem

Circuit with Both Sources Acting — When both voltage sources are connected to the resistor as shown in Figure 12.24, the current flowing through the resistor is now 2 amps. The action of this circuit is a simplified illustration of what is called the *superposition theorem*.

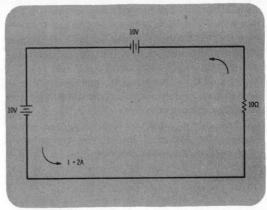

Figure 12.24

Statement of Superposition Theorem — The superposition theorem is stated as shown in Figure 12.25. *In a network with two or more sources, the current or voltage for any component is equal to the algebraic sum of the effects produced by each source acting separately*.

The superposition theorem is easy to use. As was illustrated in the simplified example, when you analyze a circuit considering only one source at a time, you can solve the remaining circuit by simply using Ohm's law and the rules you have learned for the behavior of series and parallel circuits.

SUPERPOSITION THEOREM

IN A NETWORK WITH TWO OR MORE SOURCES, THE CURRENT OR VOLTAGE FOR ANY COMPONENT IS EQUAL TO THE ALGEBRAIC SUM OF THE EFFECTS PRODUCED BY EACH SOURCE ACTING SEPARATELY.

Figure 12.25

Limitations of the Superposition Theorem — The superposition theorem, however, does have two limitations (Figure 12.26). First, all components must be *linear*, which means that as the input to the component increases or decreases, the output must increase or decrease in direct proportion. Second, all components must be *bilateral*, which means that current must flow equally well in either direction. Because of these limitations, the superposition theorem is most effectively used in analyzing the behavior of resistive circuits.

LIMITATIONS OF THE SUPERPOSITION THEOREM

1. LINEAR COMPONENTS

2. BILATERAL COMPONENTS

Figure 12.26

12-17

Sample Solution Using the Superposition Theorem

To see how the superposition theorem works, it will be used to solve for the voltage from point A to ground, across R_3, in a circuit with two voltage sources such as the one shown in Figure 12.27. Notice you could use Kirchhoff's laws to solve this problem, but not Ohm's law and the simple circuit rules alone. (Ohm's law methods alone would not allow you to determine what was happening in this circuit because two sources are interacting here to produce current flow.)

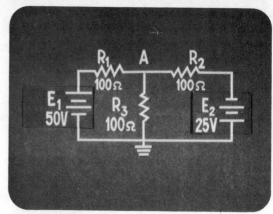

Figure 12.27

Trick in Using Superposition: Short Out E_2

The key trick in using the superposition theorem to analyze a circuit like this is to just mentally replace one of the voltage sources on your schematic, say E_2, with a short. With E_2 replaced by a short, as shown in Figure 12.28, you can now use simple circuit rules and Ohm's law to first find the voltage from point A to ground with E_1 acting alone. This voltage will be called E_{A1}.

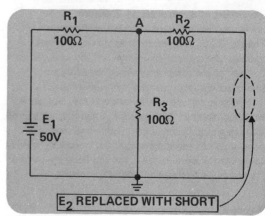

Figure 12.28

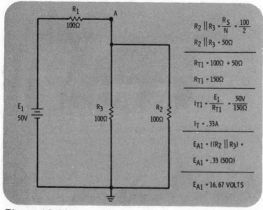

Figure 12.29

$$R_2 \parallel R_3 = \frac{R_S}{N} = \frac{100}{2}$$

$$R_2 \parallel R_3 = 50\Omega$$

$$R_{T1} = 100\Omega + 50\Omega$$

$$R_{T1} = 150\Omega$$

$$I_{T1} = \frac{E_1}{R_{T1}} = \frac{50V}{150\Omega}$$

$$I_T = .33A$$

$$E_{A1} = I(R_2 \parallel R_3) =$$

$$E_{A1} = .33 (50\Omega)$$

$$E_{A1} = 16.67 \text{ VOLTS}$$

Redrawn Circuit

This circuit can be redrawn slightly to indicate clearly how you would solve for E_{A1} (Figure 12.29). With E_2 shorted out, this circuit consists of the single power source, E_1, powering a series-parallel circuit. In the circuit, R_1 is in series with the parallel combination of R_2 and R_3. Remember that a shorthand notation that can be used to express "R_2 in parallel with R_3" is $R_2 \parallel R_3$. The first step in analyzing our original two-source circuit is to find the voltage from point A to ground in this circuit, with E_1 acting alone. This is a straightforward series-parallel circuit problem.

Begin by finding the total resistance of the circuit. To do that you need to calculate the total resistance of R_2 in parallel with $R_3(R_2 \| R_3)$. Since R_2 and R_3 are both 100-ohm resistors, use the formula $R_{eq} = R_S/N$. Substituting, you have 100 ohms divided by 2 or 50 ohms for $R_2 \| R_3$. Now the total resistance of this circuit is just $R_1 + (R_2 \| R_3)$ or 100 plus 50 or 150 ohms. The total circuit current I_{T1} just equals E_1/R_{T1} or 50 volts/150 ohms which equals 333 milliamps. Finally, E_{A1} now equals this total current times the resistance between point A and ground. $E_{A1} = I_{T1} \times (R_2 \| R_3)$ which equals 0.333 X 50 ohms or 16.67 volts.

Solution for E_{A1} — If you were to calculate this voltage with the series-parallel circuit rules and ohm's law, you would find that it is 16.67 volts as shown in Figure 12.30. The polarity of E_{A1} as shown is negative at ground and positive at point A.

At this point you know the voltage across R_3, from point A to ground, produced by one of the two sources acting alone. If you find the voltage across R_3 produced by the other source acting alone, you can add the two voltages algebraically to find the total voltage across R_3.

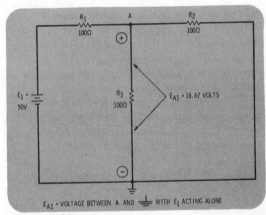

Figure 12.30

Next Step: "Short" E_1 — Your next step is to mentally reconnect E_2, and short E_1 as shown in Figure 12.31. Now you can find the voltage from point A to ground with E_2 acting alone; call it E_{A2}.

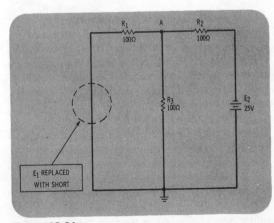

Figure 12.31

- Solving for E_{A2}
- Solution for E_{A2}
- Add E_{A1} and E_{A2} to Get Final Result

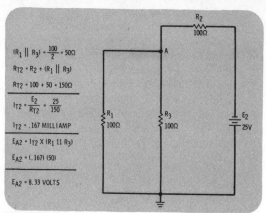

$(R_1 \| R_3) = \dfrac{100}{2} = 50\Omega$

$R_{T2} = R_2 + (R_1 \| R_3)$

$R_{T2} = 100 + 50 = 150\Omega$

$I_{T2} = \dfrac{E_2}{R_{T2}} = \dfrac{25}{150}$

$I_{T2} = .167$ MILLIAMP

$E_{A2} = I_{T2} \times (R_1 \| R_3)$

$E_{A2} = (.167)(50)$

$E_{A2} = 8.33$ VOLTS

Figure 12.32

Solving for E_{A2} — This circuit of Figure 12.31 can be redrawn as shown in Figure 12.32 to show that this too is a series-parallel circuit. The equivalent resistance of $(R_1 \| R_3)$ is now 50 ohms, similar to the previous case, and the total circuit resistance is again 150 ohms. This time the total current I_{T2} is equal to E_2/R_{T2} or 5 volts divided by 150 ohms or 167 milliamps. E_{A2} is then equal to I_{T2} times $(R_1 \| R_3)$ which equals 0.167 amp times 50 ohms or 8.33 volts.

Solution for E_{A2} — If you were to calculate this voltage with the simple circuit rules and Ohm's law, you would find that it is 8.33 volts. The polarity of E_{A2}, as shown in Figure 12.33, is opposite to the polarity of E_{A1}, that is, positive at ground and negative at point A.

To find the *total voltage* from point A to ground, *algebraically add up the effects of each of the sources acting separately*, remembering that the voltages are of opposite polarity.

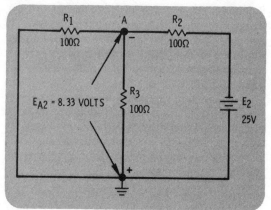

Figure 12.33

Add E_{A1} and E_{A2} to Get Final Result — In Figure 12.34, if you consider E_{A1} positive and E_{A2} negative, you should have 16.67 minus 8.33, and you get 8.34 volts for the total voltage between point A and ground. The polarity will be that of the larger voltage: positive at point A and negative at ground.

A word of caution may be in order here. Although you can talk about shorting out voltage sources in schematic diagrams when analyzing circuits with the superposition theorem, you should *never just short out an actual voltage source in a real circuit.* This can damage the source, cause electrical burns, as well as a variety of other undesirable effects. When the term "shorting out a

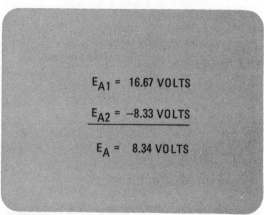

$E_{A1} = 16.67$ VOLTS

$E_{A2} = -8.33$ VOLTS

$E_A = 8.34$ VOLTS

Figure 12.34

source'' is used in circuit analysis, it refers to a *mental* process only.

Another Sample Solution Using the Superposition Theorem — To provide you with some additional practice in using the superposition theorem, it will now be used with a slightly different circuit. This time the superposition theorem will be used to find the current flowing in one of the resistors in the complex circuit situation shown in Figure 12.35.

     This is a complex two-source circuit in which you want to find the current flowing through the resistor, R_1. The two sources, E_1 which equals 10 volts, and E_2 which equals 20 volts, are pushing current through R_1 in opposite directions. Using the superposition theorem to solve this problem, you first want to find I_1, the current flowing in R_1 produced by E_1 acting alone, so you short out E_2. Then you want to find I_2, the current flowing through R_1 with E_2 acting alone — so you short out E_1. Once I_1 and I_2 are calculated, algebraically add the results to find the total current flow through R_1 with both sources acting together.

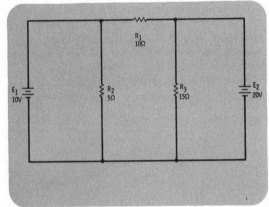

Figure 12.35

Short E_2: E_1 Acting Alone — Begin by shorting out E_2 so that E_1 is acting alone in the circuit (Figure 12.36). Notice that when E_2 is shorted out this creates a short circuit directly across R_3. There is now essentially a path with zero resistance right across R_3. This means that no current will flow through R_3 and the circuit essentially consists of R_1 in parallel with R_2 with 10 volts applied.

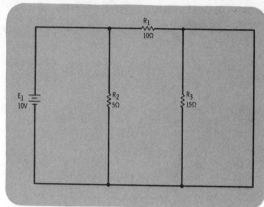

Figure 12.36

Redrawn Circuit — To clarify this, the equivalent circuit has been redrawn in Figure 12.37 with R_3 replaced by a short. The position of I_1 in the circuit is now more easily seen. To find I_1, use Ohm's law in the form $I_1 = E_1/R_1$, as shown in Figure 12.37. E_1 divided by R_1 equals 1 amp. I_1 flows in the direction shown in the circuit diagram.

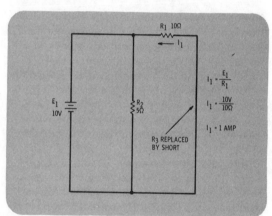

Figure 12.37

Short E_1: E_2 Acting Alone — Next you want to find I_2, the current produced in R_1 by E_2 acting alone, so you short out E_1 as shown in Figure 12.38. This puts a zero resistance path right across R_2. Now the circuit essentially consists of R_1 in parallel with R_3, since no current will flow through R_2.

To find I_2, you can use Ohm's law just as before. As shown in the figure, E_2 divided by R_1 equals 2 amps. The direction of I_2 is opposite to that of I_1, as indicated on the circuit diagram.

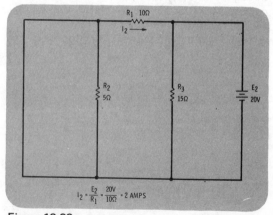

Figure 12.38

12-22

Final Solution — Back in the original circuit (Figure 12.39), the two currents I_1 and I_2 have been labeled along with their directions. Since they are flowing in opposite directions, the total current through R_1 is the difference between the two currents which is equal to 1 amp. The direction of I_{R1} is in the direction of I_2, since I_2 is the larger of the two currents.

This problem is fairly easy to work using the superposition theorem, especially when you compare it to the previous methods. If you were to use loop and node equations to analyze this circuit, you would have to write three equations, simplify them, and then manipulate the three equations in order to solve for the current you want. Using the superposition theorem, a complex two-source problem can be reduced to two single-source circuits that can be solved using methods you already know.

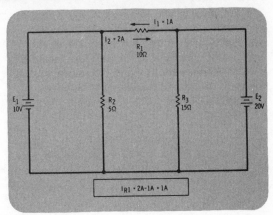

Figure 12.39

Other Methods of Circuit Analysis — The objective of the remainder of this lesson is to very briefly introduce you to some other methods of dc circuit analysis which may be useful in certain specific circuit applications.

Figure 12.40 is a list of methods and theorems which will be discussed. Relax as a general survey of these methods is presented for you. The intent is not to explain each method of analysis in depth, but to give a brief description of each method so that you will be familiar with the language and terminology of each and know generally where the different methods can be applied most effectively.

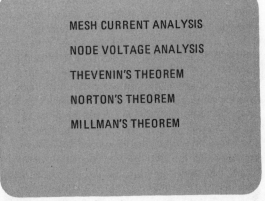

MESH CURRENT ANALYSIS

NODE VOLTAGE ANALYSIS

THEVENIN'S THEOREM

NORTON'S THEOREM

MILLMAN'S THEOREM

Figure 12.40

For those of you who wish to study these methods more fully, there is a more thorough explanation of each theorem along with worked examples at the end of this lesson. Also included is a list of reference books which discuss the various theorems and advanced methods of dc circuit analysis.

The presentation of this material is deliberately intended to serve only as an introduction for several reasons. First of all, detailed coverage of these advanced methods will be taken up and discussed in detail in more advanced courses in electricity and electronics. Secondly, most circuits you will encounter can be solved by applying the methods that have already been discussed, although some of the solutions may become quite lengthy. The methods presented here are more powerful tools that can aid in circuit analysis or greatly simplify the prediction of circuit behavior.

Mesh Current Analysis — First consider what is called the *mesh current method* of analyzing dc circuits. This method is handy for analyzing circuits with many, many branches such as the one shown in Figure 12.41. A *mesh* is defined as the *simplest form of a loop*. In a circuit such as that shown, a typical mesh looks sort of like a single window pane. Other larger paths in this circuit are loops, but not meshes. The current flowing in a mesh is called, aptly enough, a mesh current. When working with mesh currents, you usually assume that all of the currents in all of the circuit meshes flow in the same direction, usually clockwise. Also, it is assumed that the mesh current flows all the way around the mesh and doesn't break up at

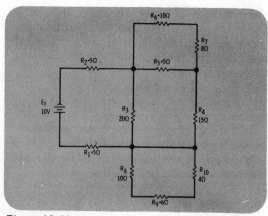

Figure 12.41

circuit nodes. If you get a negative sign in your final solution for the circuit currents, that indicates the assumed direction of the current is opposite to the actual direction of current.

Circuit with Drawn-In Mesh Currents — An important thing to remember about mesh currents is that they are *assumed currents*. Figure 12.42 shows the circuit with all the assumed branch currents drawn in. Notice that all of the branch currents are assumed to be flowing in the clockwise direction. The *actual current* flowing in any branch of the circuit may be *opposite* in direction to the *assumed* mesh current. Also, in some branches of a mesh, the current may consist of *two* mesh currents flowing in opposite directions.

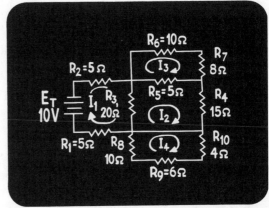

Figure 12.42

Close-Up on Central Resistor — Figure 12.43, for example, is a "close-up" of this circuit centered on the branch containing resistor R_3. Note that the current flow through R_3 is the algebraic sum of I_1 and I_2. Since these two currents flow through R_3 in different directions, $I_{R3} = I_1 - I_2$.

To carry out a complete mesh current analysis of a complex circuit like this, write mesh equations for each mesh the same way you write loop equations, except that now you use mesh currents.

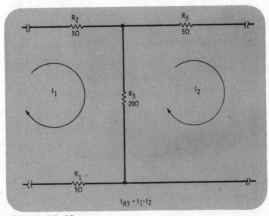

Figure 12.43

- **Left-Hand Mesh**
- **Central Mesh**
- Complete Solution

Left-Hand Mesh — For example, in the left-hand mesh of Figure 12.44, you can start with the voltage source and traverse the circuit clockwise to get: $10\,V - 5\,I_1 - 20\,I_1 - 5\,I_1 + 20\,I_2 = 0$. Notice the 20-ohm resistor also has I_2 flowing through it (opposite to I_1) so the $20\,I_2$ term in the mesh equation has a plus sign.

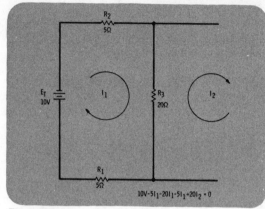

Figure 12.44

Central Mesh — In the mesh in which I_2 is flowing, the mesh equation of Figure 12.45 is $-5\,I_2 - 15\,I_2 - 20\,I_2 + 20\,I_1 + 5\,I_3 = 0$. Since I_1 also flows in R_3, the $20\,I_1$ term is positive, and because I_3 flows in R_5, the $5\,I_3$ term is also positive.

To finish the analysis of this circuit completely, you would write one equation for each mesh and solve them for all of the unknown currents. With the currents known, you could then solve for all the unknown voltages in the circuit.

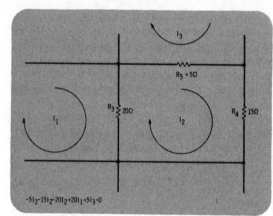

Figure 12.45

Complete Solution — The mesh equation for the top mesh, shown in Figure 12.45, starting to the left of R_5 and proceeding clockwise is: $-10\,I_3 - 8\,I_3 - 5\,I_3 + 5\,I_2 = 0$.

The bottom mesh equation may be written as: $-4\,I_4 - 6\,I_4 - 10\,I_4 = 0$. As you can see, this equation contains only terms for I_4. When added up, this equation is: $-20\,I_4 = 0$. No current flows in this loop! This fact can be seen by examining the circuit diagram. Notice that a short circuit is connected across the three resistors R_8, R_9, and R_{10}, thus no current can flow through them.

The three remaining mesh equations may now be written and simplified.

1. $10 - 5I_1 - 20I_1 - 5I_1 + 20I_2 = 0$

    $10 - 30I_1 + 20I_2 = 0$

    $-30I_1 + 20I_2 = -10$

2. $-20I_2 - 5I_2 - 15I_2 + 20I_1 + 5I_3 = 0$

    $-40I_2 + 20I_1 + 5I_3 = 0$

3. $-10I_3 - 8I_3 - 5I_3 + 5I_2 = 0$

    $-23I_3 + 5I_2 = 0$

In order to solve for any single current value, a pair of equations containing the same current values must be set up. This can be done by expressing I_3 in terms of either I_1 or I_2. The third mesh equation allows this to be done rather easily.

The equation states that $5I_2 - 23I_3 = 0$. Changing the equation around a bit, it can be seen that $23I_3 = 5I_2$. Divide both sides of the equation by 23 and you see that:

$$\frac{23I_3}{23} = \frac{5I_2}{23}$$

$$I_3 = 0.217I_2$$

Now that I_3 can be expressed in terms of I_2, a simultaneous equation may be set up using mesh equations 1 and 2. First, the I_3 term in mesh equation 2 must be written in terms of I_2.

2. $-40I_2 + 20I_1 + 5I_3 = 0$

    $-40I_2 + 20I_1 + 5(0.217I_2) = 0$

    $-40I_2 + 20I_1 + 1.09I_2 = 0$

    $+20I_1 - 38.9I_2 = 0$

This equation may be solved by canceling out a term through addition to equation 1.

1. $-30I_1 + 20I_2 = -10$

    $20I_1 - 38.9I_2 = 0$

Equation 2 must be multiplied by 1.5 in order to cancel the I_1 term.

$1.5(20I_1 - 38.9I_2) = 0(1.5)$

$30I_1 - 58.4I_2 = 0$

Now, equations 1 and 2 may be added.

1. $\quad -30\,I_1 + 20\,I_2 = -10$
   $\quad\ \ \ 30\,I_1 - 58.4\,I_2 = \quad 0$
   $$-38.4\,I_2 = -10$$

$$\frac{-38.4\,I_2}{-38.4} = \frac{-10}{-38.4}$$

$$I_2 = 0.26\ A = 260\ mA$$

The answer is positive, which means the originally assumed direction of current flow was correct.

To solve for I_1, equation 1 may be used, and the value of I_2 simply inserted.

$$-30\,I_1 + 20\,I_2 = -10$$
$$-30\,I_1 + 20\,(0.26) = -10$$
$$-30\,I_1 + 5.2 = -10$$
$$-30\,I_1 = -10 - 5.2$$
$$-30\,I_1 = -15.2$$
$$\frac{-30\,I_1}{-30} = \frac{-15.2}{-30}$$
$$I_1 = 0.507\ A = 507\ mA$$

The positive answer for I_1 indicates that the originally assumed direction of current flow was again correct.

To find I_3, the third equation may be used, and the value of I_2 substituted in.

$$5\,I_2 = 23\,I_3$$
$$23\,I_3 = 5\,I_2$$
$$23\,I_3 = 5\,(0.26)$$
$$23\,I_3 = 1.30$$
$$\frac{23\,I_3}{23} = \frac{1.3}{23}$$
$$I_3 = 0.057\ A = 57\ mA$$

Now that all the currents are known, the individual voltages may be found by using Ohm's law.

$$I_1 = 0.507\ A$$
$$I_2 = 0.26\ A$$
$$I_3 = 0.57\ A$$

$E_{R1} = I_1 \times R_1$
$E_{R1} = 0.507\,A \times 5\,\Omega$
$E_{R1} = 2.54\,V$
$E_{R2} = I_1 \times R_2$
$E_{R2} = 0.507\,A \times 5\,\Omega$
$E_{R2} = 2.54\,V$
$E_{R3} = (I_1 - I_2)\,R_3$
$E_{R3} = (0.507 - 0.26)\,20$
$E_{R3} = 0.247 \times 20$
$E_{R3} = 4.94\,V$
$E_{R4} = I_2 \times R_4$
$E_{R4} = 0.26\,A \times 15\,\Omega$
$E_{R4} = 3.9\,V$
$E_{R5} = (I_2 - I_3)\,R_5$
$E_{R5} = (0.26\,A - 0.057\,A)\,5\,\Omega$
$E_{R5} = 0.203\,A \times 5\,\Omega$
$E_{R5} = 1.02\,V$
$E_{R6} = I_3 \times R_6$
$E_{R6} = 0.057\,A \times 10\,\Omega$
$E_{R6} = 0.57\,V$
$E_{R7} = I_3 \times R_7$
$E_{R7} = 0.057\,A \times 8\,\Omega$
$E_{R7} = 0.456\,V$

Since no current flows through R_8, R_9 or R_{10}, the voltage dropped across each of these resistors is zero volts.

The real advantage of mesh current analysis is that, even though a circuit may have many loops or voltage sources, all mesh currents are assumed to flow in the same direction continuously around each mesh. This can make writing the equations much simpler; and if the *assumed direction* for one of the currents is *wrong*, this is indicated by a *negative sign* in the answer.

- **Node Voltage Analysis**
- **Sample Solution with Node Voltage Analysis**
- **Use of Node Equation**

Node Voltage Analysis — Another method for analyzing dc circuits is called *node voltage* analysis. When using this method (Figure 12.46), you no longer express the voltage drops around the circuit in terms of IR drops; now you express them in terms of the *voltage at a node*. A node is just a common connection of two or more circuit components. A *principal node* is defined as a point where *three or more* components are connected.

Figure 12.46

Sample Solution with Node Voltage Analysis — In the circuit of Figure 12.47, points A and G are principal nodes. In this circuit, point G has been selected as the ground or reference point. The voltage, E_N, between points A and G (with G used as the reference) can be used to find all other voltages in the circuit, and is called the *node voltage*.

Figure 12.47

Use of Node Equation — In the node voltage analysis of this circuit, first write a Kirchhoff's current law equation for point A in the circuit. As shown in Figure 12.48, which is a close-up of this circuit at point A, $I_3 = I_1 + I_2$.

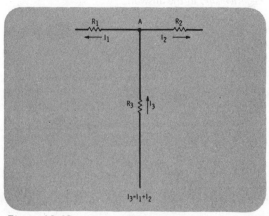

Figure 12.48

- **Express Each Current as a Voltage**
- **Express All Voltages in Terms of Source and Node Voltages**
- **Substitute in Previous Equation**

Express Each Current as a Voltage — Now each of these three currents can be expressed in terms of voltage and resistance as shown in Figure 12.49. The current flowing through R_3 can be put into an Ohm's law formula and expressed in terms of E_N and R_3: $I_3 = E_N/R_3$. Similarly, you can write that $I_1 = E_{R1}/R_1$ and $I_2 = E_{R2}/R_2$.

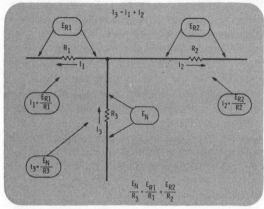

Figure 12.49

Express All Voltages in Terms of Source and Node Voltages — The next step is to take this equation and express all the voltages in it in terms of the source voltages (E_1 and E_2) and the node voltage E_N. You can do this by going around the loops containing the voltage sources, the node A and the ground reference as shown in Figure 12.50 and writing the loop equations. In the left-hand loop (starting at R_1 and traversing clockwise), you get $E_{R1} + E_N - E_1 = 0$. Transposing E_N and E_1 to the right-hand side of the equals sign (remembering to change their signs), you get $E_{R1} = E_1 - E_N$. For the right-hand loop (starting at R_2 and traversing counterclockwise), you get $E_{R2} + E_N - E_2 = 0$. Transposing this equation becomes $E_{R2} = E_2 - E_N$.

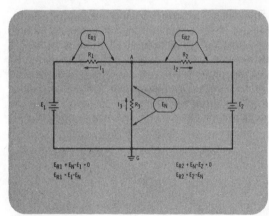

Figure 12.50

Substitute in Previous Equation — If you substitute this information into the current equation, it should appear as shown in Figure 12.51. Notice that in this final equation you know the values of all the resistances and source voltages, so you could solve the equation for E_N. Once E_N is known, all other voltages in the circuit can be found, using the equations you have just derived.

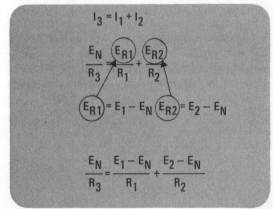

Figure 12.51

- Summary: Node Voltage Analysis
- Thevenin's Theorem
- Sample Circuit

Summary: Node Voltage Analysis — Figure 12.52 briefly summarizes the node voltage method of analyzing dc circuits. First, determine which node you want to analyze and which you want to use as a ground. Then write a node current equation for the node you have selected to analyze. Next, express each current in the node equations in terms of voltage and resistance. When these voltages are then expressed in terms of the node voltage and source voltages, the equation can be solved for the node voltage. Once the node voltage is determined, all other voltages can be found.

NODE VOLTAGE ANALYSIS

1. CHOOSE A NODE
2. WRITE A NODE CURRENT EQUATION
3. EXPRESS EACH CURRENT IN TERMS OF VOLTAGE AND RESISTANCE
4. EXPRESS THE VOLTAGES IN TERMS OF THE NODE VOLTAGE AND THE SOURCE VOLTAGES
5. SOLVE THE EQUATION FOR THE NODE VOLTAGE

Figure 12.52

Thevenin's Theorem — Another method of circuit analysis that is useful in simplifying the calculation of voltages in certain special situations is called Thevenin's Theorem (Figure 12.53). Thevenin's theorem states that *a complex circuit or network can be reduced to an equivalent series circuit with a single voltage source and a single series resistance*, as long as all components are linear.

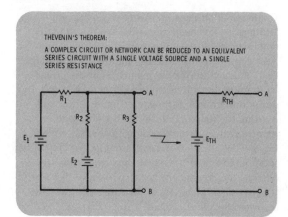

THEVENIN'S THEOREM:
A COMPLEX CIRCUIT OR NETWORK CAN BE REDUCED TO AN EQUIVALENT SERIES CIRCUIT WITH A SINGLE VOLTAGE SOURCE AND A SINGLE SERIES RESISTANCE

Figure 12.53

Sample Circuit — One type of problem (Figure 12.54) where Thevenin's theorem is useful is if you have a complex circuit and you wish to connect several different loads between two selected points, say points A and B. If you want to calculate the voltage between points A and B, you would normally have to analyze the complete series-parallel circuit every time you changed loads.

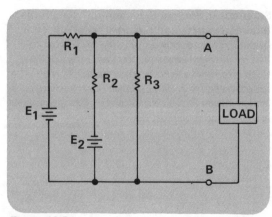

Figure 12.54

12-32

- **Thevenin Equivalent**
- **Calculation of Thevenin Voltage**
- **Calculation of Thevenin Resistance**

Thevenin Equivalent — When using Thevenin's theorem, you replace the complex circuit by an *equivalent voltage*, which is called the *Thevenin voltage* or E_{TH}, in series with a *resistance* which is called the *Thevenin resistance*, or R_{TH}, as shown in Figure 12.55. Then to find the voltage and current for each load, you connect to points A and B, and need analyze only this simple series circuit shown in Figure 12.55.

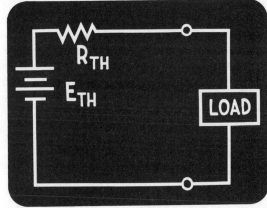

Figure 12.55

Calculation of Thevenin Voltage — To find E_{TH}, the Thevenin voltage as shown in Figure 12.56, calculate the voltage between the two selected points, when the *load is removed*.

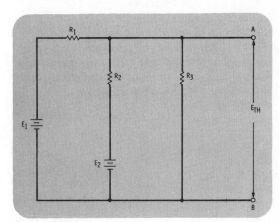

Figure 12.56

Calculation of Thevenin Resistance — The Thevenin resistance, R_{TH}, is the resistance you calculate between points A and B with *no load connected, and all the voltage sources replaced by short circuits*. So as shown in Figure 12.57 you would usually use series-parallel circuit reduction techniques to help you find R_{TH}.

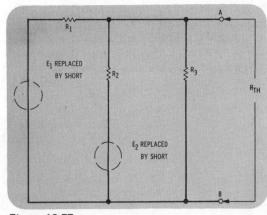

Figure 12.57

- **Norton's Theorem**
- **Norton Equivalent Current**
- **Norton Equivalent Resistance = Thevenin Equivalent Resistance**

Norton's Theorem — Another technique that you can use to analyze similar circuit situations is called Norton's theorem. Norton's theorem (Figure 12.58) states that *any complex circuit can be replaced by an equivalent parallel circuit consisting of a single current source, I_N, and a single shunt or parallel resistance, R_N.* Then, in a circuit where various loads are to be connected across points A and B, as shown, the circuit analysis is reduced to that of a simple parallel circuit shown.

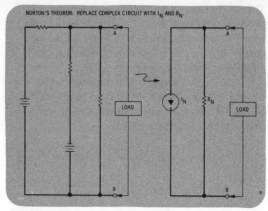

Figure 12.58

Norton Equivalent Current — The value of the Norton equivalent *current source*, I_N (Figure 12.59), is found by putting a *short circuit across points A and B*, and finding the current that flows through this short. The value of this short circuit current is the Norton equivalent current, I_N.

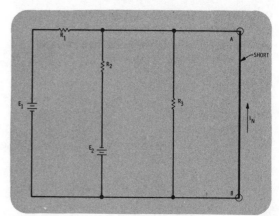

Figure 12.59

Norton Equivalent Resistance = Thevenin Equivalent Resistance — The Norton equivalent resistance, R_N (Figure 12.60), is found in the same way as the Thevenin resistance, R_{TH}. Thus, R_N equals R_{TH} for any one circuit between any two points.

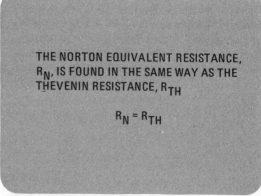

THE NORTON EQUIVALENT RESISTANCE, R_N, IS FOUND IN THE SAME WAY AS THE THEVENIN RESISTANCE, R_{TH}

$$R_N = R_{TH}$$

Figure 12.60

- **Norton Equivalent Circuit**
- **Constant Current Source**
- **Millman's Theorem**

Norton Equivalent Circuit — Once the Norton equivalent circuit (Figure 12.61) is known, you can easily calculate the voltage across and current through any resistance you place between points A and B. It should be obvious that Norton's theorem is useful in design of voltage divider circuits, where you might want to connect different loads at different times to the same two points.

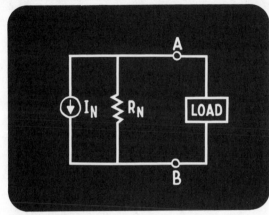

Figure 12.61

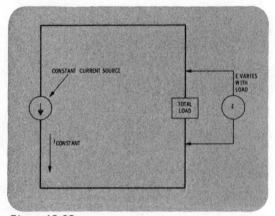

Figure 12.62

Constant Current Source — Notice that the circle with the arrow inside it used in the Norton equivalent circuit is the symbol for a *current source* (Figure 12.62). This is a special idealized source that would provide a *constant current output to a load*, but whose output voltage would vary depending on the load put across it. (This is different from the normal power supplies discussed throughout this course whose *voltage output is constant* and whose current output would vary depending on the load connected to it.)

Millman's Theorem — The final circuit analysis technique discussed in this lesson is called *Millman's theorem*. This theorem is similar to Thevenin's and Norton's theorems in that it is used to help simplify a circuit by analyzing circuit behavior between two selected points.

More specifically, Millman's theorem gives you a formula to find the total voltage across several parallel branches (Figure 12.63), each of which may contain a different voltage source and several resistors. The details of *deriving* Millman's equation are not shown here, but a complete derivation is included at the end of this lesson. The intent is to show you the results of Millman's

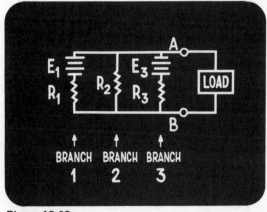

Figure 12.63

theorem and how it can help in simplifying circuit analysis problems.

Millman's Formula — Figure 12.64 shows the final formula that expresses Millman's theorem. I_1, I_2, and I_3 are the branch currents and each of these can be calculated using the branch voltages and branch resistances. Once you use this formula to calculate the voltage between points A and B, you can use that voltage to find the current through any resistive load you may place between A and B. Millman's theorem can therefore be used to greatly simplify repetitive calculations involving a parallel circuit where different loads are to be applied in circuits where there are *no series resistances between the parallel branches.*

In this lesson you have reviewed Kirchhoff's laws and seen these laws along with the superposition theorem used to analyze some typical circuits. Also, a very brief survey of some of the other more advanced methods of circuit analysis has been presented. Remember, at the end of this lesson there is additional information, including a review chart covering the advanced methods along with a list of reference texts, should you care to study these methods of analysis in more depth. The complete details of these advanced methods introduced are properly covered in more advanced courses in circuit analysis.

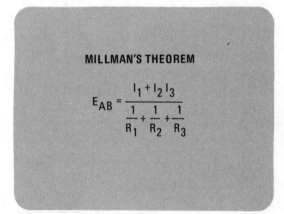

MILLMAN'S THEOREM

$$E_{AB} = \frac{I_1 + I_2 I_3}{\dfrac{1}{R_1} + \dfrac{1}{R_2} + \dfrac{1}{R_3}}$$

Figure 12.64

- **Worked Through Examples**

1. Solve for all voltages and currents in the following circuit using Kirchhoff's laws:

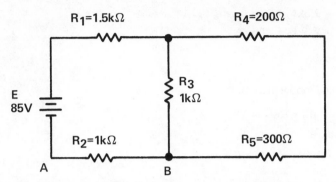

Notice first that this type of circuit could be solved using Ohm's law and circuit reduction techniques, but can also be analyzed using the more general Kirchhoff's law techniques, presented in Lessons 11 and 12. As a first step in solving this circuit, label all the currents flowing in the circuit, assigning each a direction as shown below. (This circuit will be analyzed here using *electron current*.)

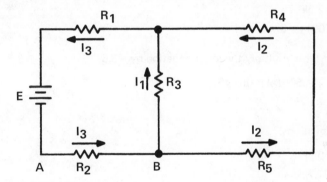

You can immediately apply Kirchhoff's current law at point B in this circuit: at that point I_3 enters, and I_1 and I_2 leave. So by Kirchhoff's current law $I_3 = I_1 + I_2$. Now proceed to use Kirchhoff's voltage law to write two loop equations for the circuit.

Starting at point A and traversing the left-hand loop counterclockwise, the voltages are: $-R_2I_3 - R_3I_1 - R_1I_3 + E = 0$. Traversing the right-hand loop counterclockwise and starting at point B, the voltages are: $-R_5I_2 - R_4I_2 + R_3I_1 = 0$. Now, these loop equations may be simplified by substituting $I_1 + I_2$ for I_3, and combining terms.

$$-R_2I_3 - R_3I_1 - R_1I_3 + E = 0 \qquad \text{(substitute } I_1 + I_2 \text{ for } I_3\text{)}$$
$$-R_2(I_1 + I_2) - R_3I_1 - R_1(I_1 + I_2) + E = 0$$
$$-R_2I_1 - R_2I_2 - R_3I_1 - R_1I_1 - R_1I_2 + E = 0$$

Now substitute in the circuit values:

$$-1kI_1 - 1kI_2 - 1kI_1 - 1.5kI_1 - 1.5kI_2 + 85 = 0$$

12-37

And combine terms:

$$-3.5kI_1 - 2.5kI_2 + 85 = 0$$
$$-3.5kI_1 - 2.5kI_2 = -85$$

or

$$3.5kI_1 + 2.5kI_2 = 85$$

Now, write the second loop equation:

$$-R_5I_2 - R_4I_2 + R_3I_1 = 0$$

Substitute circuit values:

$$-300I_2 - 200I_2 + 1kI_1 = 0$$

Combine terms:

$$-500I_2 + 1kI_1 = 0.$$

Now the two equations may be solved by canceling out one of the terms through addition.

$$3.5kI_1 + 2.5kI_2 = 85$$
$$1kI_1 - 500I_2 = 0$$

To cancel out the I_1 term, multiply the lower equation by -3.5.

$$-3.5(1kI_1 - 500I_2) = 0(-3.5)$$
$$-3.5kI_1 + 1.75kI_2 = 0.$$

Now add the two equations.

$$3.5kI_1 + 2.5kI_2 = 85$$
$$\underline{-3.5kI_1 + 1.75kI_2 = 0}$$
$$4.25kI_2 = 85$$
$$\frac{4.25kI_2}{4.25k} = \frac{85}{4.25k}$$
$$I_2 = 20 \text{ mA}$$

Substitute this value back into one of the equations and solve for I_1.

$$1kI_1 - 500I_2 = 0$$
$$1kI_1 - 500 (20 \text{ mA}) = 0$$
$$1kI_1 - 10,000 \text{ mA} = 0$$
$$1kI_1 = 10,000 \text{ mA}$$
$$\frac{1kI_1}{1k} = \frac{10,000 \text{ mA}}{1k}$$

$$I_1 = 10 \text{ mA}$$
$$I_3 = I_1 + I_2 = 10 \text{ mA} + 20 \text{ mA} = 30 \text{ mA}$$

All of the individual circuit voltage drops may now be found by using Ohm's law.

$E_{R1} = I_3 \times R_1$

$E_{R1} = 30 \text{ mA} \times 1.5 \text{ k}\Omega$

$E_{R1} = 45 \text{ V}$

$E_{R2} = I_3 \times R_2$

$E_{R2} = 30 \text{ mA} \times 1 \text{ k}\Omega$

$E_{R2} = 30 \text{ V}$

$E_{R3} = I_1 \times R_3$

$E_{R3} = 10 \text{ mA} \times 1 \text{ k}\Omega$

$E_{R3} = 10 \text{ V}$

$E_{R4} = I_2 \times R_4$

$E_{R4} = 20 \text{ mA} \times 200 \ \Omega$

$E_{R4} = 4 \text{ V}$

$E_{R5} = I_2 \times R_5$

$E_{R5} = 20 \text{ mA} \times 300 \ \Omega$

$E_{R5} = 6 \text{ V}$

2.   Using Kirchhoff's laws, solve for all voltages and currents in the circuit shown below.

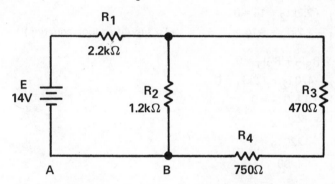

Label all currents and assign them a direction as shown in the figure below. Assuming electron current, I_3, flows from the source to point B where it splits up into I_1 and I_2 as shown.

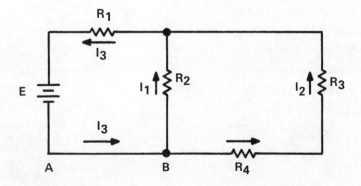

Kirchhoff's current law can therefore be applied at point B: it simply states that $I_3 = I_1 + I_2$. Now traverse two loops, and apply Kirchhoff's voltage law to each to obtain two loop equations. This will yield a total of three equations, which will allow you to solve for the three unknown currents in the problem.

First, the left-hand loop will be traversed from point A in a counterclockwise direction. The resulting loop equation is: $-R_2I_1 - R_1I_3 + E = 0$. The right-hand loop may be traversed from point B in a counterclockwise direction also. This yields $-R_4I_2 - R_3I_2 + R_2I_1 = 0$. These two equations may now be simplified by substituting in $(I_1 + I_2)$ for I_3, and combining like terms.

$$-R_2I_1 - R_1I_3 + E = 0$$
$$-R_2I_1 - R_1(I_1 + I_2) + E = 0$$
$$-R_2I_1 - R_1I_1 - R_1I_2 + E = 0$$

Now substitute the circuit values into the equations.

$$-1.2kI_1 - 2.2kI_1 - 2.2kI_2 + 14 = 0$$
$$-3.4kI_1 - 2.2kI_2 + 14 = 0$$
$$-3.4kI_1 - 2.2kI_2 = -14 \qquad \text{(1st simplified loop equation)}$$

$$-R_4I_2 - R_3I_2 + R_2I_1 = 0$$
$$-750\,I_2 - 470\,I_2 + 1.2kI_1 = 0$$
$$-1220\,I_2 + 1200\,I_1 = 0$$
$$+1200\,I_1 = 1220\,I_2$$
$$\frac{1200\,I_1}{1200} = \frac{1220\,I_2}{1200}$$

$$I_1 = 1.02\,I_2 \qquad \text{(2nd simplified loop equation)}$$

Now that I_1 has been expressed in terms of I_2, the I_1 terms in the first simplified loop equation may all be replaced with I_2 terms. The equation may then be solved for I_2 as shown below.

$$-3.4kI_1 - 2.2kI_2 = -14$$
$$-3.4k(1.02\,I_2) - 2.2kI_2 = -14$$
$$-3.47kI_2 - 2.2kI_2 = -14$$
$$-5.67kI_2 = -14$$
$$\frac{-5.67kI_2}{-5.67k} = \frac{-14}{-5.67k}$$

$$I_2 = 2.47 \text{ mA}$$

To find I_1, the value of I_2 may be substituted into the second simplified loop equation.

$I_1 = 1.02\,I_2$

$I_1 = 1.02\,(2.47\text{ mA})$

$I_1 = 2.52\text{ mA}$

Finally, since $I_1 + I_2 = I_3$, you can calculate that:

$I_3 = (2.47\text{ mA} + 2.52\text{ mA})$

$I_3 = 4.99\text{ mA}$

The three current values may now be used to find the voltage dropped across each resistor in the circuit.

$E_{R1} = R_1 \times I_3$

$E_{R1} = 2.2\text{ k}\Omega \times 4.99\text{ mA}$

$E_{R1} = 11.0\text{ V}$

$E_{R2} = R_2 \times I_1$

$E_{R2} = 1.2\text{ k}\Omega \times 2.52\text{ mA}$

$E_{R2} = 3.02\text{ V}$

$E_{R3} = R_3 \times I_2$

$E_{R3} = 470\ \Omega \times 2.47\text{ mA}$

$E_{R3} = 1.16\text{ V}$

$E_{R4} = R_4 \times I_2$

$E_{R4} = 750\ \Omega \times 2.47\text{ mA}$

$E_{R4} = 1.85\text{ V}$

3. Solve for all of the circuit *currents* in the multiple-source dc circuit shown below.

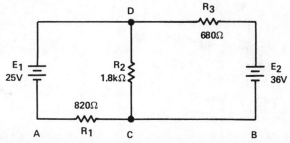

First, label all of the currents and assign them a direction, as shown below. In this analysis, electron current directions are being assumed.

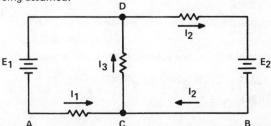

Kirchhoff's current law can be immediately applied at point C in the circuit: $I_1 + I_2 = I_3$.

Proceed to use Kirchhoff's voltage law on two of the circuit loops to get two loop equations. The two loop equations, together with the current law equation, will give you the three equations necessary to solve for the unknown currents.

First, traverse the left-hand loop counterclockwise, starting from point A, going through points C and D, and returning to point A. Algebraically adding each voltage you encounter (remembering the rules for using the voltage law) you get:

$$-R_1I_1 - R_2I_3 + 25 = 0.$$

Traversing the right-hand loop clockwise from point B (through points C and D and back to B) yields the equation:

$$-R_2I_3 - R_3I_2 + 36 = 0.$$

These two equations may now be reduced to simpler forms by substituting the expression $(I_1 + I_2)$ for I_3 each time it appears, and then combining like terms.

$$-R_1I_1 - R_2I_3 + 25 = 0$$
$$-R_1I_1 - R_2(I_1 + I_2) + 25 = 0$$
$$-R_1I_1 - R_2I_1 - R_2I_2 + 25 = 0$$
$$-820\,I_1 - 1.8kI_1 - 1.8kI_2 + 25 = 0$$
$$-2.62kI_1 - 1.8kI_2 + 25 = 0$$
$$-2.62kI_1 - 1.8kI_2 = -25$$

$$-R_2I_3 - R_3I_2 + 36 = 0$$
$$-R_2(I_1 + I_2) - R_3I_2 + 36 = 0$$
$$-R_2I_1 - R_2I_2 - R_3I_2 + 36 = 0$$
$$-1.8kI_1 - 1.8kI_2 - 680\,I_2 + 36 = 0$$
$$-1.8kI_1 - 2.48kI_2 + 36 = 0$$
$$-1.8kI_1 - 2.48kI_2 = -36$$

These two equations may now be solved simultaneously by manipulating one of the equations so that one of the "I" terms cancels out the pair.

$$(*)\ -2.62kI_1 - 1.8kI_2 = -25$$
$$-1.8kI_1 - 2.48kI_2 = -36$$

Now to arrange for one of the "I" terms to cancel, the lower equation may be multiplied by -1.46:

$$(-1.46)(-1.8kI_1 - 2.48kI_2) = -36(-1.46)$$
$$2.62kI_1 + 3.62kI_2 = +52.6$$

Now this equation may be added to the first loop equation (*) to yield:

$$-2.62kI_1 - 1.8kI_2 = -25$$
$$2.62kI_1 + 3.62kI_2 = +52.6$$
$$\overline{\hspace{1.5cm}1.82kI_2 = 27.6\hspace{1.5cm}}$$

$$\frac{1.82kI_2}{1.82k} = \frac{27.6}{1.82k}$$

$$I_2 = 15.2 \text{ mA}$$

Substitute this value back into the first equation:

$$-2.62kI_1 - 1.8k (15.2m) = -25$$
$$-2.62kI_1 - 27.36 = -25$$
$$-2.62kI_1 = -25 + 27.36$$
$$-2.62kI_1 = 2.36$$

$$\frac{-2.62kI_1}{-2.62k} = \frac{2.36}{-2.62k}$$

$$I_1 = -0.9 \text{ mA}$$

The negative sign in front of the 0.9 indicates that this current flows in the opposite direction from that direction originally assumed. The circuit, redrawn with the correct current appears as shown below.

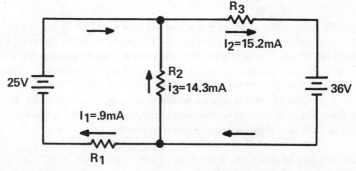

As can be seen from the figure, the 36-volt battery is actually pushing current through the 25-volt battery in a backward direction. The value of I_3 may now easily be calculated:

$$I_1 + I_2 = I_3$$
$$-0.9 + 15.2 = I_3$$
$$14.3 \text{ mA} = I_3$$

The result is positive, indicating that the correct direction was assumed for the current flow at the start of the problem.

4. Solve for all the voltages and currents in the following circuit using Kirchhoff's laws. Use *conventional current* in your analysis.

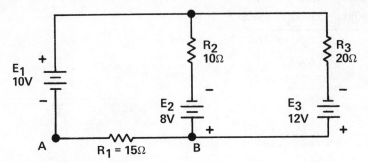

First, label all currents and assign them a direction, as shown in the circuit diagram below. The directions shown are assumed *conventional current directions*.

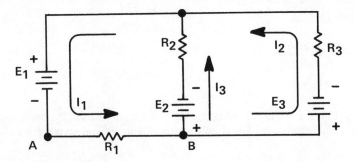

Applying Kirchhoff's current law at point B you can see that $I_1 = I_2 + I_3$, or $I_3 = I_1 - I_2$. Since these *three* currents are unknown, two more equations will be needed to finish the circuit solution. Apply Kirchhoff's voltage law to the left-hand and right-hand loops, that is, traverse the loops, add all voltages algebraically, and set the sums equal to zero. Assuming *conventional current* and starting at point A, the voltages are: In the right-hand loop, traversing clockwise, $10 + 10 I_3 + 8 + 15 I_1 = 0$. In the right-hand loop, starting at point B and traversing clockwise, you have: $-8 - 10 I_3 + 20 I_2 + 12 = 0$. Remember, since conventional current is being used here, voltage *source* terms are positive if you traverse them in the same way they push conventional current.

Now, these equations may be rewritten in terms of I_1 and I_2 by simply substituting $(I_1 - I_2)$ for I_3 each time it appears. In the first equation, this is equal to:

$$10 + 10 I_3 + 8 + 15 I_1 = 0$$
$$10 + 10 (I_1 - I_2) + 8 + 15 I_1 = 0$$
$$10 + 10 I_1 - 10 I_2 + 8 + 15 I_1 = 0$$
$$10 + 25 I_1 - 10 I_2 + 8 = 0$$
$$25 I_1 - 10 I_2 + 18 = 0$$
$$25 I_1 - 10 I_2 = -18$$

Following the same procedure in the second equation, you have:

$$-8 - 10\,I_3 + 20\,I_2 + 12 = 0$$
$$-8 - 10\,(I_1 - I_2) + 20\,I_2 + 12 = 0$$
$$-8 - 10\,I_1 + 10\,I_2 + 20\,I_2 + 12 = 0$$
$$-8 - 10\,I_1 + 30\,I_2 + 12 = 0$$
$$-10\,I_1 + 30\,I_2 + 4 = 0$$
$$-10\,I_1 + 30\,I_2 = -4$$

These loop equations may be solved by addition after multiplying the top equation by 3 (in order to make the I_2 terms cancel).

$$3\,(25\,I_1 - 10\,I_2) = (-18)\,(3)$$
$$\underline{-10\,I_1 + 30\,I_2 = -4}$$

$$75\,I_1 - 30\,I_2 = -54$$
$$\underline{-10\,I_1 + 30\,I_2 = -\ 4}$$

$$65\,I_1 \qquad = -58$$

$$\frac{65\,I_1}{65} = \frac{-58}{65}$$

$$I_1 = -0.892 \text{ A}$$

Since this answer is negative, you know that the *conventional current*, I_1, is flowing *opposite* to the assumed direction in the left-hand loop.

I_2 may now be found by substituting the I_1 value into one of the original loop equations.

$$-10\,I_1 + 30\,I_2 = -4$$
$$-10\,(-0.892) + 30\,I_2 = -4$$
$$+8.92 + 30\,I_2 = -4$$
$$30\,I_2 = -12.92$$

$$\frac{30\,I_2}{30} = \frac{-12.92}{30}$$

$$I_2 = -0.431 \text{ A}$$

The negative answer for I_2 again indicates that the originally assumed direction was incorrect and that the conventional current I_2 actually flows clockwise in the right-hand loop. To find the value of I_3, go back to the equation that expresses I_3 in terms of I_1 and I_2. I_3 is equal to $I_1 - I_2$.

$$I_3 = I_1 - I_2$$
$$I_3 = (-0.892 \text{ A}) - (-0.431 \text{ A})$$
$$I_3 = -0.461 \text{ A}$$

This answer is also negative, indicating that I_3 actually flows down through R_2, so conventional current in this circuit flows as shown below.

To go on and find the individual voltage drops in this problem, simply substitute the values of current and resistance into Ohm's law for each resistor in the circuit.

$$E_{R1} = I_1 \times R_1$$
$$E_{R1} = 0.892 \text{ A} \times 15$$
$$E_{R1} = 13.38 \text{ V}$$

$$E_{R2} = I_3 \times R_2$$
$$E_{R2} = 0.461 \times 10$$
$$E_{R2} = 4.61 \text{ V}$$

$$E_{R3} = I_2 \times R_3$$
$$E_{R3} = 0.431 \times 20$$
$$E_{R3} = 8.62 \text{ V}$$

The voltage polarities are also labeled on the diagram. Remember that conventional current always flows through resistors from + to −; while electron current flows through resistors from − to +.

5. Solve for all voltages and currents in the following circuit using the *superposition theorem*.

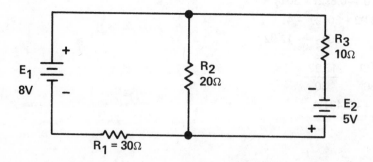

The superposition theorem says that "In a network with two or more sources, the current or voltage for any component is the algebraic sum of the effects produced by each source acting separately. The first step in solving this problem, is to remove one source and replace it with a short, or conducting path.

The circuit with E_1 "shorted out" looks like this:

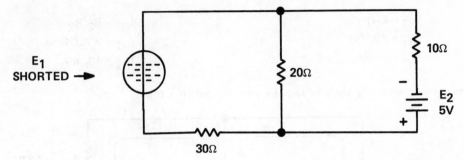

Circuit reduction laws may be applied, and the circuit reduced down to one equivalent resistance.

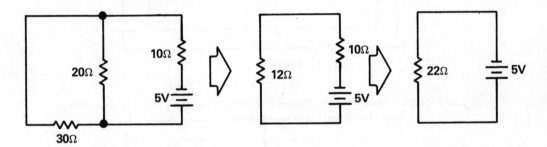

The total current may now be found by applying Ohm's law:

$$I_T = E_T/R_T$$
$$I_T = 5/22$$
$$I_T = 0.227 \text{ A} = 227 \text{ mA}$$

This "total current" flows through resistor R_3. E_{R3} may be found by applying Ohm's law.

$$E_{R3} = I_{R3} \times R_3$$
$$E_{R3} = 0.227 \times 10$$
$$E_{R3} = 2.27 \text{ V}$$

The balance of the circuit voltage is dropped across the parallel combination of resistors R_1 and R_2 ($R_{1\text{-}2}$). The voltage value may be found by applying Kirchhoff's voltage law for series circuits.

$$E_2 = E_{R1\text{-}2} + E_{R3}$$
$$5 \text{ V} = E_{R1\text{-}2} + 2.27 \text{ V}$$
$$-E_{R1\text{-}2} = -5 \text{ V} + 2.27 \text{ V}$$
$$E_{R1\text{-}2} = 2.73 \text{ V}$$

Knowing the voltage across the parallel resistors R_1 and R_2, their currents may be found by using Ohm's law.

$$I_{R1} = E_1/R_1$$
$$I_{R1} = 2.73/30$$
$$I_{R1} = 91 \text{ mA}$$

$$I_{R2} = E_2/R_2$$
$$I_{R2} = 2.73/20$$
$$I_{R2} = 137 \text{ mA}$$

The circuit, completely analyzed with E_1 shorted, looks like this:

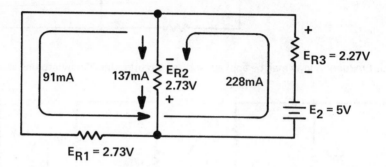

Short E_2, and solve the circuit for all voltages and currents using E_1 as the source voltage.

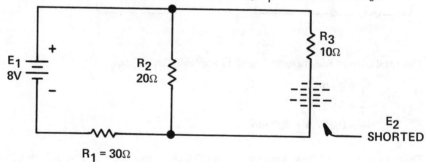

First reduce the circuit to find its equivalent resistance.

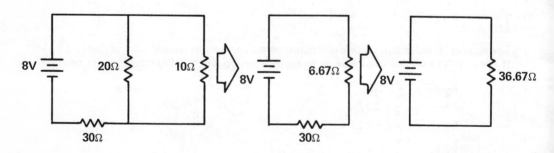

Now, use the equivalent resistance and the total voltage to find the total current.

$$I_T = E_T/R_{eq}$$
$$I_T = 8/36.67$$
$$I_T = 0.218 \text{ A} = 218 \text{ mA}$$

This current value flows through R_1. Ohm's law may be used to find the voltage dropped across R_1.

$$E_{R1} = I_T \times R_1$$
$$E_{R1} = 0.218 \text{ A} \times 30 \text{ } \Omega$$
$$E_{R1} = 6.54 \text{ V}$$

According to the series circuit voltage law, the rest of the applied voltage must be dropped across the other circuit resistance, which in this case is the parallel combination of resistors R_2 and R_3 (R_{2-3}).

$$E_{R2-3} = E_1 - E_{R1}$$
$$E_{R2-3} = 8 \text{ V} - 6.54 \text{ V}$$
$$E_{R2-3} = 1.46 \text{ V}$$

Since the 20-ohm and 10-ohm resistors are connected in parallel, the voltage across each of them is equal to 1.46 volts. The current flowing through these resistors may now be found by using Ohm's law and the known values of resistance and voltage:

$$I_{R2} = \frac{E_{R2}}{R_2} \qquad\qquad\qquad I_{R3} = \frac{E_{R3}}{R3}$$

$$I_{R2} = \frac{1.46}{20} \qquad\qquad\qquad I_{R3} = \frac{1.46}{10}$$

$$I_{R2} = 73 \text{ mA} \qquad\qquad\qquad I_{R3} = 146 \text{ mA}$$

Here is the circuit with all circuit values shown, with the source, E_1, acting alone.

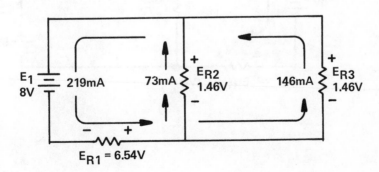

Now, superimpose this circuit over the first circuit you worked and take the algebraic sum of the values of current and voltage in the circuit.

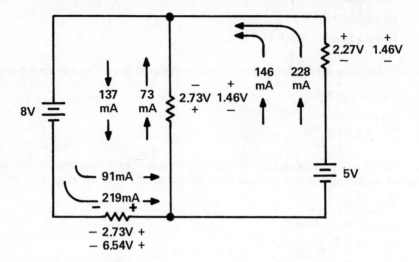

Algebraically add all the voltage and current values for each resistor to get the final circuit values as labeled below:

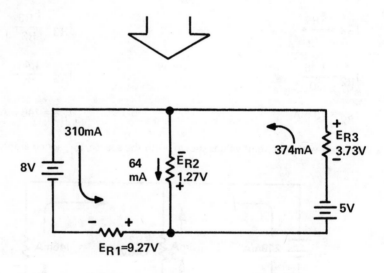

6. Solve the following circuit for all values of current and voltage using the superposition theorem:

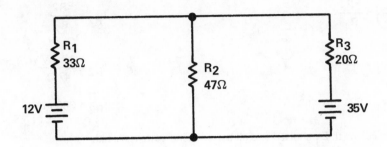

First, short one source and reduce the circuit to its equivalent resistance.

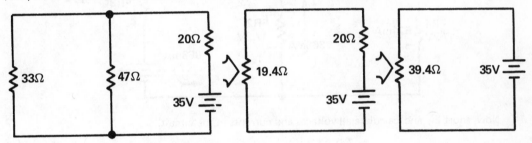

The total circuit current may be found now by using Ohm's law.

$$I_T = \frac{E_T}{R_{eq}}$$

$$I_T = \frac{35 \text{ V}}{39.4 \ \Omega}$$

$$I_T = 0.888 \text{ A} = 888 \text{ mA}$$

Looking back to the simplified circuit diagrams, you can now see that the total current I_T flows through the 20-ohm resistor and throgh the parallel combination of resistors R_1 and R_2 (R_{1-2}), which is 19.4 ohms. The voltage across these resistors may be calculated by using Ohm's law.

$E_{R3} = I_T \times R_3$ $E_{R1-2} = I_T \times R_{1-2}$
$E_{R3} = 0.888 \times 20$ $E_{R1-2} = 0.888 \times 19.4$
$E_{R3} = 17.8 \text{ V}$ $E_{R1-2} = 17.2 \text{ V}$

Now the current through resistors R_1 and R_2 may be found by using Ohm's law.

$$I_{R1} = \frac{E_{R1}}{R_1}$$

$$I_{R2} = \frac{E_{R2}}{R_2}$$

$$I_{R1} = \frac{17.2\ V}{33\ \Omega}$$

$$I_{R2} = \frac{17.2\ V}{47\ \Omega}$$

$$I_{R1} = 521\ mA$$

$$I_{R2} = 366\ mA$$

Here is the circuit with E_1 shorted and all currents and voltages listed.

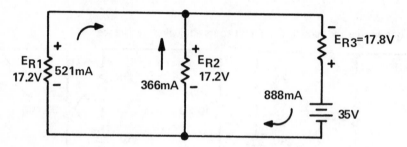

Now, short E_2 and calculate all voltages and currents in the circuit.

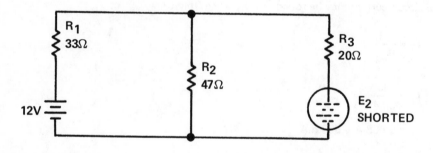

The circuit may now be reduced to its equivalent resistance.

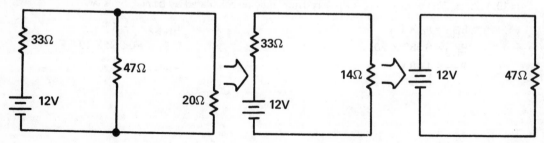

The total current may be calculated using Ohm's law.

$$I_T = \frac{E_T}{R_{eq}}$$

$$I_T = \frac{12\text{ V}}{47\ \Omega}$$

$$I_T = 0.255\text{ A}$$

This total current flows through the 33-ohm resistor producing a voltage equal to $I_T \times R_1$.

$$E_{R1} = I_T \times R_1$$
$$E_{R1} = 0.255\text{ A} \times 33\ \Omega$$
$$E_{R1} = 8.42\text{ V}$$

The balance of the 12 volts is dropped across the resistor combination $R_{2\text{-}3}$, as stated by the series circuit voltage law $E_T = E_1 + E_2$. Since, in this case, E_T = 12 volts, $12 - 8.42$ is equal to 3.58 V. This is the voltage dropped across the parallel combination of resistors $R_{2\text{-}3}$.

Now that E_{R2} and E_{R3} are known, the current through the resistors may be calculated using Ohm's law.

$$I_{R2} = \frac{E_{R2}}{R_2}$$

$$I_{R2} = \frac{3.58\text{ V}}{47}$$

$$I_{R2} = 76\text{ mA}$$

$$I_{R3} = \frac{E_{R3}}{R_3}$$

$$I_{R3} = \frac{3.58\text{ V}}{20\ \Omega}$$

$$I_{R3} = 179\text{ mA}$$

Here is the circuit with E_2 shorted and all voltages and currents listed.

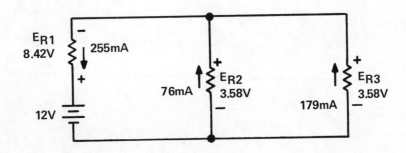

Now, superimpose the values of this circuit over the values of the circuit that had E_1 shorted.

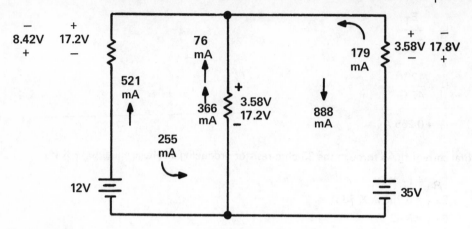

Now take the algebraic sum of all these voltages and currents.

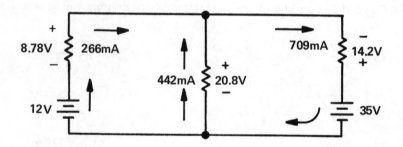

LESSON 12. ADVANCED METHODS OF DC CIRCUIT ANALYSIS

• **Practice Problems**

Depending upon the approach you use in solving these problems and how you round off intermediate results, your answers may vary slightly from those given here. However, any differences you encounter should only occur in the third significant digit of your answer. If the first two significant digits of your answers do not agree with those given here, recheck your calculations.

Fold Over

1.

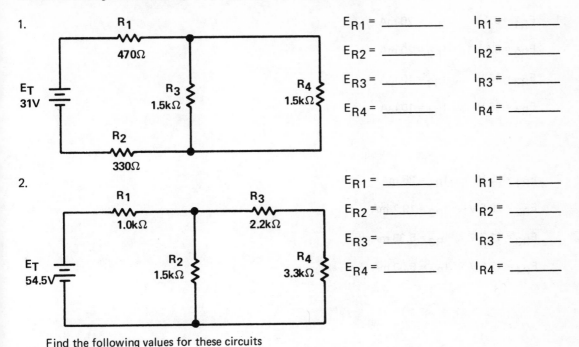

E_{R1} = _____ I_{R1} = _____

E_{R2} = _____ I_{R2} = _____

E_{R3} = _____ I_{R3} = _____

E_{R4} = _____ I_{R4} = _____

2.

E_{R1} = _____ I_{R1} = _____

E_{R2} = _____ I_{R2} = _____

E_{R3} = _____ I_{R3} = _____

E_{R4} = _____ I_{R4} = _____

Find the following values for these circuits

3. Thevenin's theorem

R_{TH} = _____

E_{TH} = _____

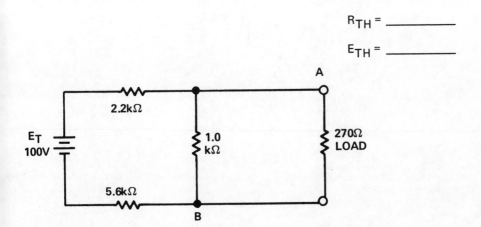

Answers

1. E_{R1} = 9.4 V I_{R1} = 20 mA

   E_{R2} = 6.6 V I_{R2} = 20 mA

   E_{R3} = 15 V I_{R3} = 10 mA

   E_{R4} = 15 V I_{R4} = 10 mA

2. E_{R1} = 25 V I_{R1} = 25 mA

   E_{R2} = 29.5 V I_{R2} = 19.7 mA

   E_{R3} = 11.7 V I_{R3} = 5.33 mA

   E_{R4} = 17.6 V I_{R4} = 5.33 mA

3. R_{TH} = 886 Ω

   E_{TH} = 11.4 V

4.

Fold Over

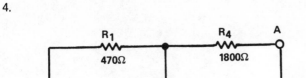

R_{TH} = _____

E_{TH} = _____

5.

R_{TH} = _____

E_{TH} = _____

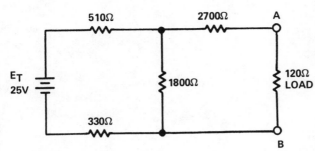

6. Norton's theorem

I_N = _____

R_N = _____

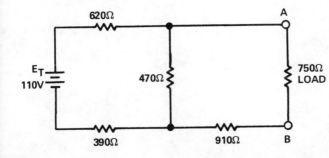

7.

I_N = _____

R_N = _____

Answers

4. $R_{TH} = 2.40 \text{ k}\Omega$

   $E_{TH} = 13.9 \text{ V}$

5. $R_{TH} = 3.27 \text{ k}\Omega$

   $E_{TH} = 17 \text{ V}$

6. $I_N = 28.4 \text{ mA}$

   $R_N = 1.23 \text{ k}\Omega$

7. $I_N = 28 \text{ mA}$

   $R_N = 600 \text{ }\Omega$

8. Millman's theorem

Fold Over

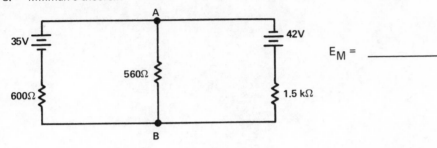

$E_M =$ _____

9.

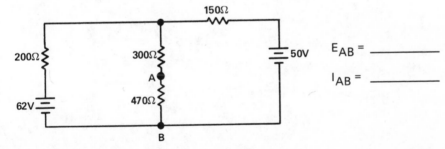

$E_{AB} =$ _____

10. Mesh currents

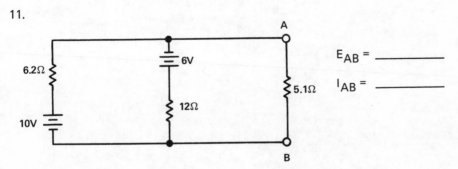

$E_{AB} =$ _____

$I_{AB} =$ _____

11.

$E_{AB} =$ _____

$I_{AB} =$ _____

Answers

8. E_M = 7.36 V

9. E_{AB} = 25.2 V

10. E_{AB} = 30.1 V

   I_{AB} = 64.0 mA

11. E_{AB} = 2.53 V

   I_{AB} = 496 mA

12. Node voltage

Fold Over

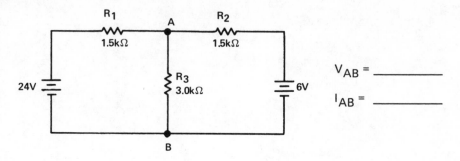

$V_{AB} =$ _____

$I_{AB} =$ _____

13.

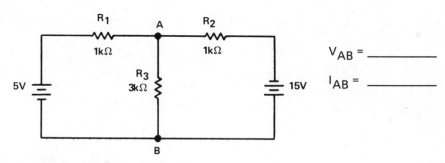

$V_{AB} =$ _____

$I_{AB} =$ _____

14. Superposition theorem

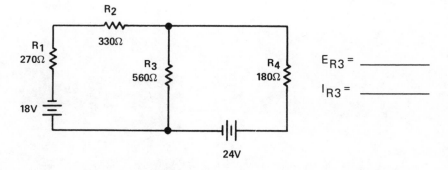

$E_{R3} =$ _____

$I_{R3} =$ _____

Answers

12. $V_{AB} = 12$ V

   $I_{AB} = 4$ mA

13. $V_{AB} = 4.29$ V

   $I_{AB} = 1.43$ mA

14. $E_{R3} = 11.5$ V

   $I_{R3} = 20.5$ mA

- **Practice Problems**

15. Fold Over

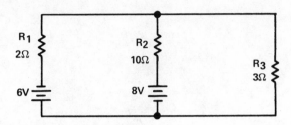

$E_{R2} =$ _____

$I_{R2} =$ _____

Answers

15. $E_{R2} = 10.4$ V

   $I_{R2} = 1.04$ A

1. A voltage source receives a _____ sign in a loop equation if one passes over it in the same direction as it normally pushes current.

   a. positive
   b. negative
   c. current
   d. voltage

2. If a voltage source is passed over when writing a loop equation in the opposite direction to that which it normally pushed current, the voltage receives:

   a. a negative sign
   b. a positive sign
   c. a current sign
   d. a voltage sign

3. When writing loop equations, if a resistor is passed over in the direction of the assumed current flow, the voltage across it is considered:

   a. negative
   b. positive
   c. zero
   d. opposite

4. The voltage across a resistor in a loop equation is considered positive if the resistor is passed over in _____ direction as the assumed current.

   a. The same
   b. A like
   c. An upward
   d. The opposite

5. $I_1 + I_2 + I_3 = 0$ is an equation using Kirchhoff's _____ law.

   a. Ohms
   b. Voltage
   c. Current
   d. Resistance

   Solve the following for the missing current. Give a value and direction. $+$ is away from the node; $-$ is toward the node.

6.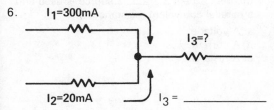

   $I_1 = 300mA$
   $I_3 = ?$
   $I_2 = 20mA$
   $I_3 =$ _____

7.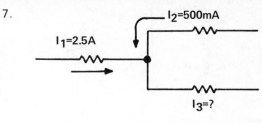

   $I_2 = 500mA$
   $I_1 = 2.5A$
   $I_3 = ?$

   $I_3 =$ _____

8.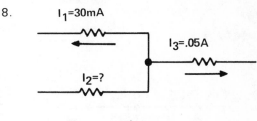

   $I_1 = 30mA$
   $I_3 = .05A$
   $I_2 = ?$

   $I_2 =$ _____

9.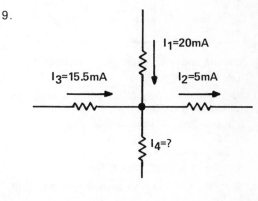

   $I_1 = 20mA$
   $I_3 = 15.5mA$
   $I_2 = 5mA$
   $I_4 = ?$

   $I_4 =$ _____

10.

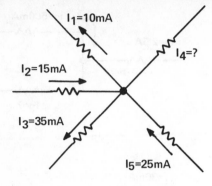

$I_4 = $ _____

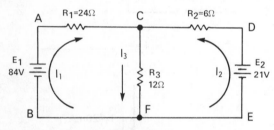

Use the above schematic for questions 11, 12, 13, 14 and 15.

11. Write the conventional current loop equation for loop A B C F A:

a. $84 - 24I_1 - 12I_3 - 12I_2 = 0$
b. $84 - 24I_1 + 12I_3 = 0$
c. $84 - 24I_1 - 12I_3 = 0$
d. $-84 - 24I_1 - 12I_3 = 0$

12. Write the conventional current loop equation for loop D E F C D:

a. $21 - 6I_2 - 12I_3 = 0$
b. $21 - 6I_2 - 12I_3 - 12I_1 = 0$
c. $-21 + 6I_2 - 12I_3 = 0$
d. $21 - 6I_2 + 12I_3 = 0$

13. Write the Kirchoff's current law for node C:

a. $I_1 + I_2 + I_3 = 0$
b. $I_1 = I_2 + I_3$
c. $I_1 = -I_2 + I_3$
d. $I_1 + I_2 = I_3$
e. d only
f. c and d above

14. Solve for I_1, I_2, and I_3:

a. $+3.0, -2.0, +1.0$
b. $+2.5, +0.5, +3.0$
c. $+2.29, -0.36, +1.93$
d. $+2.5, -0.5, +2.0$

15. What are the voltages across R_1, R_2, and R_3?

a. 81, 24, 3
b. 55, 8, 29
c. 60, 3, 24
d. None of above

16. When using the Superposition Theorem, all components in the circuits must be:

a. Voltage dependent
b. Linear and bilateral
c. Have low temperature coefficients
d. Be stable

17. When analyzing a circuit using mesh currents, it is usually assumed that all mesh currents:

a. Flow backwards
b. Flow in the same direction
c. Are indefinitely small
d. Can't flow opposite to the direction assumed

18. In the node voltage analysis method for circuit analysis, the voltage drops around a circuit are expressed in terms:

a. Of a node voltage
b. Familiar to all
c. That requires power dissipation
d. Of superposition

19. When a complex circuit is replaced with an equivalent voltage and an equivalent source resistance for circuit analysis, _____ theorem is being used.

a. Ampere
b. Coulombs
c. Thevenin's
d. Ohm's

20. Norton's Theorem is similar to Thevenin's theorem except _____ source is used and a parallel equivalent resistance.

a. A voltage
b. A current
c. A resistor
d. A series

LESSON 12. SUPPLEMENT
AN OUTLINE OF ADVANCED METHODS OF DC CIRCUIT ANALYSIS
AND HOW THEY ARE USED

In the previous lessons, Kirchhoff's voltage and current laws have been thoroughly discussed. This included not only a complete discussion of how they are applied in solving some fairly complex circuits, but also an introduction into some more specific applications of these rules as applied to complex circuit analysis. The methods discussed included node and loop equations and the superposition theorem; and also briefly introduced mesh current analysis, node voltage analysis, Thevenin's theorem, Norton's theorem, and finally Millman's theorem.

With this introduction as a background, the purpose of this additional material is to give a more complete treatment of each of these methods of circuit analysis. Specifically, each method will be discussed as to *where it is useful*, as well as the *specific steps to follow* in using the method in solving problems.

Then, each will have a *complete worked through example* illustrating details of the methods used.

The methods of circuit analysis will be discussed in this order:
1. Mesh currents
2. Node voltages
3. Thevenin's theorem
4. Norton's theorem
5. Millman's theorem

These five methods can be placed into two similar groups.

The first group consists of the mesh and node analysis methods. These two are actually used as extensions of Kirchhoff's current and voltage laws and are used primarily to analyze a circuit *completely* by finding all of the various current and voltage values throughout the circuit.

The second group, Thevenin's, Norton's, and Millman's theorems, is used to analyze circuits with a specific solution as an objective. For example, Thevenin's theorem is useful for analyzing the effect of substituting various loads across two specific test terminals in a circuit. Norton's theorem allows analysis similar to Thevenin's; however, the specific test point in the circuit is analyzed with respect to current rather than the Thevenin voltage consideration. Finally, Millman's theorem provides a shortcut method of finding the voltage across any number of parallel circuit branches, where each branch may contain different voltage sources, as well as resistances.

If further information is desired concerning these analysis methods, refer to the reference list following this supplement.

Where Useful

Mesh current solutions are particularly useful in solving for currents and voltages in complex circuits with several branch points, such as the circuit shown in Figure 12S.1.

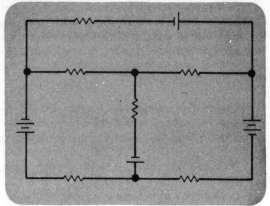

Figure 12S.1

Definitions and Methods of Use

The concept of mesh currents analyses of a circuit is similar to the analysis of loops and equations using Kirchhoff's laws. The basic differences center around the initial rules, or assumptions, used *before* writing the equations to solve for the currents in the circuits.

Rule — Assign mesh currents to all meshes in the circuit so that each element in the circuit is included at least once. A *mesh* is defined as the simplest closed path, or loop, in a circuit. Within a circuit, a mesh resembles a single window pane, and may or may not include a voltage source. Notice in Figure 12S.2 that the circuit shown has only two meshes. (Other closed circuit pathways will be *loops*, but not meshes.)

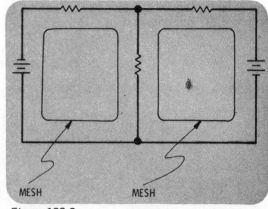

MESH   MESH

Figure 12S.2

Now, choose a current convention for use in the circuit (either electron current or conventional current) and assign all of the mesh currents the same direction (either all clockwise or all counterclockwise), as shown in Figure 12S.3. Note that with a resistor such as R_2 there are *two* mesh currents flowing through it. The actual value of the current flowing through R_2 will be the *difference* of the two mesh currents, with the *direction* being that of the *larger* current.

After these rules are employed, mesh equations are written in the same way as loop equations, using Kirchhoff's voltage law. Note: When writing the equations, shared components, like R_2 in Figure 12S.3, produce two terms in each mesh equation, one positive and one negative. (See sample solution.)

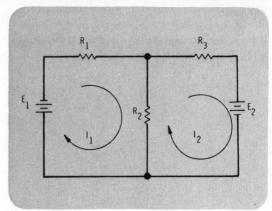

Figure 12S.3

Problem

Solve the circuit shown in Figure 12S.4 for the currents through R_1, R_2, and R_3, and voltages across R_1, R_2, and R_3.

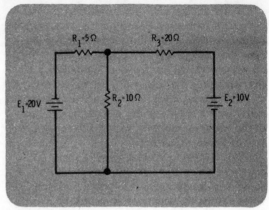

Figure 12S.4

Solution

First choose a current convention (here electron current is chosen), and assign mesh currents to each mesh, all in the same direction, as shown in Figure 12S.5. Then, write the mesh equation for each mesh current following Kirchhoff's voltage law:

Mesh 1. Beginning at Point A and traversing clockwise in the direction of I_1, you get: $-5\,I_1 - 10\,I_1 + 10\,I_2 + 20 = 0$ or $-15\,I_1 + 10\,I_2 + 20 = 0$. Note the $(-10\,I_1 + 10\,I_2)$ for R_2, due to the opposite mesh currents through R_2.

Mesh 2. Begin at point B and follow clockwise in the direction of I_2. This results in: $-10\,I_2 + 10\,I_1 - 20\,I_2 + 10 = 0$, or $+10\,I_1 - 30\,I_2 + 10 = 0$. Again note the R_2 term. The polarities reverse for the second mesh for $+10\,I_1 - 10\,I_2$.

Then solve the two resulting equations shown in Figure 12S.6. There will be one equation for each mesh so that there is one equation for each unknown mesh current.

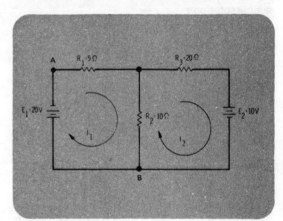

Figure 12S.5

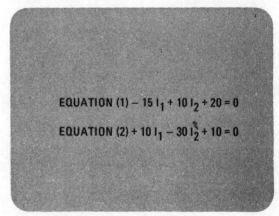

EQUATION (1) – 15 I_1 + 10 I_2 + 20 = 0

EQUATION (2) + 10 I_1 – 30 I_2 + 10 = 0

Figure 12S.6

Figure 12S.7 begins the solution. The first thing to do is to try to eliminate one of the unknowns, and the procedure followed here is aimed at eliminating I_2. To do this, multiply the first equation by +3 to get common coefficients for I_2 in both mesh equations. Then (Figure 12S.8), add the equations to eliminate I_2. This leaves the equation at the top of Figure 12S.9 with only one unknown. Solving this equation, I_1 is found to be 2 amps.

FIRST – MULTIPLY EQUATION (1) BY 3

$$3 \times (-15 I_1 + 10 I_2 + 20 = 0)$$

THIS GIVES

$$-45 I_1 + 30 I_2 + 60 = 0$$

Figure 12S.7

EQUATIONS (1) AND (2) NOW HAVE THE SAME COEFFICIENT FOR I_2, THUS I_2 CAN BE ELIMINATED BY ADDITION:

$$(1) \quad -45 I_1 + 30 I_2 + 60 = 0$$

$$+ (2) \quad +10 I_1 - 30 I_2 + 10 = 0$$

$$\overline{\qquad\qquad\qquad}$$

$$-35 I_1 \qquad\qquad + 70 = 0$$

Figure 12S.8

$$-35 I_1 + 70 = 0$$

$$-35 I_1 = -70$$

$$I_1 = \frac{-70}{-35}$$

$$I_1 = 2A$$

Figure 12S.9

Once I_1 is known, substitute I_1 into either of the two equations and solve for I_2 as shown in Figure 12S.10. I_2 is found to be 1 amp.

EQUATION (2)

$$+ 10\,I_1 - 30\,I_2 + 10 = 0$$
$$\text{(SUBSTITUTE } I_1 = 2)$$
$$+ 10\,(2) - 30\,I_2 + 10 = 0$$
$$20 - 30\,I_2 + 10 = 0$$
$$- 30\,I_2 + 30 = 0$$
$$- 30\,I_2 = 0$$

$$I_2 = \frac{-30}{-30} = 1A$$

Figure 12S.10

Then solve for the current through R_2 by subtracting the smaller mesh current from the larger mesh current, giving the 1 amp shown in Figure 12S.11. This current flows *down*, through the central resistor R_2, in the direction of the larger mesh current I_1.

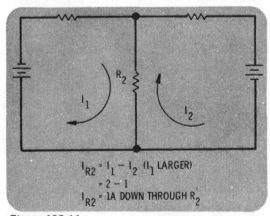

$$I_{R2} = I_1 - I_2 \ (I_1 \text{ LARGER})$$
$$= 2 - 1$$
$$I_{R2} = 1A \text{ DOWN THROUGH } R_2$$

Figure 12S.11

The rest of the solution is shown in Figure 12S.12 and involves finding each component's voltage using Ohm's law.

$$E_{R1} = I_1 \times R_1$$
$$E_{R1} = 2A \times 5\,\Omega = 10\,V$$

$$E_{R2} = I_{R2} \times R_2$$
$$E_{R2} = 1A \times 10\,\Omega = 10\,V$$

$$E_{R3} = I_2 \times R_3$$
$$E_{R3} = 1A \times 20\,\Omega = 20\,V$$

Figure 12S.12

The final solution with polarities is shown in Figure 12S.13.

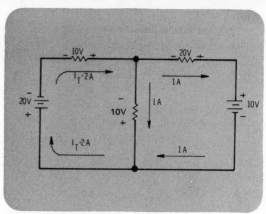

Figure 12S.13

Where Useful

This method is useful when solving for a particular voltage at a node, or branch point, without having to solve for complete current and voltage values within the circuit.

Definitions and Methods of Use

A node is a connection of two or more circuit components. A *principal node* has three or more connections (such as points A and B in Figure 12S.14). The first step in utilizing the method of node voltage analysis is to select *one* principal node in the circuit to act as the *reference node* (point B in Figure 12S.14). Then a current equation is written for each of the other principal nodes in the circuit. With this method, there will be one less node equation written than there are principal nodes. (Figure 12S.14 would then require only one equation.)

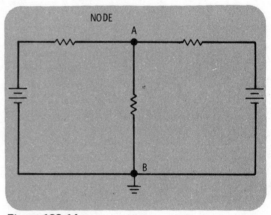

Figure 12S.14

To actually write the equation, begin by *choosing a current convention* (in the circuit shown in Figure 12S.15 electron current will be assumed), and by *labeling all* of the *currents* flowing in the circuit *with an assumed direction*. Then, using Kirchhoff's current law, *write a Kirchhoff's current law equation for every node except the reference node*. For the circuit shown in Figure 12S.15, you would have only one node equation: $I_3 = I_1 + I_2$.

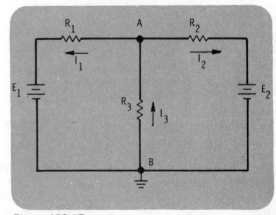

Figure 12S.15

Now the real trick in using node voltage analysis is this: Each of these *currents* is now *expressed in terms of the voltages* in the circuit. As shown in Figure 12S.16, I_3 equals the voltage across R_3 divided by R_3 or E_{R3}/R_3. Similarly I_1 equals E_{R1}/R_1 and $I_2 = E_{R2}/R_2$ as shown in the figure.

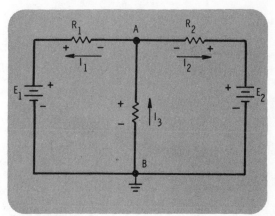

$$I_3 = I_1 + I_2$$

OR

$$\frac{E_{R3}}{R_3} = \frac{E_{R1}}{R_1} + \frac{E_{R2}}{R_2}$$

Figure 12S.16

Finally, all of the voltages can be expressed in terms of the *source voltages* and the *node voltage* E_{AB}. To do this, assign voltage polarities (Figure 12S.17) to each resistor in the circuit (using your assumed current direction). Then, keeping Kirchhoff's voltage law in mind, examine each *voltage* term in the equation

$$\frac{E_{R3}}{R_3} = \frac{E_{R1}}{R_1} + \frac{E_{R2}}{R_2}$$

and look for a way to express each in terms of the node voltage E_{AB} (which equals E_{R3}) and the applied voltages.

For example, if you traverse the left-hand loop if the circuit (Figure 12S.17) starting at point B and proceeding counterclockwise and write down the loop equation, you'd have $-I_3R_3 - I_1R_1 + E_1 = 0$. Or expressing each of these terms as a voltage directly, you'd have: $-E_{R3} - E_{R1} + E_1 = 0$. Remembering that $E_{R3} = E_{AB}$, the node voltage, this becomes $-E_{AB} - E_{R1} + E_1 = 0$. The key point is that, using this equation, E_{R1} can now be expressed in terms of the node voltage E_{AB} and the applied voltage E_1:

$$-E_{R1} = -E_1 + E_{AB}$$

or

$$E_{R1} = E_1 - E_{AB}.$$

If you do this same operation for the right-hand loop, you'll find that $E_{R2} = E_2 - E_{AB}$ and so the equation

Figure 12S.17

$$\frac{E_{R3}}{R_3} = \frac{E_{R1}}{R_1} + \frac{E_{R2}}{R_2}$$

can now be written

$$\frac{E_{AB}}{R_3} = \frac{E_1 - E_{AB}}{R_1} + \frac{E_2 - E_{AB}}{R_2}$$

The only unknown in this equation is now the
node voltage, E_{AB}, and this equation may then be
solved for it.

Problem

Solve Figure 12S.18 for the voltage across R_3. Use node voltage analysis.

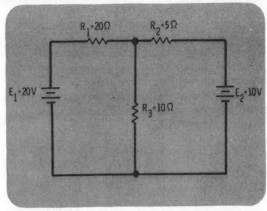

Figure 12S.18

Solution

First, identify the principal nodes and select a reference node. Here B will be the reference node (and is labeled with a ground in Figure 12S.19), and the only other principal node in the circuit is A. Then, choose a current convention (electron current will be used here) and label all the currents on the circuit assigning each a direction as shown in Figure 12S.19. Then, label voltage polarities across each resistor.

Next, write the current equation for the principal node A using Kirchhoff's current law. This gives $I_3 = I_1 + I_2$.

Then, express the node equation in terms of circuit voltages.

$$I_3 = \frac{E_{R3}}{R_3}, \; I_1 = \frac{E_{R1}}{R_1}, \text{ and } I_2 = \frac{E_{R2}}{R_2}$$

With these terms substituted in the original current equation, you have

$$\frac{E_{R3}}{R_3} = \frac{E_{R1}}{R_1} + \frac{E_{R2}}{R_2}$$

Now, express the voltages in this equation in terms of the desired node voltage, E_{AB}, and the applied voltages E_1 and E_2. First, E_{R3} is the node voltage, so $E_{R3} = E_{AB}$.

To obtain the other voltage relations you need, first write a loop equation for the left-hand loop in this circuit (starting at point B and traversing counterclockwise):

This gives: $-E_{R3} - E_{R2} + E_1 = 0$

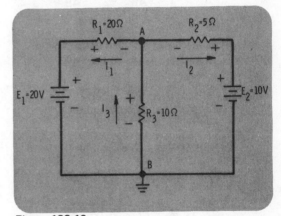

Figure 12S.19

Then, rearranging terms:

$E_{R1} = E_1 - E_{R3}$, and substituting E_{AB} for E_{R3}, $E_{R1} = E_1 - E_{AB}$.

Following a similar procedure for the right-hand loop gives you $-E_2 + E_{R2} + E_{AB} = 0$. Then rearranging: $E_{R2} = E_2 - E_{AB}$.

At this point, rewrite the node equation with substituted terms, and then substitute known values into the equation.

$$I_3 = I_1 + I_2$$

or

$$\frac{E_{R3}}{R_3} = \frac{E_{R1}}{R_1} + \frac{E_{R2}}{R_2}$$

or

$$\frac{E_{AB}}{R_3} = \frac{E_1 - E_{AB}}{R_1} + \frac{E_2 - E_{AB}}{R_2}$$

With known values: $E_1 = 20$ V, $E_2 = 10$ V, $R_1 = 20\ \Omega$, $R_2 = 5\ \Omega$, and $R_3 = 10\ \Omega$, the equation becomes:

$$\frac{E_{AB}}{10} = \frac{20 - E_{AB}}{20} + \frac{10 - E_{AB}}{5}$$

Then solve for E_{AB}. Multiply the equation by 20 for:

or

$$2E_{AB} = 20 - E_{AB} + 4(10 - E_{AB})$$

$$2E_{AB} = 20 - E_{AB} + 40 - 4E_{AB}$$

Combine like terms

$$2E_{AB} = 60 - 5E_{AB}$$

Transpose

$$7E_{AB} = 60$$

Divide

$$E_{AB} = \frac{60}{7} = 8.57 \text{ V}$$

Where Useful

Thevenin's theorem is useful where one particular component in a circuit must be repeatedly replaced, such as in a complex circuit where several different loads are to be applied. For example, what will the current and voltage values be for R_4 in Figure 12S.20 with R_4 equal to 20 ohms, 5 ohms, 30 ohms, and 50 ohms? Normal solution methods for this would involve four separate solutions of a complex circuit. However, Thevenin's theorem allows the rest of the circuit (without R_4) to be analyzed just once, and a very simple analysis to be made each time a new R_4 is "plugged in."

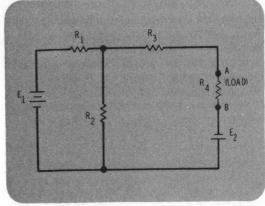

Figure 12S.20

Definitions and Methods of Use

Thevenin's theorem states that a circuit such as Figure 12S.20 above can be replaced by an equivalent series circuit consisting of one voltage (Thevenin's voltage, E_{TH}) and one series resistance (Thevenin's resistance, R_{TH}), as shown in Figure 12S.21.

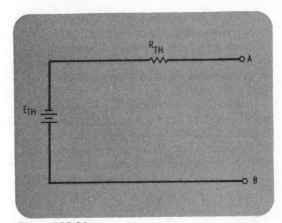

Figure 12S.21

Once E_{TH} and R_{TH} are known, various loads can be placed across points A and B (Figure 12S.22) and the desired current and voltage values for this load can then be easily determined.

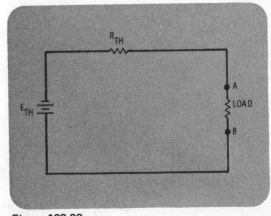

Figure 12S.22

Thevenin's voltage, E_{TH}, is found by first *removing* the load component to be tested (R_4 in Figure 12S.20) and then finding the voltage between these two open terminals (see Figure 12S.23). The voltage across the open terminals A and B in Figure 12S.23 will be E_{TH} for this circuit.

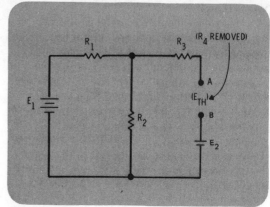

Figure 12S.23

Thevenin's resistance, R_{TH}, is found also with the test component (R_4 of Figure 12S.20) removed. R_{TH} is the resistance as measured between the *open test terminals* A and B, with all of the sources replaced by short circuits (see Figure 12S.24).

Once E_{TH} and R_{TH} are found, the circuit has been Thevenized and the equivalent circuit (Figure 12S.22) can be used to solve for the voltages across, and the current through, any load attached to the terminals A and B.

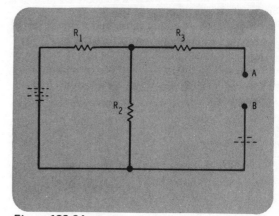

Figure 12S.24

Problem

Find the current and voltage for R_4 in Figure 12S.25 for these values of R_4: $R_4 = 20\ \Omega$ and $R_4 = 5\ \Omega$. Use Thevenin's theorem.

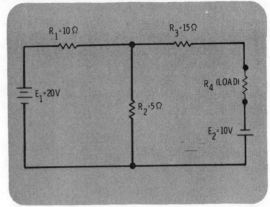

Figure 12S.25

Solution

First label the test points and remove the load to be tested (Figure 12S.26).

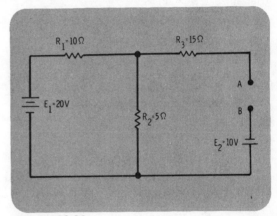

Figure 12S.26

Next, find E_{TH}, the open circuit voltage between test points A and B. In Figure 12S.27, E_{TH} will be the algebraic sum of E_{R3}, E_{R2}, and E_2. Since A and B are open, no current flows through R_3; therefore, $E_{R3} = 0$. E_{R2} can be solved using series circuit solution methods, because with A and B *open*, the only complete circuit path for current flow is the single series loop containing E_1, R_1, and R_2. Once E_{R2} is found, it can be algebraically added to E_2 to find the total voltage across points A and B (which is the Thevenin voltage).

Using electron current to analyze the problem as shown in Figure 12S.27, I_1 flows through R_2 and R_1 and gives rise to the voltage polarities

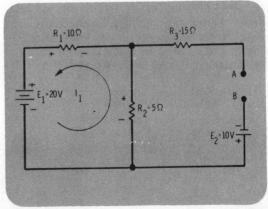

Figure 12S.27

labeled. (Note that you'd arrive at the same polarities using conventional current in your analysis.)

To find E_{R2} just calculate the total current flowing in the left-hand loop, I_1:

$$I_1 = E_1/R_T$$

where R_T just equals $R_1 + R_2$ which equals $5 + 10 = 15\ \Omega$.

Substituting

$$I_1 = 20\ V/15\ \Omega = 1.33\ A$$

Then E_{R2} equals I_1 times R_2 or

$$1.33\ A \times 5\ \Omega$$

or

$$E_{R2} = 6.65\ V$$

So at this point E_{R3}, E_{R2}, and E_2 are known. E_{TH} is just the algebraic sum of these. (Remember $E_{R3} = 0$.)

$$E_{TH} = E_{R3} + E_{R2} + E_2$$
$$E_{TH} = 0\ V + 6.65 + 10\ V$$
$$E_{TH} = 16.65\ V$$

Note: The polarities of the voltages must be considered. E_{R2} and E_2 were in the same relative direction so they were added. Thus, E_{TH} is 16.65 V, negative at point B, positive at point A.

Next solve for R_{TH} by mentally replacing all source voltages with short circuits, and finding R_{TH} between the open test points A and B (Figure 12S.28) using the circuit reduction techniques you've seen earlier (Figure 12S.29).

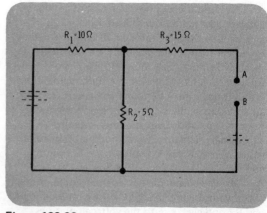

Figure 12S.28

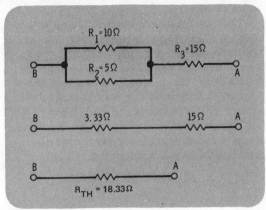

Figure 12S.29

Then draw the equivalent circuit and substitute the desired loads for solution (Figure 12S.30).

If $R_4 = 20\ \Omega$ find I and E_{R4},

$$I = \frac{E_{TH}}{R_T} \text{ where } R_T = R_{TH} + R_4$$

$$I = \frac{16.65\ V}{18.33 + 20} = 0.434\ A$$

$$E_{R4} = I \times R_4 = 0.434\ A \times 20 = 8.68\ V$$

If $R_5 = 5$ ohms.

$$I = \frac{16.65}{18.33 + 5} = 0.714\ A$$

$$E = I \times R_4 = 0.714 \times 5 = 3.57\ V$$

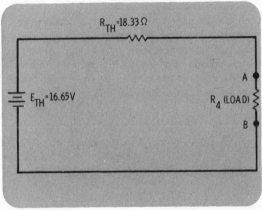

Figure 12S.30

Note that once a circuit is "Thevenized," it is easy to solve for E_{load} and I_{load} for any given load. A complete repeat of the circuit analysis is not required as different loads are plugged in.

Where Useful

As with Thevenin's theorem, Norton's theorem is useful when repeated substitutions of one component are desired in a circuit, and you have no desire to do repeated complex solutions for the circuit for each load. For example, in Figure 12S.31, Norton's theorem provides a method that will allow you to easily calculate the voltage across and current through any load placed across terminals A and B without completely analyzing the circuit for each load.

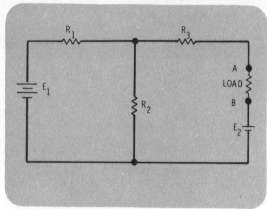

Figure 12S.31

Definitions and Method of Use

Norton's theorem states that a circuit with several sources and components can be replaced for evaluation at two test points by an equivalent circuit consisting of one *current source* (Norton current, I_N) and one parallel, or shunt, resistance (Norton resistance, R_N). See Figure 12S.32.

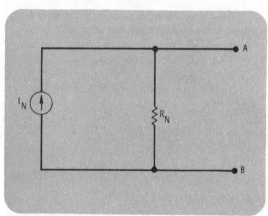

Figure 12S.32

I_N is found by mentally shorting the test terminals, A and B of Figure 12S.31, together and calculating the current that would flow through the short (see Figure 12S.33). The value of current found, I_N, will be the value of the current source in the equivalent circuit (Figure 12S.32), whose output will be shared by R_N and the load placed across A and B.

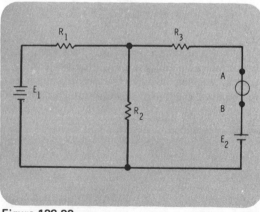

Figure 12S.33

R_N is found by shorting all voltage sources and computing the resistance from the open load terminals with the load removed (R_4), Figure 12S.34. Note that R_N and R_{TH} (Thevenin resistance) are found in an identical manner; thus, $R_N = R_{TH}$.

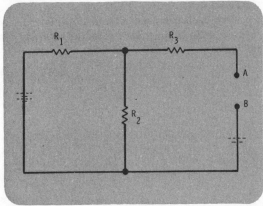

Figure 12S.34

Once I_N and R_N are known, the loads to be tested are placed across the equivalent circuit and the current and voltages calculated (Figure 12S.35) using parallel circuit analysis techniques.

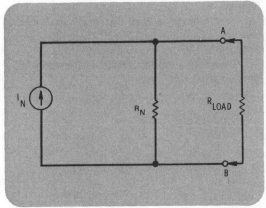

Figure 12S.35

Problem

Find the current and voltage for R_4 in Figure 12S.36 for $R_4 = 30\ \Omega$. Use Norton's theorem.

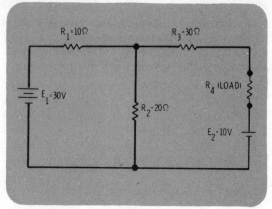

Figure 12S.36

Solution

First remove the load (R_4) and then short the load terminals and solve for I_N through the short (Figure 12S.37).

Several methods are available to solve for I_N. Here, superposition is used.

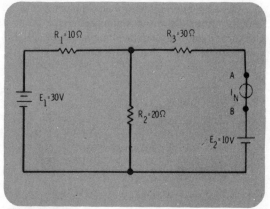

Figure 12S.37

First mentally short out E_2 and find the current produced by E_1 acting alone as shown in Figure 12S.38. To do this, find the total resistance for the circuit and then solve for the total circuit current.

$$R_T = \frac{R_2 \times R_3}{R_2 + R_3} + R_1 = \frac{30 \times 20}{30 + 20} + 10$$

$$R_T = 12 + 10 = 22\ \Omega$$

$$I_T = \frac{E}{R} = \frac{30}{22} = 1.36\ A$$

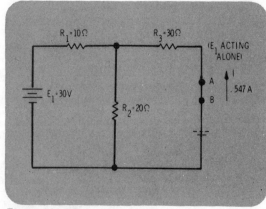

Figure 12S.38

Then solve for the voltage across R_1. This subtracted from E_1 will give you E_{R3}. Given E_{R3}, I_{R3} can be calculated, and this gives you the current past points A and B. Then

$$E_{R1} = I \times R_1 = 1.36 \text{ A} \times 10 = 13.6$$

$$E_{R3} = 30 - 13.6 = 16.4 \text{ V}$$

$$I_{R3} = \frac{E}{R3} = \frac{16.4 \text{ V}}{30 \ \Omega} = 0.547 \text{ A}$$

The I through the shorted terminals for E_1 alone is 0.547 amp *entering B to A* for electron current.

Then solve again with E_2 in the circuit and E_1 shorted (Figure 12S.39). To do this, again first find R_T and solve for I_T which is through the A, B terminal short.

$$R_T = R_3 + \frac{R_1 \times R_2}{R_1 + R_2}$$

$$R_T = 30 + \frac{10 \times 20}{10 + 20} = 30 + 6.67$$

$$R_T = 36.67$$

$$I_T = \frac{10 \text{ V}}{36.67} = 0.272 \text{ A}$$

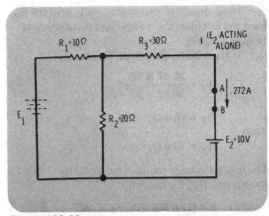

Figure 12S.39

This second current through the shorted terminal is in an opposite direction to the first; therefore, the value of I_N is the difference of the two, with the direction of the larger (Figure 12S.40). So

$$I_N = 0.547 - 0.272$$

or

$$I_N = 0.275 \text{ amp from B to A.}$$

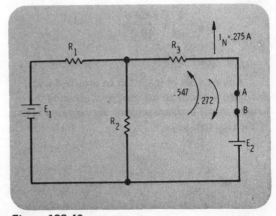

Figure 12S.40

Then to complete "Nortonizing" this circuit, find R_N, the resistance between the open load terminals A and B with all sources replaced with shorts (Figure 12S.41).

$$R_N = R_3 + \frac{R_1 \times R_2}{R_1 + R_2} = 30 + \frac{200}{30}$$

$$R_N = 36.67 \ \Omega$$

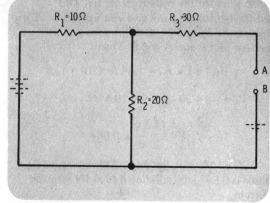

Figure 12S.41

Now, draw the equivalent circuit, add the R_4 load and calculate the current and voltage values (Figure 12S.42).

If $R_4 = 30 \ \Omega$, then solve first for R_T.

$$R_T = \frac{36.67 \times 30}{36.67 + 30}$$

$$R_T = 16.5 \ \Omega$$

Thus

$$R_T = 16.5 \ \Omega.$$

The applied voltage can then be found by multiplying this R_T times I_N.

$$E = I_N \times R_T = 0.275 \times 16.5$$
$$E = 4.54 \ V$$

Then

$$I_{R4} = \frac{E}{R4} = \frac{4.54 \ V}{30 \ \Omega}$$

$$I_{R4} = 0.15 \ A$$

Any number of loads can be attached and evaluated in the same manner, thus avoiding the lengthy initial problem solution for repeated values of the load resistance.

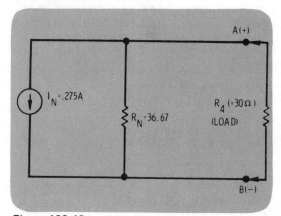

Figure 12S.42

Where Useful

Millman's theorem is particularly useful in finding the common value of voltage across several parallel branches each having different voltage sources as shown in Figure 12S.43.

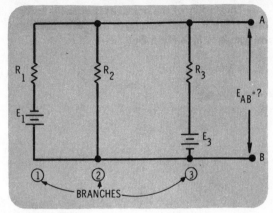

Figure 12S.43

Definitions and Methods of Use

Basically, Millman's theorem states that all parallel branches of a circuit such as Figure 12S.43 can be converted to current sources by taking each branch's total source voltage and dividing it by the total resistance of that branch. Thus for *Branch 1*

$$I_1 = \frac{E_1}{R_1}$$

for *Branch 2*

$$I_2 = \frac{E_2}{R_2}$$

and for *Branch 3*

$$I_3 = \frac{E_3}{R_3}$$

Once this is done for each branch, the results are combined by adding the currents $I_1 + I_2 + I_3$ and then dividing by the sum of the conductance of each branch, $1/R_1 + 1/R_2 + 1/R_3$. This gives a formula of this form:

$$E = \frac{I_1 + I_2 + I_3}{\dfrac{1}{R_1} + \dfrac{1}{R_2} + \dfrac{1}{R_3}}$$

And since this is simply the total current divided by total conductance, it can also be written $E = I_T/G_T$.

This I_T/G_T of the branches is actually $I_T R_T$, since $1/G = R$, thus resulting in the desired branch voltage since $I_T \times R_T = E_T$.

Millman's Formula

This can be expressed in the formula shown in Figure 12S.44. This formula will work for any number of branches and is simply extended as necessary. However, *some precautions should be observed*. First: All branches must be parallel with no series resistances between them. Second: If branches contain more than one source, or multiple resistances, combine them for totals for each branch before solving. Third: The *polarity* used in the formula *for each source* is taken to be *the polarity it is applying to the top point* (point A of Figure 12S.43) *of the branches*, with respect to point B as a reference point. For example in Figure 12S.43, E_1 is negative, E_3 is positive. Notice also that the second branch with R_2 has no source, so E_2 would simply be equal to zero for that branch.

Once these precautions are observed, it is a simple matter to plug in the known values and solve for the desired voltage. Once this voltage is known, the other voltages and currents in the circuit can easily be found.

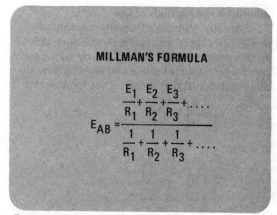

MILLMAN'S FORMULA

$$E_{AB} = \frac{\dfrac{E_1}{R_1} + \dfrac{E_2}{R_2} + \dfrac{E_3}{R_3} + \ldots}{\dfrac{1}{R_1} + \dfrac{1}{R_2} + \dfrac{1}{R_3} + \ldots}$$

Figure 12S.44

Problem

Solve for the voltage between points A and B (or E_{AB}) in Figure 12S.45. Use Millman's theorem.

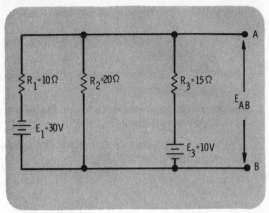

Figure 12S.45

Solution

Since there is only one source and one resistance in each parallel branch, simply place the values in the formula and solve.

$$E_{AB} = \frac{\dfrac{E_1}{R_1} + \dfrac{E_2}{R_2} + \dfrac{E_3}{R_3}}{\dfrac{1}{R_1} + \dfrac{1}{R_2} + \dfrac{1}{R_3}}$$

By substituting the voltages and resistances, you get

$$E_{AB} = \frac{\dfrac{-30}{10} + \dfrac{0}{20} + \dfrac{10}{15}}{\dfrac{1}{10} + \dfrac{1}{20} + \dfrac{1}{15}}$$

(Note the −30 for E_1, the 0 for E_2 and the +10 for E_3.) Then, simply reduce the terms and solve.

$$E_{AB} = \frac{-3 + 0 + 0.667}{0.1 + 0.05 + 0.067}$$

$$E_{AB} = \frac{-2.333}{0.217}$$

$$E_{AB} = -10.75 \text{ V}$$

Note that the minus indicates that the voltage is negative at point A with respect to point B as the reference point.

Additional Reference Material on Complex Circuit Analysis Methods

Grob, B., *Basic Electronics*, Third Edition, (New York, N.Y.: McGraw-Hill Book Co., 1971) pp. 119-166.

Herrick, C. N., *Unified Concepts of Electronics*, (Englewood Cliffs, N.J.: Prentice-Hall, 1970), pp. 187-232.

Singer, B. B., *Basic Mathematics for Electricity and Electronics*, Second Edition, (New York, N.Y.: McGraw-Hill Book Co., 1965), pp. 178-238.

Tocci, R. J., *Introduction to Electric Circuit Analysis*, (Columbus, Ohio: Charles E. Merrill Publishing Co., 1974), pp. 263-300.

Lesson 13

Capacitors and the RC Time Constant

This lesson introduces a new type of circuit component: the capacitor. Capacitor construction, units of capacitance measurement, and effects of capacitors in dc circuits are discussed. The very important concepts of the resistor-capacitor (RC) time constant and Universal Time Constant graph are introduced and discussed in detail, along with the effects of capacitor charge storage and rapid discharge.

LESSON 13. CAPACITORS AND THE RC TIME CONSTANT

• **Objectives**

In this lesson you will be introduced to an entirely new type of circuit component that produces some very useful effects in dc circuits: the capacitor. At the end of this lesson you should be able to:

1. *Sketch* the construction of a capacitor, *label* each of its component parts, and *draw* its schematic symbol.

2. *Write* and *show* with sketches what is meant by a charged and discharged capacitor, including a description of the procedures that may be used to charge and discharge a capacitor.

3. *Write* a definition of capacitance; explaining its relationship to the amount of charge stored and voltage across a capacitor's plates. *List* the three factors that determine the capacitance of a capacitor, and *define* the unit of capacitance; the farad.

4. For the circuit shown in Figure A below:

    a. *Calculate* the resistor-capacitor (RC) time constant.
    b. *Calculate* the voltage across the capacitor's plates one time constant after switch S is thrown to position 1.
    c. *Calculate* the time it takes for the capacitor to *fully charge.*
    d. *Sketch* a graph which describes how the voltage across the capacitor varies with time after the switch is thrown to position 1.
    e. With the capacitor in Figure A fully charged, the switch is thrown to position 2. *Calculate* the voltage on the capacitor 1 time constant later. *Calculate* the time it takes for the capacitor to fully discharge.

    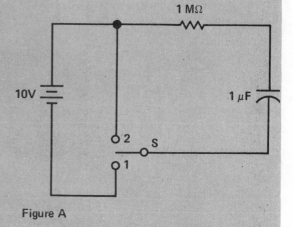

    Figure A

    f. *Sketch* a graph which describes the behavior of the voltage across the capacitor with time, after the switch is thrown to position 2.

5.

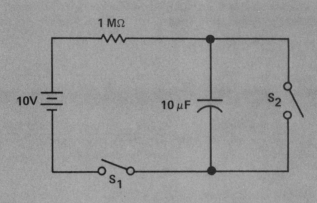

Figure B

In Figure B above, switch S_1 is closed for 5 time constants, then opened. *Write* a description of what happens when switch S_2 is closed.

- **Lesson Objectives**
- **Capacitor Construction**

By now you have come quite a long way in your study of dc electricity. You have probed the nature of electricity itself, learned much of the language and conventions used in describing electricity, and should be getting more and more familiar with the mathematical tools that enable you to predict and control the behavior of dc circuits. The circuits that have been discussed so far, however, have only contained combinations of voltage sources and resistors. In this lesson an entirely new type of circuit component will be introduced: the capacitor.

Lesson Objectives — To begin, it is always a good idea to set down objectives for the topics you will be studying. At the end of this lesson you should be able to sketch the construction of typical capacitors, and mathematically describe their behavior in circuits. You will also be able to define the important new concept of an "RC (resistor-capacitor) time constant," and sketch and explain what is called the *universal time constant graph*. You should also be familiar with common applications of capacitors in dc circuits, and be able to explain *why* capacitors are useful in these applications.

> **AT THE END OF THIS LESSON YOU SHOULD BE ABLE TO:**
>
> DRAW TYPICAL CAPACITOR
>
> DESCRIBE CAPACITOR BEHAVIOR MATHEMATICALLY
>
> DEFINE "RC TIME CONSTANT"
>
> USE "UNIVERSAL TIME CONSTANT GRAPH"

Figure 13.1

Capacitor Construction — In its most basic form, a capacitor consists of two conductors separated from each other by an insulator. In a capacitor, this insulator is called a *dielectric*. A sketch of a simple capacitor is shown in Figure 13.2. It basically consists of two metal plates separated by air, which is just one type of insulator or dielectric material commonly employed in capacitors. Connected to each plate is a lead or wire so that the capacitor can be connected to other circuit components. Capacitors used to be (and sometimes still are) referred to as *condensors*. The term capacitor is by far in more widespread use today.

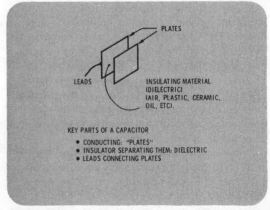

Figure 13.2

Capacitor Symbols — The schematic symbol for a capacitor is easy to associate with the real capacitor. As you see in Figure 13.3(A), the symbol shows two plates electrically separated from one another, with leads attached to each plate.

Figure 13.3(B) shows the more commonly accepted symbol for a capacitor. Notice that the major difference between this and the previous symbol is that in this symbol one plate is curved while the other plate is symbolized with a straight line. Generally, the curved line indicates the plate that should be connected to a more *negative voltage* than the other plate. Figure 13.3(C) shows some symbols you may see for *variable* capacitors or trimmer capacitors used in a variety of electronic applications that will be discussed for you in later courses in electronics.

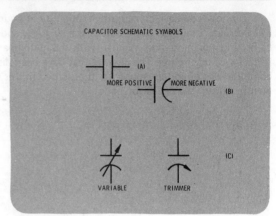

Figure 13.3

Electrolytic Capacitor Symbol — One other important capacitor symbol is shown in Figure 13.4. This symbol has a "plus" sign next to the "flat" plate. This symbol is the most common one used to signify an *electrolytic capacitor*. Electrolytic capacitors should *always* have the plate marked with the "plus sign" connected to a more positive voltage than the other plate. Electrolytic capacitors are designed to be used in dc or pulsating dc applications only.

A variety of other symbols are in use for electrolytic capacitors, and some additional ones are shown in Figure 13.4. In any of them, however, the polarity of the plates is identified; one of the plates is either labeled positive, or its shape tells

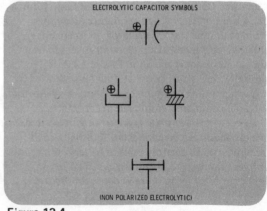

Figure 13.4

you that it is positive. (Certain specially constructed electrolytic capacitors are available that can be used in ac applications, and the symbol used to indicate these "nonpolarized" electrolytic capacitors is also shown in Figure 13.4.)

   If this is your first opportunity to learn about the capacitor, you may be wondering just how the thing works in dc circuits. There is no direct conduction path for current flow through the device, so what good is it? Just what does it do? These questions about capacitors will be answered. First, however, a little discussion of the history of capacitors may be interesting to you. The fact is that the capacitor was discovered by accident in 1746 in Leyden, Holland by a physicist named Pieter Van Musschenbroek.

Leyden Jar — Pieter was doing some experiments in an attempt to "electrify" water. The water "electrification" device consisted of a large jar lined inside and out with copper foil as shown in Figure 13.5. This "Leyden jar" as it is called, has all of the elements of a capacitor. As shown in the detail view, the rod sticking through the lid of the jar had a chain on the end that hung down and supplied connection to the inside layer of foil. This formed one plate of the capacitor, the glass wall of the jar served as the dielectric, and the outer foil served as the other plate.

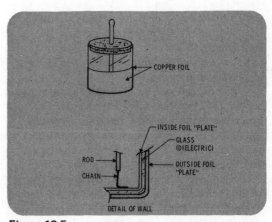

Figure 13.5

Leyden Jar Operation — As the story goes, Van Musschenbroek connected the Leyden jar to a voltage source for a period of time (Figure 13.6), then the voltage source was disconnected, and the jar was removed.

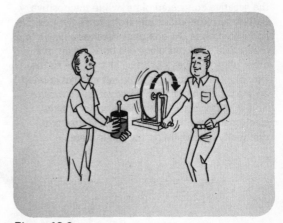

Figure 13.6

Zap – At this point Van Musschenbroek's assistant is said to have held the jar with one hand while disconnecting the high-voltage lead with the other hand. The lab assistant received an unexpected shock of considerable intensity (Figure 13.7). Unfortunately, history didn't record the words spoken by the assistant.

The shock received by the assistant points up a most important aspect of capacitors: *They are devices that can store an electrical charge.* Electrical charge, as well as electrical energy, can be stored or held in a capacitor and then released at a later time. Note that capacitors *must be given* the charge they store. A capacitor cannot produce electrical energy by itself, the way a battery does with chemical action.

Figure 13.7

Capacitor Action – How does a capacitor store charge? It does this through the action of an *electrostatic field*. To see just how this works, focus your attention on the sketch of capacitor plates shown in Figure 13.8.

As has been said, a capacitor consists of two conductors separated from each other by a layer of insulating material called a dielectric. Normally, the two metal conducting plates will have equal amounts of net positive and negative charge. As was discussed in Lesson 1, objects that contain equal amounts of positive and negative net charge are said to be *electrically neutral*. What will happen to these two plates if a potential difference is applied to them, say with a battery? The negative terminal of the battery pushes electrons out onto the negative connected plate, while the positive battery terminal draws electrons from the positive connected plate. As one plate receives a negative charge due to excess electrons building up, the other plate receives a positive charge due to the lack of electrons created. The net charges created on the capacitor's plates are *equal* and *opposite*. This is an important point. The battery takes electrons from one plate of the capacitor and essentially puts them on the other plate.

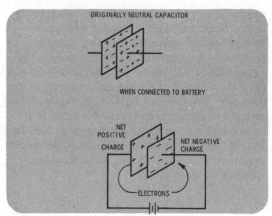

Figure 13.8

Charges Pack on Negative and Positive Plates —
Negative charges (electrons) cannot build up on the
negative plate forever. As more and more electrons
move toward the negative plate, they start getting
pushed back or repelled by the electrons already
there. After a while the battery cannot push any
more electrons onto the negative plate. The same
thing is true with the positive plate. After a while,
so many electrons have been removed from the
positive plate that the battery cannot pull any
more off.

Consequently the capacitor develops a net
positive charge on one plate and a net negative
charge on the other plate. Because of this, a
potential difference or voltage exists between the
two plates. At the point where no more charge is
flowing, the voltage across the capacitor's plates
equals the battery's voltage. Notice in Figure 13.9
that the voltage across the capacitor opposes the
battery's voltage. The capacitor's negative plate is
pushing electrons back in opposition to the push of
the negative battery terminal, and the capacitor's
positive plate attracts electrons and thus prevents
their further removal from the positive plate. At
the point where the voltage on the capacitor equals
the voltage of the battery, no more current flows,
since these voltages are in opposing directions.

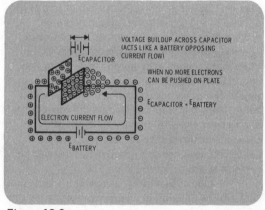

Figure 13.9

Capacitor Equivalent Circuit — As illustrated in
Figure 13.10, once the capacitor's plates have
accumulated enough negative and positive charges,
the capacitor acts like a battery wired to act
against the original battery in this circuit.

Review in your mind for a moment the
important points about a capacitor which have
been discussed. When a capacitor originally having
neutral plates is connected to a battery, *charge
flows* as a *current exists* in the circuit. Electrons
flow out of the battery's negative terminal and
build up on the negative connected plate, while
electrons are drawn from the positive connected
plate. The charge created on each plate causes a
potential difference or voltage, to build up on the

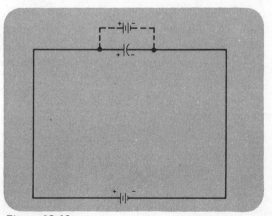

Figure 13.10

capacitor. As the charge on the capacitor's plates increases, the voltage across the plates increases, until finally the potential difference of the capacitor equals that of the battery. Since these two voltages are in opposition, when they equal each other there can be no more electron current flow. So notice: Charges flow in the *circuit*, but none flow *through* the capacitor because of the insulating gap between the two plates. Also, charge flow or *current only goes on for the short time* necessary for the voltage across the capacitor to become equal to the battery voltage.

Charged Capacitor — Whenever a net charge exists on each of the capacitor's plates, a *potential difference* or voltage exists across the capacitor. Likewise, when a voltage is *placed* across a capacitor, "charge" gets stored inside. Here's an important definition for you to remember: whenever a potential difference or voltage exists between the plates of a capacitor, the capacitor is said to be *charged*. A primary function of capacitors is this ability to store a charge. Capacitors are rated or measured by how well they perform this function.

   The factors that affect a capacitor's ability to perform the function of charge storage are the *size of its plates*, the *spacing between the plates*, and the *type of insulating material* separating the plates.

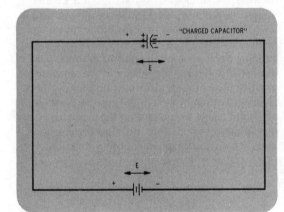

Figure 13.11

- Plate Area and Capacitance
- Capacitance
- Formula for Capacitance

Plate Area and Capacitance — Each of these factors will be discussed in detail and you will probably find the first factor, plate size, is the most obvious thing about a capacitor that will affect its charge storage ability. As shown in Figure 13.12, if each of a capacitor's plates is made larger (that is, if the plate area is increased), and then connected to a battery, more charge will be stored on the larger plates than on the smaller plates. More charge would have to flow until the potential difference across the capacitor equals that of the battery. When current flow stops, the capacitor would be storing more charge than a capacitor with smaller plates, even though both capacitors were charged to the same voltage.

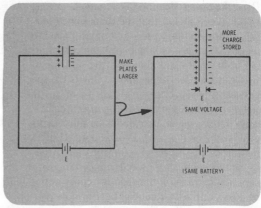

Figure 13.12

Capacitance — Since charge storage is really one of the most basic capacitor functions, a quantity is needed to describe how well a capacitor does this. This quantity is called the *capacitance* of the capacitor. As shown in Figure 13.13, *capacitance* is defined as the charge stored on a device, divided by the voltage across the device when that charge was stored.

CAPACITANCE

THE RATIO OF THE CHARGE STORED DIVIDED BY THE VOLTAGE ACROSS THE DEVICE.

Figure 13.13

Formula for Capacitance — Using the letter C to represent capacitance, Q for charge, and E for potential difference, an equation for capacitance may be written: $C = Q/E$. The capacitance of a device equals the charge it is storing divided by the voltage across it (Figure 13.14).

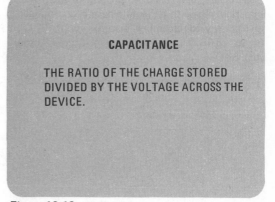

C = CAPACITANCE

Q = CHARGE

E = POTENTIAL DIFFERENCE

$C = Q/E$

Figure 13.14

- **Other Factors Affecting Capacitance**
- Dielectric Strength and Dielectric Constant

Other Factors Affecting Capacitance – It has already been shown that the capacitance of a capacitor depends on the area of its plates, the bigger the plate area, the bigger the capacitance. As has been mentioned, there are two additional factors that affect capacitance. One is the spacing between the capacitor's plates. It turns out that if the *plates* are pushed *closer together*, the *capacitance* will be *increased*. The third factor deals with the *type of dielectric* used. If different dielectrics are placed between the plates, the capacitance will vary. Details concerning *why* capacitance varies with capacitor construction will be covered in a later course, but for now just remember that the capacitance of a device depends on these three things: the spacing between plates, the area of the plates, and the dielectric material (specifically, the *dielectric constant* of the material). These three factors have been arranged into an easy-to-remember form for you in Figure 13.15. The first letters of the three factors spell SAD.

FACTORS AFFECTING CAPACITANCE

SPACING BETWEEN THE PLATES

AREA OF THE PLATES

DIELECTRIC MATERIAL USED

Figure 13.15

Dielectric Strength and Dielectric Constant – Notice that the dielectric in a capacitor is actually doing two things, First of all it is the ***insulating material*** that prevents charges from flowing from one plate to the other. Second, dielectric materials because of their makeup, actually act to ***help*** the capacitor store charge. As different dielectrics are placed between the plates of a capacitor, its capacitance will vary.

Two special quantities are used to describe how well a dielectric performs these ***two*** functions. One is ***dielectric strength***. This describes how ***resistant to breakdown*** a dielectric is. In capacitors, dielectrics consisting of very thin sheets are often subjected to very high voltages. When the voltage

DIELECTRIC STRENGTH	
ABILITY OF A MATERIAL TO WITH STAND ELECTRICAL BREAKDOWN	
MATERIAL	DIELECTRIC STRENGTH (VOLTS/MIL)
AIR	20
CERAMICS	600-1250 VARIES WITH TYPE
PYREX GLASS	330
MICA	600-1500 VARIES WITH TYPE
TEFLON	1525
OIL	375
PAPER	400-1250 VARIES WITH TYPE

Figure 13.16

applied across the dielectric becomes high enough, the dielectric will "break down," and electrons will "punch their way through" the dielectric. This creates a conducting path from one plate to the other through the dielectric and the capacitor malfunctions. *Dielectric strength* is a measure of how *resistant* a dielectric is to this type of breakdown. The dielectric strength of a material is commonly measured in volts per mil (V/mil); and some common values are listed in Figure 13.16. (One mil = 1/1000th of an inch.) These values tell you how many volts a one-mil thickness of dielectric can withstand before breaking down.

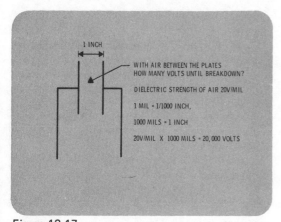

Figure 13.17

Example — For example, the dielectric strength of air is 20 volts/mil. How many volts would be required to break down 1 inch of air and jump a spark through it? As 1 mil is 0.001 inch; so 1 inch is 1000 mils. Air can withstand 20 volts for each mil of thickness so 20 volts/mil times 1000 mils equals 20,000 volts. In a capacitor with 1 inch of air between its plates, 20,000 volts applied would be enough to cause breakdown, as shown in Figure 13.17.

DIELECTRIC CONSTANT	
A MEASURE OF HOW WELL A DIELECTRIC HELPS A CAPACITOR STORE CHARGE (AS COMPARED TO AIR)	
DIELECTRIC MATERIAL	DIELECTRIC CONSTANT
AIR	1
CERAMICS	80-1200 VARIES WITH TYPE
GLASS	8
MICA	3-8 VARIES WITH TYPE
TEFLON	2.1
OIL	2-5 VARIES WITH TYPE
PAPER	2-6 VARIES WITH TYPE

Figure 13.18

Dielectric Constant — The other factor of importance that describes how well a dielectric functions in a capacitor is called its *dielectric constant*. This is a measure of how well a dielectric helps a capacitor store charge. Dielectric constants for some common materials are listed in Figure 13.18. Notice that the dielectric constant for air is listed as 1. The dielectric constant for any other material tells you how much more (or less) effective a material is (as compared to air) in helping a capacitor store charge. Glass, for example, has a dielectric constant of 8. If you had a capacitor with air originally between its plates, and replaced the air with a glass slab of the same thickness, the capacitor's ability to store charge would have increased *8 times*. Just how dielectrics work to help capacitors store charge has to do with how they affect the *electric field* between the capacitor's plates. Details of exactly how this process works are beyond the scope of this text, and are covered for you in later courses.

Farad — The units used to measure capacitance are called *farads*, named after the scientist Michael *Farad*ay. Following the equation C = Q/E, a capacitor has 1 farad of capacitance when it can store 1 coulomb of charge with a 1-volt potential difference placed across it.

In reality, 1 farad turns out to be an extremely *large* unit of capacitance, so common capacitors are rated in microfarads or picofarads as listed in Figure 13.19. An important point to note is that on many capacitors the letter m is used as an abbreviation for micro. Keep in mind that on capacitors m does not mean milli or mega, it is always used to indicate micro. Also you may notice the abbreviation mmF used to indicate *micro micro farads*, which are identical to picofarads. Pico is simply a newer term.

CAPACITANCE IS MEASURED IN FARADS

$$C = Q/E$$

$$1 \text{ FARAD} = \frac{1 \text{ COULOMB}}{1 \text{ VOLT}}$$

COMMON CAPACITOR VALUES IN

MICROFARADS = μF = mF

PICOFARADS = pF = mmF

Figure 13.19

Charged Capacitor — As has been mentioned, in order to *charge* a capacitor, you must connect it to a dc supply and apply a voltage. After a very short while, current stops flowing and the plates have a potential equal to the supply voltage.

An important point: if the capacitor is *disconnected* from the battery or supply while in its charged condition, *the charge still remains on its plates*. How does the capacitor hold this charge on its plates?

Recall from an earlier lesson, the first law of electrostatics states that *unlike charges attract* each other. Look at Figure 13.20, and you can see that even with the battery disconnected, the positive charges on one plate will attract the negative charges on the other plate and hold them there. Because of these unlike charges on the plates, an *electric field* exists in the dielectric region between them. This field is actually the mechanism that holds the charge on the plates, and also while acting to do that, actually *stores energy*. Since this electric field exists in the dielectric in the absence of current flow, it is called an electro*static* field.

Since the charges on the plates cannot move to reach each other because of the insulating dielectric between the plates, in this charged condition the capacitor can store charge and energy for long periods of time. This means that a charged capacitor can be used to provide a current or do some work for you at some later time.

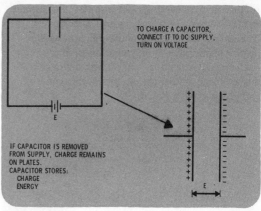

Figure 13.20

Discharging a Capacitor — The energy and charge stored in a capacitor may be *recovered* if a conducting path is provided between the plates. This procedure is called *discharging* the capacitor. The excess electrons on the negative plate will flow to the positive plate, until both plates have no net excess charge, or are neutral. In this condition, the capacitor is said to be *discharged*. The current that flows is called the discharge current, and the path taken by the current is called the discharge path. A charged capacitor may be discharged by providing an appropriate conducting path between its plates as shown in Figure 13.21. An important observation for you to make should be emphasized at this point. Even though the power may be shut

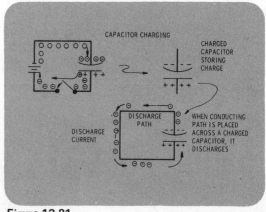

Figure 13.21

off to a circuit, every capacitor in the circuit may retain its charge for a long period of time. Therefore, before working on high-voltage electronic circuitry, you should be sure to discharge all capacitors. The stored charge and energy in capacitors can discharge through you, *giving you a nasty shock.*

Charge Formula — The amount of charge present on the capacitor's plates and the voltage across the plates are related. To restate, the capacitance of a capacitor in farads equals the charge on the capacitor in coulombs divided by the voltage across it, or C = Q/E. This equation may now be rearranged as shown in Figure 13.22 to read Q = CE, or the charge stored in a capacitor (in coulombs) equals its capacitance (in farads) times the voltage between its plates. Look at this new equation carefully. It states that the amount of charge stored in a capacitor is directly related to the voltage across the capacitor's plates. The more voltage across the plates, the more charge on the plates, and vice versa. For a given voltage, the higher the capacitance, the more charge will be stored on the plates, and vice versa.

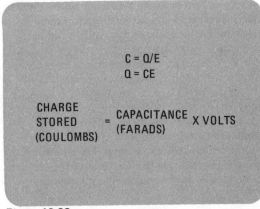

$$C = Q/E$$
$$Q = CE$$

CHARGE STORED (COULOMBS) = CAPACITANCE (FARADS) X VOLTS

Figure 13.22

Capacitor Charging: No Resistance — Up to this point, capacitor construction and charging and discharging of a capacitor have been introduced and discussed for you. When a capacitor is connected to a voltage source, current flows for a short time until the capacitor charges up to equal the source voltage. A capacitor can hold that charge for long periods of time. Consider what will happen if a *resistor* is placed in series with a capacitor as it charges and discharges.

The original circuit presented in this lesson consisted only of a capacitor and a power supply connected in series. When the battery was connected to the capacitor, electrons surged onto the negative-connected plate, and away from the positive-connected plate. When a capacitor is connected to a dc source in this way, it charges very rapidly. In fact, with virtually no resistance in the circuit, the capacitor would become fully charged almost *instantly*, as described in Figure 13.23.

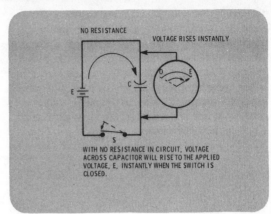

Figure 13.23

Capacitor Charging: Resistance Present — If a resistor is placed in series with this circuit, current cannot flow as freely as before. The current flowing in the circuit must "fight" its way through the resistor in order to charge the capacitor. Since there will be reduced current flow, *more time* will be required to charge the capacitor. Resistance has the important effect of causing a delay in the time required to charge a capacitor.

When the switch, S, is closed in a circuit consisting of a resistor, capacitor, and voltage source in series, the voltage across the capacitor's plates will take a *longer time* to reach the battery voltage than before (as shown in Figure 13.24). This is an important new effect. With a resistor in

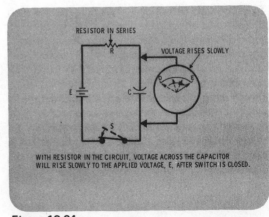

Figure 13.24

the circuit, the voltage across the capacitor rises more slowly than before, taking more time to reach the battery voltage. The current that flows in the circuit behaves in the opposite fashion. When the switch is first closed, a lot of current flows; and as the opposing voltage across the capacitor rises, less and less current flows, until finally, when the battery voltage and opposing capacitor voltage are equal, current flow ceases.

Factors Affecting Delay — This time delay required for the capacitor's voltage to reach the supply voltage, is a very useful effect — and you can control it. To enable you to *control* this delay, consider the factors that affect it.

The time required for the capacitor to charge and the voltage across it to rise up to the supply voltage depends on *two* factors (Figure 13.25): 1) *how much resistance* is in the circuit opposing current flow, and 2) *how big* the capacitor is.

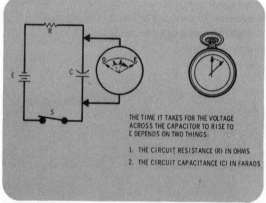

THE TIME IT TAKES FOR THE VOLTAGE ACROSS THE CAPACITOR TO RISE TO E DEPENDS ON TWO THINGS:

1. THE CIRCUIT RESISTANCE (R) IN OHMS
2. THE CIRCUIT CAPACITANCE (C) IN FARADS

Figure 13.25

Time Constant Definition — This time delay is such an important effect in electricity that engineers and technicians use a special way to describe how fast or how slow a capacitor charges. The time required for the capacitor to charge may be described in a standard way by defining what is known as the *capacitive time constant*. One time constant is defined as the *time required for a capacitor to charge up to 63% of the battery or supply voltage* (Figure 13.26). The time constant is also used to describe capacitor *discharge*, as will be discussed in a moment.

DEFINITION: TIME CONSTANT

1 TIME CONSTANT — THE TIME REQUIRED BY A CAPACITOR TO CHARGE TO 63% OF ITS FULL CHARGE VALUE (OR DISCHARGE DOWN 63% FROM FULL CHARGE).

Figure 13.26

- **Time Constant Formula**
- Time Constant Example
- Second Example

Time Constant Formula — Why this rather unusual definition for time constant? As it turns out, this specific time interval may be easily calculated from a simple formula as shown in Figure 13.27. You can calculate the capacitive time constant using the formula $T = RC$, where T is the capacitive time constant in seconds, R is the circuit resistance in ohms, and C is the capacitance in farads. For a series resistive-capacitive (RC) circuit, you find the time constant by simply *multiplying* the circuit's resistance in ohms, times the capacitance in farads.

CAPACITIVE TIME CONSTANT FORMULA

$$T = RC$$

T = TIME CONSTANT IN SECONDS

R = CIRCUIT RESISTANCE IN OHMS

C = CAPACITANCE IN FARADS

Figure 13.27

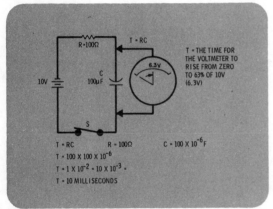

Figure 13.28

Time Constant Example — As an example, calculate the time constant for the circuit shown in Figure 13.28. In the circuit diagram the resistance is shown as 100 ohms, and the capacitance as 100 microfarads. To calculate the time constant, simply use the formula T = RC. Substituting: T = $100 \times 100 \times 10^{-6}$, which equals 1×10^{-2} or 10×10^{-3} or *10 milliseconds*. Remember, this is the time it would take for the voltage to rise from zero to 63% of the applied voltage. So in this case the voltage will rise to 63% of 10 volts or 0.63×10 or 6.3 volts in 10 milliseconds.

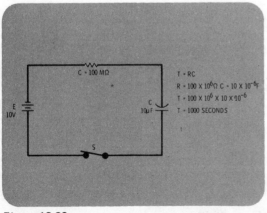

Figure 13.29

Second Example — Consider next the circuit of Figure 13.29. Here the resistance is a much larger 100 megohms, while the capacitance has been reduced slightly to 10 microfarads. Again, using the formula T = RC and substituting, you get T = $100 \times 10^6 \times 10 \times 10^{-6}$ or T = 1000 seconds. In this circuit you have to wait 1000 seconds (16-2/3 minutes) for the capacitor's voltage to rise very slowly to 63% of the applied voltage or 6.3 volts. The extremely large resistance really slows things up. This predictable rising voltage can be put to many uses in electricity and electronics.

Universal Time Constant Graph — At this point you know that the time constant of a circuit such as that shown in Figure 13.29 (called an "RC" circuit) equals R times C, and that in one time constant, the capacitor's voltage rises to 63% of the applied voltage, E. Focus your attention on the details of how this voltage behaves as time goes on after switch, S, is closed. This is a new dimension in the study of dc — *time* is involved now. You know that when the switch is closed in this circuit, the voltage across the capacitor starts to rise. To describe how this happens, the behavior of the circuit may be plotted on the graph shown in Figure 13.30. The voltage across the capacitor, that is the voltmeter's reading at different times, will be plotted on the vertical axis. Time (as measured by, say, a stopwatch) will be plotted on the horizontal axis. The switch is closed and the stopwatch started. As the watch measures off one time constant, the voltage will have risen to 63% of the battery voltage. As time goes on during the next and each successive time constant, the voltage continues to rise 63% of the *remaining voltage*, until full charge is obtained. During the second time constant, the voltage rises 63% of the remaining voltage or to 86.4% of full charge, and so on. This process continues until *after five time constants* the capacitor is for all practical purposes fully charged. The line on the graph shows the voltage behavior with time. This curve is important and deserves some close examination.

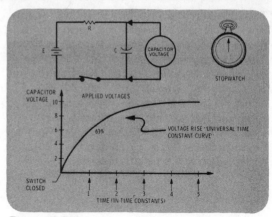

Figure 13.30

Universal Time Constant Graph (Charge) — The graph shown in Figure 13.31 is called the universal time constant graph, and may be used to describe any circuitry with a time constant type of behavior. This graph marks out in detail exactly what percentage of the applied voltage a capacitor will have charged to during specific time intervals after the voltage is applied to an RC circuit. If you know a circuit's time constant, this curve will enable you to accurately predict RC circuit behavior as time goes on. For example, suppose that you had calculated a circuit's time constant to be one second and you want to know what the capacitor's voltage will be one-half second after applying a voltage of 10 volts to it. In this case

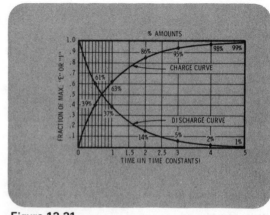

Figure 13.31

one-half second is one-half of a time constant or 0.5 time constant, so find that point on the bottom (or horizontal axis) of the graph. Follow the vertical line up from that point until it touches the charge curve, and you see that after 0.5 time constant, the capacitor would be at 39% of 10 volts, or 3.9 volts. Notice that there are *two curves* on this graph, one is the charging curve that has already been discussed. Now consider the process of *discharging* a capacitor through a resistor.

Universal Time Constant Graph (Discharge) — In Figure 13.32, the same capacitor used before is now fully charged but is rewired to discharge through the resistor, R. Notice that this is an RC circuit whose *time constant is identical* to the one considered in Figure 13.30. This time when the switch, S, is closed, the capacitor *discharges*, and the behavior of the capacitor's voltage is the *reverse* of that you saw previously. As the stopwatch ticks off the first RC time constant, the capacitor's voltage *falls 63%* of its fully charged voltage, so that at the end of one RC time constant, the voltage remaining on the capacitor is 37% of its fully charged value. During each successive time constant, the voltage continues to fall 63% of the remaining voltage value. After *five time constants*, the voltage may be assumed to be zero. Notice this important point: it takes five time constants for a capacitor to either fully charge or fully discharge. This is an important fact to remember concerning RC circuits.

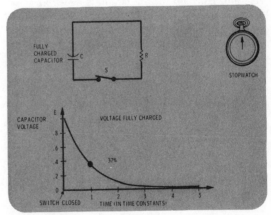

Figure 13.32

- **Example: RC Circuit Demonstration**
- **Storage Oscilloscope**

Example: RC Circuit Demonstration — To understand RC circuits more fully, a complete RC circuit example of a type you could easily build and study in the lab will now be discussed. Follow the circuit analysis as if you were actually watching the circuit perform. First, you will calculate the time constant for the circuit (shown in Figure 13.33), and then examine its behavior in detail. The circuit contains a 10-microfarad capacitor, and a 100-kilohm resistor and a switch, S, as shown. These components will be connected to a 100-volt dc supply. First calculate the time constant for this circuit, using the formula T = RC. Substituting R = 100 kΩ or 1 X 10^5 Ω and C = 10 μF or 1 X 10^{-5} farads. Multiplying 1 X 10^{+5} and 1 X 10^{-5} gives you 1 X 10^0 or 1. So the time constant for this circuit is *1 second*.

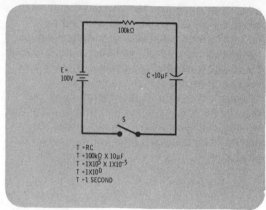

Figure 13.33

Storage Oscilloscope — To check the circuit's behavior, you could connect it to a special instrument called a *storage oscilloscope*, if one was available in your laboratory. This special instrument will actually plot a graph of the capacitor's voltage on the vertical axis, and time on the horizontal axis. On a typical storage scope you can set up the scope face so that each division on the scope's vertical axis represents 20 volts, and each one of the scope's horizontal divisions represents 1 second (Figure 13.34). When the switch, S, is closed, the oscilloscope *actually measures* the voltage across the capacitor for you, and plots it at different time intervals.

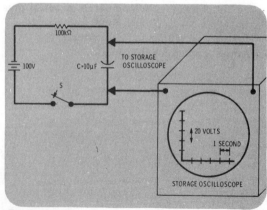

Figure 13.34

- **Scope Face: Capacitor Charging**
- **Discharge Demonstration Circuit**
- **Scope Face (Discharge)**

Scope Face: Capacitor Charging — When the switch in the circuit is closed, as shown in Figure 13.34, the scope face traces the patterns as shown in Figure 13.35 during the first five time constants. Figure 13.35(A) shows what the scope trace (picture) would look like at the end of 1 second. At this point, 63 volts is indicated on the scope face, which is 63% of 100 volts. In Figure 13.35(E), after five time constants or 5 seconds, the graph line has risen up to 100 volts or full charge.

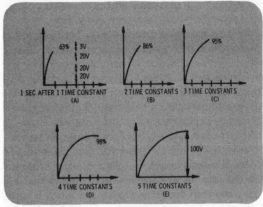

Figure 13.35

Discharge Demonstration Circuit — If the 100-volt power supply is removed from the circuit and the capacitor is connected so that it discharges through the same 100-kilohm resistor, the capacitor's discharge curve may be observed on the storage oscilloscope face (Figure 13.36), set at the same scales as before.

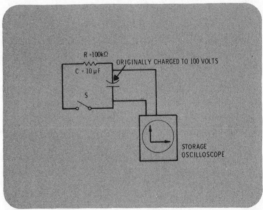

Figure 13.36

Scope Face (Discharge) — What the storage oscilloscope would display for you is shown in Figure 13.37. In Figure 13.37(A), which shows the scope face after one time constant or 1 second, the voltage has fallen from full charge of 100 volts down to about 38 volts. In the successive figures the line continues to descend until in Figure 13.37(E) at five time constants, the voltage is at zero and the capacitor is discharged.

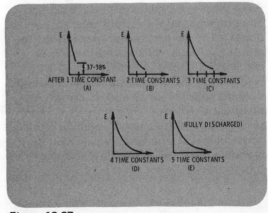

Figure 13.37

- Slow Discharge of Capacitor: Low Current
- Rapid Discharge: High Current

Slow Discharge of Capacitor: Low Current — At this point, you have seen what capacitors are, and how they operate in dc circuits. As has been demonstrated, a capacitor can *store charge*. This effect finds application in many dc circuits, for the following reason. When a charged capacitor is discharged, the rate at which the voltage across it drops and the amount of current that flows in the discharge circuit depend on the resistance in the discharge path. As you have seen, more resistance in the circuit causes a longer RC time constant, and hence it takes a longer time for a charged capacitor to discharge. In an RC circuit with high resistance, the amount of discharge current that flows is small. This trickle of discharge current flows for a long time, until the capacitor is discharged as shown in Figure 13.38.

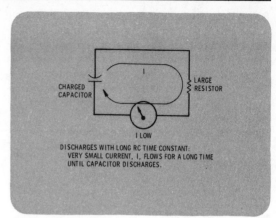

Figure 13.38

Rapid Discharge: High Current — Consider the following situation. If a charged capacitor is discharged by *shorting* its leads with a conductor, as shown in Figure 13.39, the resistance in the circuit that is formed approaches zero. The RC time constant then is also close to zero. As a result, a charged capacitor can be made to deliver an extremely large burst of current for a very short time. This makes the capacitor useful for providing power for special loads which require short, very high bursts of current to operate.

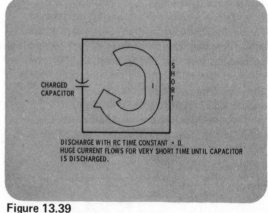

Figure 13.39

Example — One type of load that requires a high burst of current for a short time is a flash tube of the type used with many cameras. In cases such as this, a dc supply, usually having a low-current capability, may be used to gradually charge a large capacitor. This capacitor may then be discharged through the loads that require a short burst of very high current. In Figure 13.40, a high-voltage supply with a low-current capability is first used to charge a capacitor when the switch is thrown to the left. Then after the capacitor is fully charged, the switch is thrown to the right to provide a large burst of current to fire the flash tube. This, by the way, is a good time to remind you that in circuits containing capacitors, even though the power is off, there may still be a "jolt" awaiting the careless technician. Be careful.

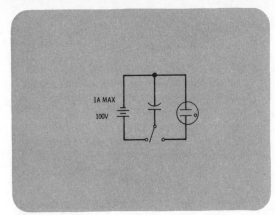

Figure 13.40

Capacitors Oppose Changes in Voltage — Now that you have seen capacitors in action, consider for a moment another of their effects that find use in a variety of applications. In all the circuits studied in the earlier lessons of this course, when power was applied to the circuit, the voltage at all parts of the circuit instantly reached its final value. No "time delays" were ever considered. In RC circuits of the type that have been discussed for you, the voltage across the capacitor rises more slowly, depending on the circuit's *time constant*. So it may be said that capacitance tends to *fight or oppose* changes of *voltage* in a circuit. As you have seen, if a rising voltage (such as a power supply which is abruptly switched on) is applied to a capacitor, the

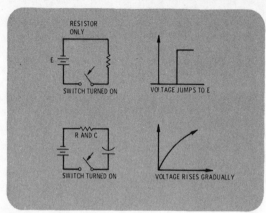

RESISTOR ONLY

SWITCH TURNED ON

VOLTAGE JUMPS TO E

R AND C

SWITCH TURNED ON

VOLTAGE RISES GRADUALLY

Figure 13.41

capacitor will act to *slow up* or oppose the rise of voltage, making it more gradual. Alternately, if the voltage is turned off in a circuit containing a capacitor, the capacitor will give up some of its charge and keep the voltage up longer. For this reason the capacitor finds application as a *filter* in certain circuits. In these types of circuits (Figure 13.41), a capacitor may be used to "smooth out" any abrupt voltage changes that may occur. Another common use for a capacitor is in a variety of *timing* applications. Both of these applications, as well as many others, will be covered for you in depth in later courses.

Capacitor Types — Now that you have seen some aspects of how capacitors work, consider some of the actual components you may find available in the laboratory. Figure 13.42 is a chart listing various types of capacitors that are available. Capacitors are usually *named* by the dielectric material used in them.

Because of the many applications of capacitors and the different properties of the dielectric, each capacitor you encounter will probably be labeled with a WVDC or "Working Voltage dc." This is the maximum voltage the capacitor can tolerate without its dielectric breaking down. As you apply capacitors in circuits, the voltage across them must be kept below this WVDC.

Capacitor Type	Range of Capacitance	Range of WVDC (in volts)	Range of Temperature (°C)	R_i = Insulation Resistance I_L = Leakage Current (at 25°C)	Comments
Ceramic	1 pF – 2.5 μF	20 – 200	–55 +125	R_i = 100 GΩ/μF	Small size Low cost
Paper	0.001 – 200 μF	50 – 200,000	–55 +105	R_i = 3 – 20 GΩ/μF	Low cost
Electrolytic	0.5 – 1,000,000 μF	2.5 – 700	–80 +125	I_L = 0.1 μA or more	Very small size Very low cost
Mylar	0.001 – 20 μF	50 – 1000	–55 +150	R_i = 50 GΩ/μF	Small size Relatively high cost
Air	10 – 400 pF	200/0.01 in air gap	–	–	Variable
Mica	1 pF – 1 μF	50 – 100,000	–55 +150	R_i = 10 – 100 GΩ/μF	Cap. change with age very small
Oil Filled	0.001 – 15 μF	100 – 12,500	–55 +85	R_i = 2 – 100 GΩ/μF	Low cost

Figure 13.42

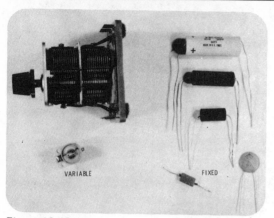

Figure 13.43

Fixed and Variable Capacitors — Capacitors are available in both fixed and variable types as shown in Figure 13.43. Several different common types including paper, mica, and ceramic capacitors are shown in the figure. As mentioned, these are named for the *dielectric material* employed in manufacturing them, and are produced in a set of preferred values, with tolerances similar to those of resistors. In these devices the capacitance is usually labeled on the device or follows a color code (listed for you in the Appendix).

Figure 13.44

Capacitor Construction — To keep the size of these devices as small as possible, a series of foil plates is usually employed with thin sheets of dielectric rolled up in between them as shown in Figure 13.44. Also shown in the figure is a typical *variable* capacitor. Variable capacitors are most often constructed so that their effective plate area can be varied by rotating a shaft connected to one set of plates. These plates can be moved between a stationary set of plates changing the capacitance value of the device.

Electrolytic Capacitor vs Oil-Filled Capacitor — Often in electronics, large amounts of capacitance may be needed in a small space. Most standard fixed capacitors are limited to values of about 1 microfarad or less due to cost and size considerations. There are capacitors available, however, that use a special chemical action to cram a large amount of capacitance into a small space. These are called *electrolytic* capacitors. An electrolytic capacitor having a capacitance of 42,000 microfarads may be about the same size as a 10 microfarad standard oil-filled capacitor (Figure 13.45). A price is paid, however, because the maximum working voltage of electrolytic capacitors is usually much lower than oil-filled or

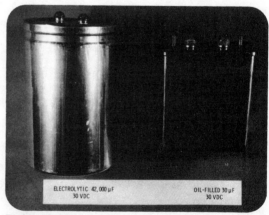

Figure 13.45

other standard types. As mentioned, the maximum working voltage or WVDC of a capacitor is governed by its plate spacing and dielectric. If voltages on the capacitor's plates are higher than the WVDC, the dielectric will usually break down, allowing charge from one plate to pass through the dielectric to the other plate. When this happens, the capacitor is no longer properly functioning. With severe breakdown, the plates may actually short together, rendering the capacitor useless. A good rule of thumb is to choose capacitors that have a working voltage well above the highest voltage with which they will come in contact.

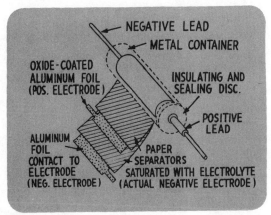

Figure 13.46

Electrolytic Construction — Most newer dry-type electrolytic capacitors commonly available are manufactured from two aluminum sheets separated by a saturated paper layer (Figure 13.46). The paper is saturated with a special chemical called an *electrolyte*, and rolled together with the aluminum sheets and packaged in a compact roll. When the capacitor is manufactured, a dc voltage is applied to it causing a thin *oxide layer* to be formed on one sheet. This oxide is *very thin* and acts as the insulating dielectric between the two plates. One of the capacitor's plates is now the aluminum sheet with the oxide deposited on it (positive plate), and the other plate is actually the electrolyte, which is connected to external circuits by the second aluminum sheet. Since the oxide layer is extremely *thin*, very large capacitances are available in electrolytic form. Since the oxide is fairly fragile, only lower voltages can normally be used with electrolytics. But most important, because of the way electrolytic capacitors are constructed, they can never be used in ac applications. They are restricted to only dc or pulsating dc applications, and must *always* be wired into dc circuits in the correct polarity, positive terminal to more positive voltages, negative to more negative voltages. If wired in the opposite direction, the electrolytic behaves as a low-value resistor, and the capacitor may actually explode due to heat generated by large amounts of current flow through it.

Leakage Resistance — It should be pointed out that even in the best capacitors, some "leakage" of charge will occur over periods of time. For good capacitors, however, significant charge can be stored almost indefinitely. Leakage occurs for a variety of reasons in capacitors and tends to be higher in electrolytic types. Some charge actually makes it through the dielectric, as if there were a very high-value resistor connected between the plates as shown in Figure 13.47. Often a minimum value of leakage resistance R_L is specified for capacitors in applications where leakage may be critical.

When discharging capacitors, it is generally *not* recommended that the leads simply be shorted together with a conductor. Although many capacitors can take this abuse, the very large internal currents created can damage them. So it is always a good idea to discharge capacitors gradually through an appropriate resistor. This keeps internal currents low and prevents damage to what are often expensive and difficult to replace parts.

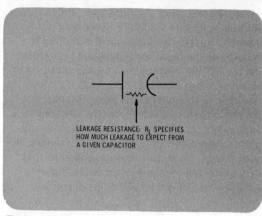

LEAKAGE RESISTANCE: R_L SPECIFIES HOW MUCH LEAKAGE TO EXPECT FROM A GIVEN CAPACITOR

Figure 13.47

Capacitor Applications — The charge storage capability of capacitors is utilized in a variety of devices and applications. These are listed in Figure 13.48. Briefly consider several of these applications: discharging capacitors can produce currents large enough to weld metals together, which is a common capacitor application in spot-welding devices. Flash tubes, as has been mentioned, also require very large, very short bursts of current to operate. A capacitor is used to provide this burst of current. Also, in capacitive discharge ignition systems, the same principle is used to get a "hotter spark" in an automobile engine. More recently, in medical emergency rooms a device known as a *defibrillator* discharges a

TYPICAL CAPACITOR APPLICATIONS

SPOT WELDER

FLASH TUBE

CAPACITOR DISCHARGE IGNITION SYSTEM

MEDICAL DEFIBRILLATOR

ELECTRONICS — TIMING, COUPLING, RESONANT CIRCUITS, ETC.

Figure 13.48

capacitor through two paddles so that a controlled amount of energy is delivered to a patient's heart, restoring normal rhythm to a heart that has stopped beating. You will find capacitors applied in a variety of ways as you continue your study of electricity.

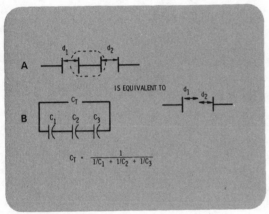

Figure 13.49

Capacitors in Series — Before leaving the topic of capacitors, one more topic should be mentioned. Often to obtain a desired value of capacitance, capacitors are combined in series and parallel connections. Consider what happens when two capacitors are connected in series as shown in Figure 13.49(A). The two inner plates of these capacitors are wired directly together so effectively that they act as one plate. The result is that two capacitors in series act as a single capacitor whose plates are separated by *both* plate separations. As you have learned, the *larger* the spacing between the plates, the *lower* the capacitance. For this reason, the total capacitance of any series combination of capacitors is less than that of any individual capacitor in the circuit. As it turns out, the total capacitance of capacitors in series is calculated in the same way as the total resistance of parallel resistors. The formula is

$$C_T = \frac{1}{1/C_1 + 1/C_2 + 1/C_3}$$

etc., as shown in Figure 13.49(B).

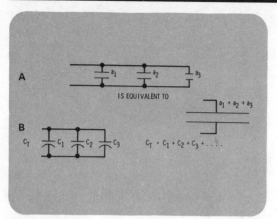

Figure 13.50

Capacitors in Parallel — When several capacitors are connected in parallel, an interesting thing happens. As shown in Figure 13.50(A), since all the *plates* are wired together in tandem, a parallel connection of capacitors acts like a single capacitor having a total plate area equal to the sum of the plate areas of the individual capacitors. Since capacitance varies directly with plate area, the total capacitance of several capacitors connected in parallel is found by adding all the individual capacitances, as with series resistors, as shown in Figure 13.50(B).

A new and useful component has been examined in this lesson and some of the wide variety of its applications have been shown. In the next lesson, the behavior of dc in circuits containing other new components, called *inductors*, will be introduced. You will find many similarities, some big differences, and some interesting and important new effects.

LESSON 13. CAPACITORS AND THE RC TIME CONSTANT

- **Worked Through Examples**

1. Find the time constant of a circuit containing a 10-kilohm resistor in series with a 0.82-microfarad capacitor.

    To solve this problem, you must use the time constant formula T = RC. Substituting in the circuit values, the formula reads T = 10 kΩ X 0.82 μF. In scientific notation the values are: T = 1.0 X 10^4 X 8.2 X 10^{-7}.

$$1.0 \text{ X } 10^4$$
$$\underline{\text{X } 8.2 \text{ X } 10^{-7}}$$
$$T = 8.2 \text{ X } 10^{-3} \text{ seconds (s) or 8.2 milliseconds (ms)}$$

2. Find the time constant of this circuit:

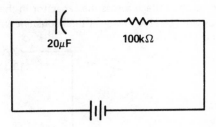

20μF   100kΩ

    Use the formula: T = RC. First substitute in the circuit values: R = 100 kΩ, C = 20 μF

$$T = 100 \text{ k}\Omega \text{ X } 20 \text{ }\mu\text{F}$$
$$T = 1.0 \text{ X } 10^5 \text{ X } 2.0 \text{ X } 10^{-5}$$
$$T = 2.0 \text{ seconds}$$

3. How long will it take the capacitor in the following circuit to reach full charge?

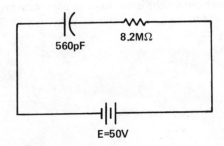

560pF   8.2MΩ

E=50V

    First, use the time constant formula T = RC.

$$T = RC$$
$$T = 8.2 \text{ M}\Omega \text{ X } 560 \text{ pF}$$
$$T = 8.2 \text{ X } 10^6 \text{ X } 5.6 \text{ X } 10^{10}$$
$$T = 4.59 \text{ X } 10^{-3} \text{ s or 4.59 ms}$$

You must remember that the RC time constant formula you just worked gives you *one* time constant (in seconds). *Five* time constants are required for full charge. So, multiply the time constant by 5 to arrive at the correct answer.

$$\begin{array}{r} 4.59 \times 10^{-3} \\ \underline{\times \quad 5 \quad\quad} \\ 22.95 \times 10^{-3} \text{ or } 2.3 \times 10^{-2} \text{ seconds} \end{array}$$

The capacitor will be fully charged after 2.3×10^{-2} seconds or 23 milliseconds.

4. Find the voltage across the capacitor in the circuit shown below 500 milliseconds after the switch is closed. (Use the universal time constant graph.)

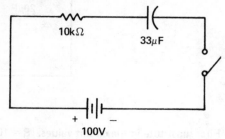

First, you should calculate the time constant of the circuit. T = RC.

$$T = RC$$
$$T = 10 \text{ k}\Omega \times 33 \text{ }\mu F$$
$$T = 1.0 \times 10^4 \times 3.3 \times 10^{-5}$$
$$T = 3.3 \times 10^{-1} \text{ or } 330 \text{ ms}$$

Now look at the universal time constant graph. Time (horizontal axis) is measured in time constants. To convert this chart to seconds, multiply 330 milliseconds by each of the time divisions. For example:

1 X 330 ms = 330 ms

1.5 X 330 ms = 495 ms

2 X 330 ms = 660 ms

3 X 330 ms = 990 ms

4 X 330 ms = 1.32 s

5 X 330 ms = 1.65 s

Now these values are applied to the universal time constant graph.

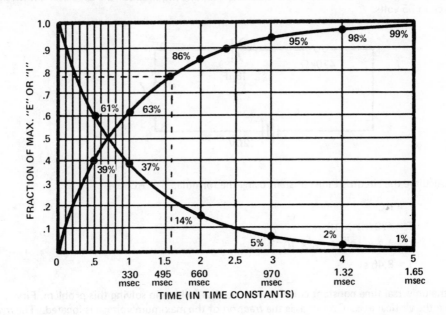

FRACTION OF MAX. "E" OR "I"

| | | | | | | | | | |
95%   98%   99%
86%
61%   63%
39%   37%
14%
5%   2%   1%

0   .5   1   1.5   2   2.5   3   4   5
         330   495   660   970   1.32   1.65
         msec msec msec   msec   msec   msec
              TIME (IN TIME CONSTANTS)

Look at the chart and locate the 500 millisecond position on the horizontal axis. Now trace directly upward (following the dotted line) and note the point on the charging curve that is reached at 500 ms. Tracing to the left from that point, across the graph, you can see that the amplitude at the intersection point is about 0.78 or 78% of the full charge voltage; 0.78 X 100 V = 78 V. So after 500 ms, the capacitor is charged to 78 volts.

5.   Find the charge in coulombs of the capacitor in problem 4, at the end of 500 milliseconds.

The formula for calculating the charge stored in a capacitor is

$$Q = CE$$

where

Q = the stored charge in coulombs
C = the capacitance in farads
E = the voltage between the capacitor plates

Substituting the values of capacitance and voltage:

$$Q = 33 \, \mu F \times 78 \, V$$

$$Q = 3.3 \times 10^{-5} \times 7.8 \times 10^{1}$$

$$Q = 2.57 \times 10^{-3} \text{ coulombs (or 2.57 millicoulombs)}$$

6. Using the universal time constant graph, calculate the time required for the capacitor shown below to charge to 55 volts.

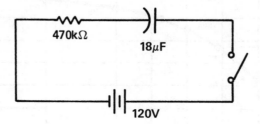

First, calculate the circuit's time constant using the formula: T = RC

> T = RC
>
> T = 470 kΩ X 18 μF
>
> T = 4.7 X 10^5 X 1.8 X 10^{-5}
>
> T = 8.46 s

Now, the universal time constant curve may be used as follows in solving this problem. First, examine the vertical axis. On this axis the *fraction* of the maximum voltage is located. The *maximum* voltage here is 120 volts: the total applied voltage. What *fraction* of 120 volts is 55 volts? Thus, 55/120 equals 0.458. This is the *fraction* of the applied voltage 55 volts represents. Now, locate 0.458 on the vertical axis of the universal time constant graph. Trace to the right horizontally (a dotted line is drawn in for you to follow) until you intersect the charging curve.

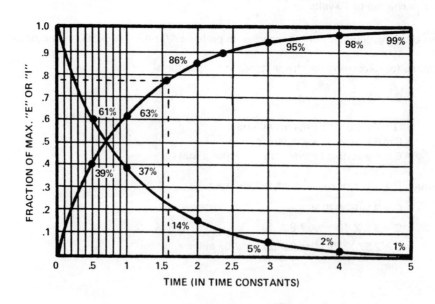

Locate that point on the curve, and then trace directly *down* to the horizontal axis. At this point you read the time elapsed: 0.6 *time constants*. You know that 1 time constant is 8.46 seconds, so the total elapsed time is 0.6 X 8.46 or 5.08 seconds.

7. A "strobe" flash attachment for a camera has a bulb that requires 0.02 coulomb of charge at 450 volts in order to flash properly. What is the minimum size capacitor that could be satisfactorily used?

    Since both the quantity of charge (Q) and voltage (E) are known, the equation C = Q/E can be used to solve this problem. Simply substitute in the capacitor values and solve for C.

    $$C = Q/E$$
    $$C = \frac{0.02\ C\ (coulomb)}{450\ V}$$
    $$C = 0.0000444\ F\ or\ 44.4\ \mu F$$

8. Find the approximate frequency of oscillation in the circuit shown here.

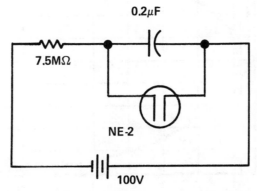

The circuit shown above is a "relaxation oscillator." It operates on the basis of its RC time constant. The bulb shown connected across the capacitor is an NE-2 neon glow lamp. These lamps require a certain voltage (called the "firing voltage") in order to light. Once lit, the voltage across the lamp must fall significantly below the firing voltage before it will turn "off." Typical "on" and "off" voltages for neon glow lamps are: 75 volts "on" and 50 volts "off." This means that the typical NE-2 will not "light" until the voltage across it reaches 75 volts, but once lit, will continue to glow until the voltage drops below 50 volts. Before the lamp lights, it has a very high resistance (essentially an open circuit). Once the lamp is on, its resistance drops to a low value.

Consider what will happen when one of these lamps is connected across a capacitor as shown in the circuit above. When power is applied to the circuit, the capacitor will begin to charge up to the source voltage. The rate of charging will be controlled by the RC time constant. When the capacitor reaches 75 volts, the neon bulb (which is connected in parallel with the capacitor) will also have 75 volts applied across it. At this instant, the bulb will light, allowing heavy current flow, and thus discharging the capacitor very quickly. As the capacitor discharges, its voltage will drop down below the 50 volts required to keep the neon bulb lit. The bulb goes out and the capacitor again charges up to the 75 volts required to fire the bulb, and the cycle is repeated again and again. As you can see, there are several factors that affect the rate of blinking (or oscillation) of the bulb: the resistor size, the size of the capacitor, the supply voltage, and the characteristics of the individual neon bulb.

To analyze this problem, first calculate the RC time constant of the circuit and plot it on a universal time constant graph.

$$T = RC$$
$$T = 7.5 \text{ M}\Omega \times 0.2 \text{ }\mu\text{F}$$
$$T = 7.5 \times 10^6 \times 2.0 \times 10^{-7}$$
$$T = 1.5 \text{ s}$$

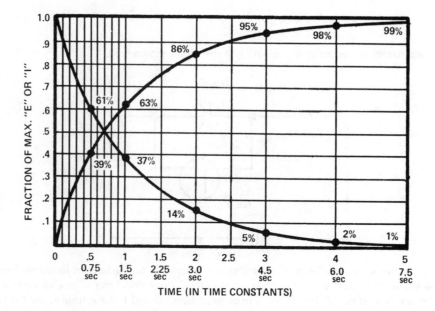

$$1 \times 1.5 \text{ s} = 1.5 \text{ s}$$
$$1.5 \times 1.5 \text{ s} = 2.25 \text{ s}$$
$$2 \times 1.5 \text{ s} = 3.0 \text{ s}$$
$$3 \times 1.5 \text{ s} = 4.5 \text{ s}$$
$$4 \times 1.5 \text{ s} = 6.0 \text{ s}$$
$$5 \times 1.5 \text{ s} = 7.5 \text{ s}$$

To give a clearer picture of the operation of this circuit, these values are plotted on the horizontal axis of the universal time constant graph above.

The lamp fires at 75 volts, and causes the voltage across the capacitor to rapidly drop to 50 volts so that the lamp then goes out. Voltage across the capacitor, plotted as time goes on, will appear as shown below.

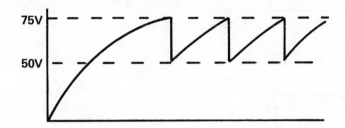

In order to find the time duration between flashes, simply look back at the Universal Time Constant graph you just filled in. Locate 75 volts and 50 volts, and measure the time elapsed between these two points. Seventy-five volts occurs at approximately 1.4 time constants or 2.1 seconds. Fifty volts occurs at 0.7 time constants or 1.05 seconds. The time elapsed is the *difference* between the two times. Subtract and you get 2.1 s − 1.05 s = 1.05 s. So the lamp will blink once every 1.05 seconds. Dividing 60 by 1.05 yields a frequency of 57 flashes per minute.

9. Calculate the total capacitance of this circuit.

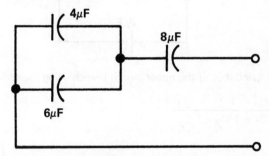

Problems of the type shown above give many students headaches because capacitors "add" just the opposite of the way resistors do. Parallel capacitors are added by using a formula similar to the series resistance formula: $C_T = C_1 + C_2 + C_3 \ldots$ Series capacitors must be added by using a formula similar to the parallel resistance formula:

$$C_T = \frac{1}{1/C_1 + 1/C_2 + 1/C_3 \ldots}$$

To solve this problem, the 4-microfarad and the 6-microfarad capacitors should be combined by using the parallel capacitance formula $C_T = C_1 + C_2 + C_3 \ldots$

$C_T = 4\,\mu F + 6\,\mu F$

$C_T = 10\,\mu F$

This 10 microfarads of capacitance must be combined with the 8 microfarads of capacitance by using the series capacitance formula.

$$C_T = \frac{1}{1/C_1 + 1/C_2 + 1/C_3}$$

$$C_T = \frac{1}{1/10 + 1/8}$$

$$C_T = \frac{1}{0.1 + 0.125}$$

$$C_T = \frac{1}{0.225}$$

$$C_T = 4.44 \ \mu F$$

10. Calculate the total capacitance of the following circuit.

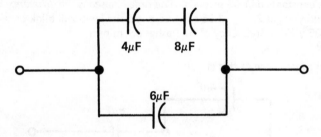

First, find the total capacitance of the upper circuit branch using the series capacitance formula:

$$C_T = \frac{1}{1/C_1 + 1/C_2 + 1/C_3}$$

$$C_T = \frac{1}{1/4 + 1/8}$$

$$C_T = \frac{1}{0.25 + 0.125}$$

$$C_T = \frac{1}{0.375}$$

$$C_T = 2.67 \ \mu F$$

Now the total capacitance may be found by combining the two parallel capacitances using the parallel capacitance formula $C_T = C_1 + C_2 + C_3 \ldots$

$$C_T = 2.67 \ \mu F + 6 \ \mu F$$

$$C_T = 8.67 \ \mu F$$

LESSON 13. CAPACITORS AND THE RC TIME CONSTANT

● **Practice Problems**

Depending upon the approach you use in solving these problems and how you round off intermediate results, your answers may vary slightly from those given here. However, any differences you may encounter should only occur in the third significant digit of your answer. If the first two significant digits of your answers do not agree with those given here, recheck your calculations.

1. Calculate the RC time constant for the following circuits. Fold over **Fold Over**
the page to check your answers.

a.

1.5MΩ

4.7µF

T = _____

b.

750kΩ

.22µF

T = _____

c.

43pF   110MΩ

T = _____

d.

56 MΩ

10µF

T = _____

e.

100kΩ

56pF

T = _____

2. Calculate the total capacitance in the following circuits. (All capacitors are 2 µF).

a.

$C_T =$_____

b.

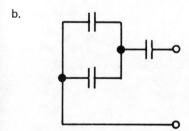

$C_T =$_____

•   **Practice Problems**

Answers

1.
a.   T = 7.05 s

b.   T = 165 ms

c.   T = 4.73 ms

d.   560 s

e.   T = 5.6 μs

2.
a. C_T = 1 μF

b. C_T = 1.33 μF

Fold Over

c.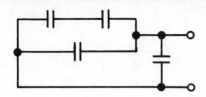

$C_T =$ _____

d.

$C_T =$ _____

e.

$C_T =$ _____

3.   Find the following unknown values using the formula $Q = CE$.

a.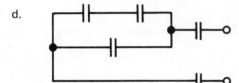

$C = 6\mu F$

150V

$Q =$ _____

b.

$600\mu F$

6V

$Q =$ _____

c.

$Q = 19.5$ ncoul.

50V

$C =$ _____

Answers

c. $C_T = 5\,\mu F$

d. $C_T = 0.75\,\mu F$

e. $C_T = 10\,\mu F$

3.
a. $Q = 900\,\mu C$

b. $Q = 3.6\,mC$

c. $C = 390\,pF$

d.

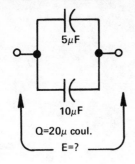

Fold Over

E = _____

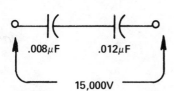

e.

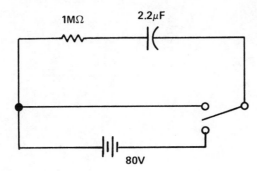

Q = _____

4. For the circuit shown below, calculate, or use the universal time constant graph to find:

a. RC time constant. _____

b. Time required for capacitor to charge fully. _____

c. Voltage across the capacitor after 1.5 seconds. _____

d. Voltage across the capacitor after 6.5 seconds. _____

e. Time required for the capacitor to charge to 30 volts. _____

Answers

d.   E = 1.33 V

e.   Q = 72 μC

4.
a.   T = 2.2 s

b.   11 s

c.   39.5 V

d.   75.8 V

e.   1.03 s

1. A device which, in its basic form, consists of two conductors separated from each other by an insulator is called a:

   a. Battery
   b. Generator
   c. Motor
   d. Capacitor

2. Capacitors are devices that can:

   a. Store electric charge
   b. Be charged and discharged repeatedly
   c. Hold a charge for a long time
   d. All of the above
   e. None of the above

3. When a potential difference exists between the plates of a capacitor, the capacitor is said to be:

   a. Discharged
   b. Open
   c. Charged
   d. Disconnected

4. The equation of Capacitance C in farads is _____ where Q is charge in coulombs and E is potential difference in volts.

   a. $C = QE$
   b. $C = \dfrac{Q}{E}$
   c. $C = \dfrac{E}{Q}$
   d. $C = Q^2E$

5. Capacitance is the ratio of the charge stored _____ the voltage across the capacitor.

   a. Multiplied by
   b. Divided by
   c. Added to
   d. Subtracted from

6. When a capacitor can store 1 coulomb of charge with 1 volt potential difference across it, it is said to have _____ of capacitance.

   a. 10 farads
   b. 1 farad
   c. 0.1 farad
   d. A small value

7. The charge stored in a capacitor with C farads of capacitance and E volts applied is:

   a. $Q = CE$
   b. $Q = CE^2$
   c. $Q = \dfrac{C}{E}$
   d. None of above

8. When a capacitor is placed across a battery without resistance in the circuit, the capacitor charges:

   a. Very slowly
   b. To twice the voltage
   c. Instantaneously
   d. To one-half the voltage

9. When a capacitor is placed across a battery with resistance in the circuit, the capacitor charges:

   a. Instantaneously
   b. Much slower than without resistance
   c. To twice the voltage
   d. To one-half the voltage

10. The capacitive time constant is defined by the following equation:

    a. $T = R^2C$
    b. $T = CR$
    c. $T = \dfrac{R}{C}$
    d. $T = RC$
    e. b and d above

11. When a capacitor and resistor are placed across a voltage, the time required to charge the capacitor to 63% of the applied voltage is called:

    a. The rise time
    b. The discharge curve
    c. The capacitive time constant
    d. The peak value

12. When evaluating a capacitive time constant, the R in the equation is in ohms and the C is in farads. As a result T is in:

    a. Seconds
    b. Minutes
    c. Hours
    d. Relative time

13. The capacitor is considered charged for all practical purposes after _____ time constants.

    a. 2
    b. 3
    c. 1
    d. 5

14. The discharge time constant of a capacitor is the same as the charge time constant if:

    a. The voltage is reversed
    b. The circuit is open
    c. The resistor and capacitor are the same
    d. Other paths are removed

15. What is the discharge time of a 10 microfarad capacitor charged to 10 volts shunted by a 10 K resistor?

    a. 1 sec
    b. 0.1 sec
    c. 10 sec
    d. 100 sec

Calculate the following quantities:

16.

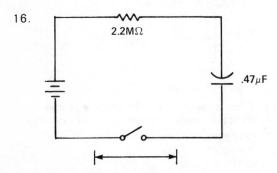

2.2MΩ

.47μF

Time Constant _____ seconds

17.

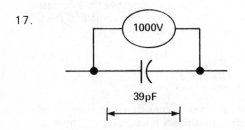

1000V

39pF

Stored charge _____ coulombs

18.

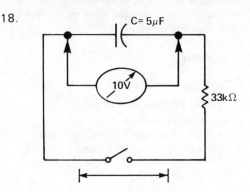

C= 5μF

10V

33kΩ

Time to discharge _____ seconds

19.

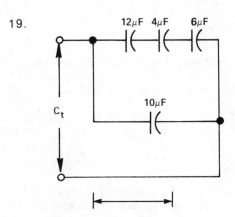

12μF 4μF 6μF

C_t

10μF

C_T, Total capacitance _____ μF

20.

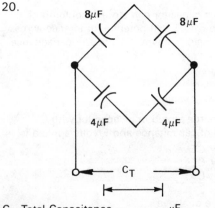

8μF

8μF

4μF

4μF

C_T

C_T, Total Capacitance _____ μF

13-48

Lesson 14

Inductors and the L/R Time Constant

In this lesson an entirely new type of circuit component — the *coil* or *inductor* — will be introduced and discussed. You will see that the behavior of coils in dc circuits may be described in a similar fashion to the action of *capacitors* discussed in the previous lesson. Coils, however, act to oppose *changes in current*, rather than voltage, and store energy in a *magnetic field*, rather than an electrostatic field. The concept of the L/R time constant used in describing circuits containing resistance (R) and inductance (L) will also be introduced.

• **Objectives**

This lesson gives you a brief introduction to a new type of circuit component that you will see called by many names, such as:

Coil

Inductor

Choke

Solenoid

The behavior of coils in dc circuits can be described using many of the terms that were introduced to you in the last lesson. At the end of this lesson, you should be able to

1. *Sketch* the construction of a typical inductor, labeling its basic component parts. *Sketch* the schematic symbols for:

    a. Air or insulating core inductor

    b. Iron core inductor

    c. Powdered iron core inductor

2. *Write* a brief description of the magnetic field created by a coil and the key effect this magnetic field has on a coil's behavior in circuits. *Sketch* the magnetic field lines around a simple current carrying coil. *State* the units used to measure the inductance.

3. Given a schematic for any circuit of the type shown below:

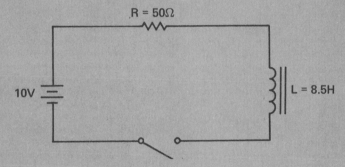

$R = 50\Omega$

10V

$L = 8.5H$

a. *Calculate* the circuit's time constant

b. *Calculate* the value of the steady-state current

c. *Calculate* the value of the current flowing in the circuit after one time constant

d. *Calculate* the time it takes for the current in this circuit to reach its steady-state value

e. *Sketch* a graph that shows how the current rises in this circuit from the time the switch is closed through five time constants

f. *Write* a description of the effect that would occur if the switch is opened after the current in this circuit has been allowed to reach its steady-state value.

- **Coil Construction**
- **Iron Core Coil**

Lesson 13 covered one of the most important circuits in electronics — the resistor-capacitor (or RC) circuit. In that lesson you were shown how to predict the behavior of a circuit containing a resistor and capacitor connected in series. The characteristic behavior of these circuits, especially the characteristic time required to charge and discharge the capacitor in RC circuits was discussed. The RC time constant was discussed and it was shown how RC circuits may be used to perform many useful tasks in electronics. It was also shown how capacitors store charge and energy, and how they can be used to provide large bursts of current for short periods of time for special loads requiring such power.

Now in this lesson, *another* basic electronic component the "coil," or as it is often called, the "inductor," or "choke," will be examined. You will be seeing that the behavior of a coil, or inductor, in a circuit is, in many ways, similar to, and in some ways opposite from, the behavior of a capacitor. Puzzling? By the end of this lesson, you should have a fairly good understanding of coils and how they operate in circuits.

Coil Construction — To begin, a *coil* simply consists of wire that is wrapped or coiled around a "core." The wire may be any size, or length, and typical core material may be anything from iron to air. The most common schematic symbol for a coil looks just like several turns of wire adjacent to one another. Figure 14.1 shows the symbol used to signify an air core or insulating core coil. Typically, cores of this type are used in high-frequency ac applications.

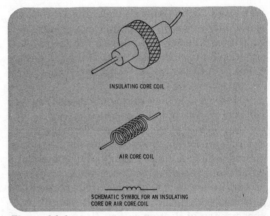

Figure 14.1

Iron Core Coil — If the coil symbol also contains two parallel lines as shown in Figure 14.2, an iron core coil is indicated. These inductors are typically used in lower frequency ac applications and dc applications. A typical iron core coil is also shown in Figure 14.2. In this type of coil, the core material may actually surround the wire and forms the most substantial component of the coil.

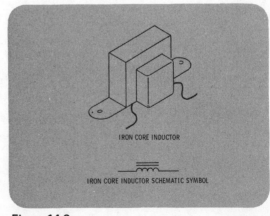

Figure 14.2

- Powdered Iron Core Coil
- Wire Inside Coils

Powdered Iron Core Coil — Figure 14.3 shows a schematic symbol indicating a coil that has an iron core indicated by dashed lines. These dashed lines indicate a coil that has a *powdered iron* core. A powdered iron core coil is used in applications where radio-frequency waves are being processed. A common use for this type of coil is for the antenna in a standard AM radio.

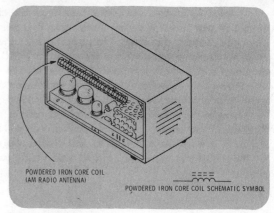

POWDERED IRON CORE COIL
(AM RADIO ANTENNA)

POWDERED IRON CORE COIL SCHEMATIC SYMBOL

Figure 14.3

Wire Inside Coils — What do coils do in dc circuits? How do they work? To get into the processes by which coils function, it is necessary to focus your attention on the individual parts of the coil one at a time (Figure 14.4). First, consider the wire making up the coil itself.

Very early in your study of dc electricity, you saw how a single strand of conducting wire contains *billions* of free electrons. Normally these electrons are moving around in the wire in random motion. You have already seen that if a potential difference is applied across the wire, electrons begin drifting from the negative to the positive potential, as discussed earlier. This is the phenomenon of electron current flow.

The action of coils depends upon a phenomenon that will be introduced at this point: the electromagnetic field.

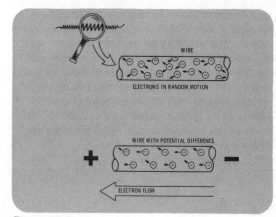

WIRE

ELECTRONS IN RANDOM MOTION

WIRE WITH POTENTIAL DIFFERENCE

ELECTRON FLOW

Figure 14.4

- **Electromagnetic Field**
- **Electrostatic Field and Lines of Force**
- **Wire with Electromagnetic Field**

Electromagnetic Field — Here's a new and important fact about electrons in motion: "Whenever current flows in a conductor, a *magnetic field* is set up around the conductor" (Figure 14.5). A magnetic field is a type of field that has some properties similar to that of the electrostatic field examined earlier.

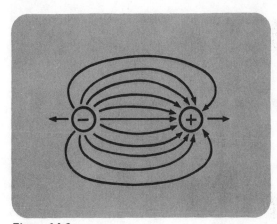

"WHENEVER CURRENT FLOWS THROUGH A CONDUCTOR, A **MAGNETIC FIELD** IS SET UP AROUND THE CONDUCTOR."

Figure 14.5

Electrostatic Field and Lines of Force — Recall that in an earlier lesson it was shown that an *electrostatic field* exists in the area around any charged body, and that this field may be visualized with electrostatic lines of force, as shown in Figure 14.6. Considerable time has been spent discussing the *effects* of the electrostatic field on electrons.

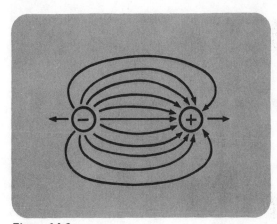

Figure 14.6

Wire with Electromagnetic Field — An *electromagnetic field* is a field which surrounds any current-carrying conductor, and can also be visualized by using what are called "magnetic lines of force." The magnetic lines of force go right around the current, and thus around the wire in little rings as shown in Figure 14.7. The center of these rings is the current itself.

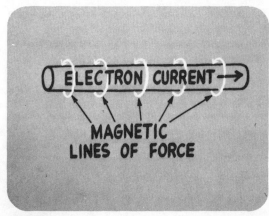

ELECTRON CURRENT

MAGNETIC
LINES OF FORCE

Figure 14.7

- Magnetic Lines of Force
- Direction of Lines of Force
- **Simple Coil**

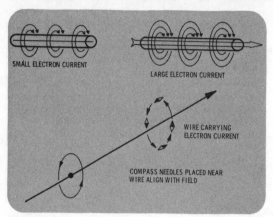

Figure 14.8

Magnetic Lines of Force — An electromagnetic field is created around any wire carrying current. The larger the current in the wire, the stronger the field will be. In a diagram such as shown in Figure 14.8, this is represented by drawing more and denser lines of force. The magnetic field around a current-carrying wire may be detected with a small compass needle placed near the wire. The compass needle, being magnetized, will line up with the magnetic lines of force near the wire. The magnetic lines of force are assigned a direction (indicated by the small arrows on them). This direction is the direction that the north pole of the compass will point when placed into the field.

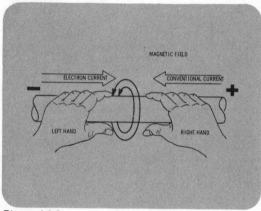

Figure 14.9

Direction of Lines of Force — To find the direction of the field lines, you can use one of the "hand rules." In Figure 14.9, a wire is shown with electron current flowing from left to right (this is equivalent and identical to conventional current flowing from right to left). To find the direction of the magnetic field, you mentally grasp the wire with your *left* hand, the thumb pointing in the direction of the *electron* current. Your fingers will curl around the wire, pointing in the direction of the magnetic field. (Do the same thing, only with your *right* hand, if you are considering *conventional* current; the magnetic field direction will be the same.)

Simple Coil — In most current-carrying wires, the surrounding magnetic field is small and goes unnoticed. However, if the wire were to be wrapped into a coil, the wire would be concentrated into a smaller area, thus concentrating the lines of force around it into a smaller area, as shown in Figure 14.10. This increases the strength of the magnetic field, especially inside the loop.

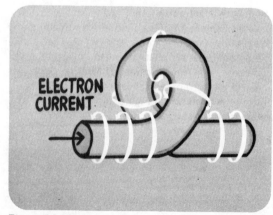

Figure 14.10

- **Multiple Loops**
- **Large Coil**
- **Bar Magnet**

Multiple Loops — If the wire is looped two or more times, an interesting and very useful effect occurs. The lines of force produced by the first loop of wire join together and reinforce the lines of force produced by the second loop, strengthening the magnetic field inside the coil as shown in Figure 14.11.

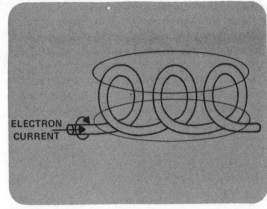

Figure 14.11

Large Coil — If many loops of current-carrying wire are wrapped into a coil, a strong electromagnetic field can be created inside the coil, as shown in the cutaway view in Figure 14.12.

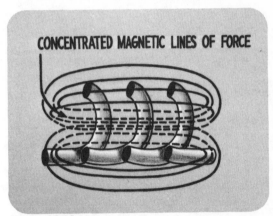

Figure 14.12

Bar Magnet — A coil, when carrying current, contains a *strong magnetic field*. Because of this, a coil carrying current will behave just like a regular bar magnet (Figure 14.13).

Most of you have probably seen magnets and are familiar with how they attract metal objects. A coil, when carrying current, does the same thing with the added advantage that it may be turned on and off. With the current turned on, a piece of steel may be drawn into the coil. If no current flows through the coil, no magnetic field exist and metal objects will be released.

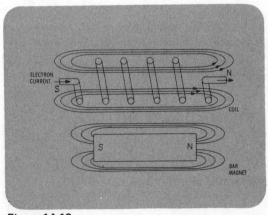

Figure 14.13

Relay — This feature makes coils useful in many applications. The device, shown in Figure 14.14, is called a "relay." In a relay, a current is used to create a magnetic field in a coil which causes the coil to draw in a metal bar connected to a switch. The current may be made to open or close the switch, as the application requires. So by using a relay, one current (called the "control current") may be used to switch an entirely different current.

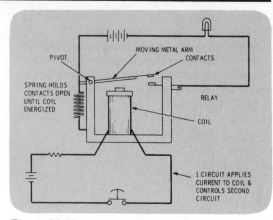

Figure 14.14

Automotive Starting System — Relays find many uses in a variety of applications in electricity and electronics. One typical situation in which they are used is where a very large *current* needs to be switched on and off from a remote location. One such situation is in the starter circuit of your automobile. The starter motor for most cars is an extremely large load: drawing currents of 100 amperes or more for short intervals. It would be impractical and undesirable to run a large length of heavy cable capable of handling 100 amps to your dashboard to a heavy-duty key switch. Instead, a special relay is actually used to switch the starter motor current. This relay is commonly called a *solenoid* (pronounced "soul-annoyed"), and may be mounted right in the casing with the starter motor or separately elsewhere in your car. The word solenoid is another one of those words that is often used to mean different things. It is used in different contexts to mean a coil, a relay, or an electromagnet, depending on what is being discussed. At any rate, the solenoid in your car works as described in Figure 14.15. When you turn your ignition key switch, it turns on only a small "control current" which activates the windings of the solenoid coil. The solenoid then completes the circuit, handling the very large current that cranks over your engine. (At the same time, another coil is at work, the spark coil, which will be discussed later in this lesson.)

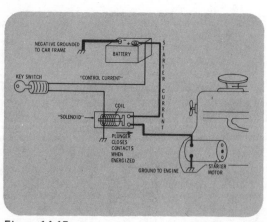

Figure 14.15

Effects of Coils in Circuits — Up to this point you have seen that when current flows through a coil, a magnetic field builds up in the coil. This magnetic field may be used for a variety of purposes, as mentioned, but its presence in the coil has some other interesting effects on the behavior of the circuit containing the coil.

Anytime you try to force current through a coil, a magnetic field must build up inside it. The key point is that it takes a certain amount of time to build up this field. Because of the mechanisms involved in this field buildup (Figure 14.16), the *rise of the current in circuits containing coils is slower. Coils act to oppose changes in current.*

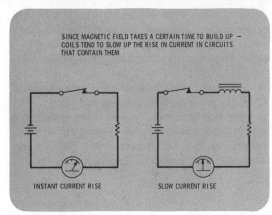

Figure 14.16

Current Increase — Exact details of the mechanism by which coils oppose or fight changes in current will be discussed at great length in later courses. One way to quickly visualize what is going on is as follows. Magnetic fields (like electric fields) store *energy* inside them. (Energy is actually the ability to do work. In capacitors you saw how the electric field of a charged capacitor stored energy and gave up this energy when the capacitor was discharged).

A magnetic field may actually be considered to be an energy storage device that is present in a circuit whenever a coil is connected. The workings of this system may be visualized as shown in Figure 14.17. When current tries to *increase* through the coil, the coil will take some energy from the circuit and dump it into the magnetic field. The current now finds itself building up the magnetic field as it tries to start flowing through the circuit. As a result of this magnetic field buildup, *it takes the current longer to build up in the circuit with the coil present than with no coil.* For this reason, it may be said that coils fight or oppose current increasing through them. Again, it takes longer for current to build up in a circuit containing a coil than it does in a circuit with no coil.

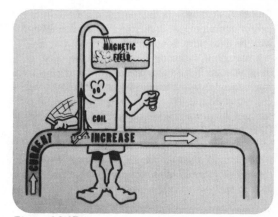

Figure 14.17

- **Steady Current Flow**
- **Current Decrease**
- **Coil Rule**

Steady Current Flow — After a period of time, the magnetic field increases to a maximum value, and the current in the circuit reaches a steady-state value. Here's another important point: *As long as the current is not changing, the magnetic field remains built up at a steady-state (Figure 14.18). When the magnetic field is in a steady-state, it has no effect on the current flowing in the circuit.* In a steady-state condition, the only thing that affects the amount of current flowing in the circuit is the total resistance present (and the applied voltage).

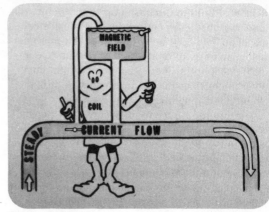

Figure 14.18

Current Decrease — If the switch is opened in a circuit containing an inductor, the circuit current will try to rapidly fall to zero. At this point, the energy stored in the coil's magnetic field gets dumped back into the circuit and tries to help keep the current flowing. It appears as if the coil saw the current trying to fall and flushed the energy into the circuit to try to keep current flowing, as visualized in Figure 14.19. So it is said that a coil *also* acts to fight or oppose any current *decrease* through it. *It takes longer for current to fall to zero in a circuit containing a coil than it does in a circuit with no coil.*

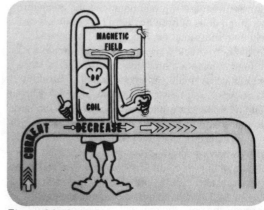

Figure 14.19

Coil Rule — Think about the actions of a coil for a moment. Through the actions of the magnetic field, a coil acts to oppose any current increase or decrease through it. *It may be said that coils act to oppose any change in current through them* (Figure 14.20).

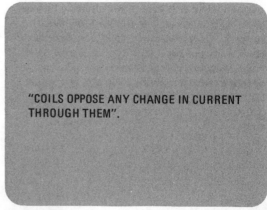

"COILS OPPOSE ANY CHANGE IN CURRENT THROUGH THEM".

Figure 14.20

Energy Storage — As you will recall from the last lesson, a *capacitor stores electrons*. The imbalance of electrons (many on one plate, very few on the other) produces an electrostatic field in the region between the plates. It was stated that *energy* was stored in a capacitor in this electrostatic field. This stored energy was demonstrated to you as it was released in a capacitor discharge. Now, it has been seen that in a coil, energy is stored in the *electromagnetic field* created by a current flowing through it (Figure 14.21). Because of these similar effects, the voltage and current characteristics of coils and capacitors have an interesting interrelationship.

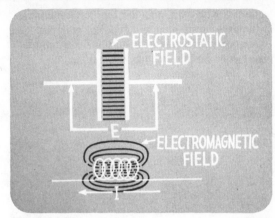

Figure 14.21

Capacitor Action (Charge) — *Capacitors* in circuits *oppose the change of voltage* across the circuit. When the switch in the circuit of Figure 14.22 is thrown to position A, a voltage is applied to the RC circuit. The capacitor takes a certain amount of time to charge up, with the voltage across it rising slowly. When the voltage across the capacitor equals the applied voltage, *no further current flow occurs in the circuit*, and the capacitor is said to be fully charged.

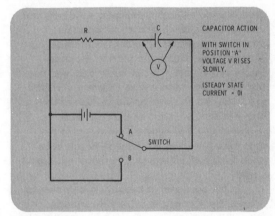

Figure 14.22

Capacitor Action (Discharge) — When the switch in this circuit is thrown to position B (Figure 14.23), the applied voltage is removed and the capacitor discharges, giving up its stored charge and energy. The voltage across the capacitor falls gradually to zero. Therefore, it may be said that a capacitor fights *changes* in *voltage* across it.

As has been discussed, a coil opposes *changes* in the *current flowing* through a circuit by means of storing and giving up the energy contained in its magnetic field. The process by which a coil fights changes in current is called electromagnetic induction. A coil sets up a voltage called an induced voltage, which actually acts to fight against changes in current. In later courses on

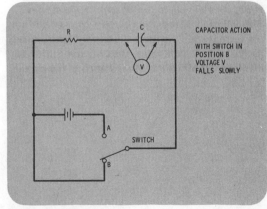

Figure 14.23

alternating current, induction and induced voltage will be discussed in more detail. For now, just remember that a coil tends to slow up or oppose changes in current through it.

Demonstration Circuit Schematic — To help you visualize how a coil operates in a dc circuit, consider what would happen in a simple dc demonstration circuit like the one shown in Figure 14.24. In this circuit schematic, you have a coil connected in series with a battery, a switch and a resistor. To simplify the analysis of the circuit at first, assume that the coil has no resistance and that all of the resistance in the circuit is supplied by the resistor, which has a labeled value of 500 ohms. The battery voltage is 6 volts.

As has been said, if the switch is thrown to position B_2, so that the battery is connected, the coil will fight or oppose the *change or buildup* in the circuit current. After the current is *finished changing* and the magnetic field is at its *maximum value, the coil will no longer oppose the current.* The coil itself opposes the current *change*, but not the current itself. So once the current has reached its final steady-state value, the only opposition to it will be the 500 ohms of resistance in the circuit.

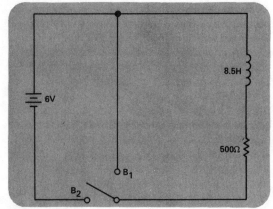

Figure 14.24

Ohm's Law (I) — Because the only factor controlling the circuit's steady-state current is the circuit resistance, Ohm's law can be used to find this current, as shown in Figure 14.25. After the magnetic field around the coil has reached its final value, you can use Ohm's law in the form $I = E/R$ to calculate the current. Substituting, $I = 6/500$, which equals 12 milliamps. Keep in mind what will happen when the voltage is applied to the circuit of Figure 14.24. *The current will slowly rise, finally reaching this steady state value of 12 milliamps.*

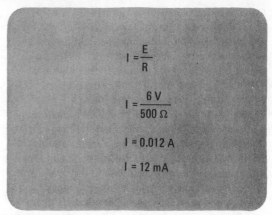

Figure 14.25

Current Rise in Inductive Circuits — Trace this process step by step. When the switch is first switched to position B_2, connecting the battery, the current jumps up from zero and starts to flow. The coil opposes this drastic change in current by taking some circuit energy and storing it in its magnetic field. Gradually, as the magnetic field gets completely built up and reaches a steady-state, the resistor provides the only opposition to current flow in the circuit.

At that point, the circuit current has reached a steady-state and the final current flowing is 12 milliamps as shown in Figure 14.26.

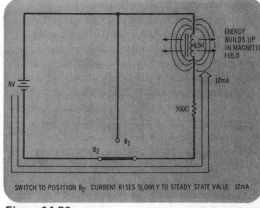

Figure 14.26

Current Fall in Inductive Circuits — If the switch in this circuit is instantly switched to position B_1, the circuit current tries to immediately change back to zero. The coil will fight this change by dumping energy back into the circuit from its magnetic field, thus the current falls *gradually* to zero as seen in Figure 14.27. Coils act to oppose any *changes in current.*

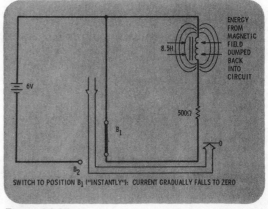

Figure 14.27

Demonstration Circuit — Figure 14.28 is a line drawing of what an actual circuit of the type being examined would look like in your laboratory. When the switch is closed, current flows from the power supply through the switch, through the 100-ohm resistor, through the coil, and then back to the battery. You will notice back in Figure 14.27, the schematic diagram indicated that a *500-ohm* resistor was connected in series with the coil. In an actual circuit of this type, probably about 400 ohms of resistance would be contained in the large amount of wire wound inside the coil. The coil probably contains about 100 feet of fairly small gage wire, so it is reasonable to expect the coil to have a considerable resistance. Keep this in mind. You must remember to include the internal resistance of coils when analyzing practical circuits. As seen in the schematic of Figure 14.27, *the resistance of a coil appears to be connected in series with the coil itself*. So the actual circuit represented by this schematic diagram would consist of a 100-ohm resistor in series with the coil for a total equivalent series resistance of 500 ohms.

In order to actually observe the effect of the coil in the circuit, a "storage oscilloscope" may be connected across the 100-ohm resistor. If you remember, the storage oscilloscope was used in the last lesson. This type of "scope" will measure and plot the voltage across this resistor on its vertical axis, and time on its horizontal axis.

Stop and consider what is being performed, keeping in mind Ohm's law. The oscilloscope will now plot the *voltage* across the resistor versus time. The voltage across any resistor, however, is directly proportional to the current flowing through it. The graph plotted by the storage scope will, in effect, be a picture of how the *current* in the circuit behaves as time goes on. On the screen will be a graph representing *current* on the vertical axis, and *time* on the horizontal axis.

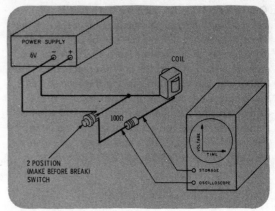

Figure 14.28

Current Rise in L/R Circuit — When the switch is thrown so that the 6-volt power source is applied to the circuit, the waveform shown in Figure 14.29 is produced. Immediately the shape of this curve should look somewhat familiar to you. It is a universal time constant graph, similar to the graph produced by an RC circuit, with some exceptions. Figure 14.29 is a plot of *current* flowing in the circuit versus time, instead of voltage as it was when you were examining a capacitor. A capacitor opposes change in voltage across a circuit, where a coil opposes any change in current through a circuit. In series circuits with inductance and resistance, the *current* rises with a characteristic "time constant" type of behavior.

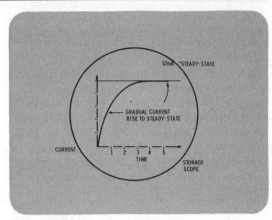

Figure 14.29

Factors Affecting Time Constant in Circuits Containing Coils — Circuits containing inductance demonstrate a time-constant type of behavior similar to the action you have seen for RC circuits. Previously it was seen that the amount of resistance in the circuit and the size of the capacitor (in farads) were the two factors that affected the time constant for an RC circuit. In a circuit containing a resistor and a coil, you will see that the time constant behavior again depends on how much resistance is present in the circuit, and also on how well the coil does its job of slowing up current changes (Figure 14.30). Focus your attention on each of these factors one at a time.

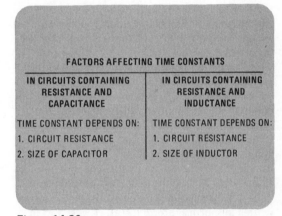

Figure 14.30

Ohm's Law — Consider the effect of resistance on the time constant. If more resistance is added to this circuit, what will be the result?

You know from Ohm's law that more resistance in a circuit causes *less* total circuit current to flow (Figure 14.31).

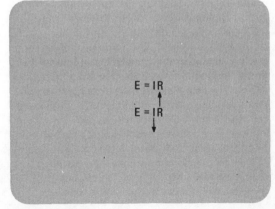

Figure 14.31

Time Constant and Resistance — With increased resistance in the circuit, when the power supply is turned on, the change from zero current to maximum current will be less as shown in Figure 14.32. Since the *change in current flowing* is less, the coil will offer less opposition to the change in current.

If the coil offers less opposition, the current flowing in the circuit will reach its maximum value in a shorter period of time, thus providing a shorter time constant. So the *higher the circuit's series resistance* in a circuit containing a resistor and a coil, the *shorter* the time constant will be.

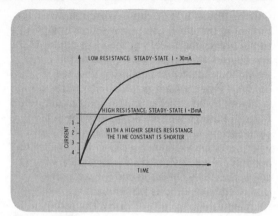

Figure 14.32

Inductance — What other factor will affect the current buildup? The better a coil is at storing energy, the more it will be able to oppose changes in current through a circuit.

The ability of a coil to store energy and fight changes in current flowing through it is specified by what is called its *"inductance."* It is for this reason that coils are often called inductors. The symbol you will see used to indicate inductance in formulas is "L." The units used to measure inductance are called "henries," named after the American scientist Joseph Henry. The unit *henry* is abbreviated "H". So the mathematical statement: "The inductance of this coil is 10 henries" may be written in shorthand form L = 10 H, as shown in Figure 14.33. The more henries of inductance a coil has, the more energy it will store in its magnetic field. As a result, the coil will be better able to oppose current changes through it. The inductance of a coil depends on how it is constructed. In general, the more turns of wire a coil has, the bigger the cross-sectional area, and the shorter its length is, the bigger the coil's inductance will be. The core material used in its construction also drastically affects coil inductance. In general, coils that employ an iron core can pack a lot more inductance in a smaller space than is possible with air or insulating cores. More details on inductance and the mechanics of how coils fight current change are really part of an ac course, and therefore will not be covered in this course.

INDUCTANCE — "L" MEASURED IN HENRIES

ABBREVIATION . . . H

"THE INDUCTANCE IS 10 HENRIES" MAY BE ABBREVIATED: "L = 10H"

Figure 14.33

In circuits containing coils and resistors (often termed RL or LR circuits), the time constant will depend directly on the number of henries of inductance present. The more inductance, the longer the time constant, and vice versa. As you have already seen, the time constant depends *inversely* on the resistance. The *more series resistance* in the circuit, the *shorter* the time constant will be, and vice versa.

L/R Time Constant Formula — In formula form, the time constant for an RL circuit can be expressed as: $T = L/R$. In the formula, T represents time constant in seconds; L is inductance in henries, and R is the series resistance in ohms, as shown in Figure 14.34.

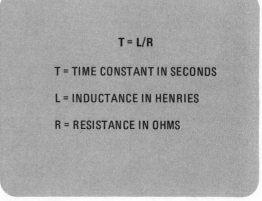

$$T = L/R$$

T = TIME CONSTANT IN SECONDS

L = INDUCTANCE IN HENRIES

R = RESISTANCE IN OHMS

Figure 14.34

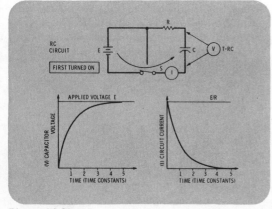

Figure 14.35

RC Circuit: First Turned On — You have now seen that inductive and capacitive dc circuits behave in somewhat similar ways, with a time constant associated with each. As a review, examine the behavior of both of these type circuits, during the various phases of their operation. First, consider what happens to the circuits in Figures 14.35 and 14.36 when power is first applied. In the RC circuit, the voltage across the capacitor starts at zero and gradually rises until it reaches the applied voltage. The current in the RC circuit flows only a short time necessary to charge the capacitor (five time constants).

14-19

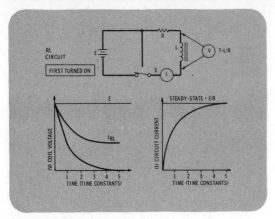

Figure 14.36

RL Circuit: First Turned On — In the RL circuit (Figure 14.36), the current in the circuit starts at zero and rises slowly to the steady-state value E/R. The voltage across the coil behaves in an interesting fashion. It starts out equal to the applied voltage when the switch is first closed, and gradually falls as the steady-state is reached. If the coil had no internal resistance, the coil voltage would gradually fall to zero. If the internal resistance of the coil is R_L, the coil's voltage will fall to a value equal to the steady-state current times R_L or $I \times R_L$.

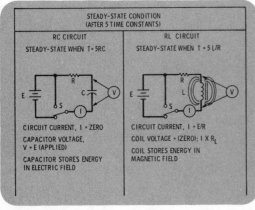

Figure 14.37

RC and RL Circuits: Steady-State — As has been seen, when the steady-state is reached in the RC circuit (after five time constants as shown in Figure 14.37), no more current is flowing in the circuit. At this point, the voltage across the capacitor equals the applied voltage. The capacitor stores energy in an electrostatic field between its plates. In the RL circuit, after five time constants, the circuit current has risen to a value equal to E/R. The coil's voltage would be zero *if the coil had no internal resistance*. Actually, the voltage across the coil will be equal to the circuit current times the coil's internal resistance, R_L. The coil stores energy in the steady-state in its *magnetic field*.

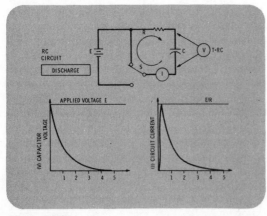

Figure 14.38

Voltage Fall: RC Circuits — If the switch in the RC circuit shown in Figure 14.38 is thrown after the capacitor has been allowed to reach steady-state, the capacitor will give up its stored energy. A burst of current will flow for a short while, and the capacitor's voltage will gradually fall to zero.

- Current Fall: RL Circuits
- **Example: Time Constant Calculation**
- **Current Rise**

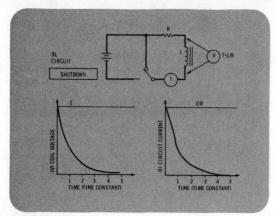

Figure 14.39

Current Fall: RL Circuits — If the RL circuit shown in Figure 14.39 has been allowed to reach the steady-state and then the switch is *instantly* switched to the short position, the current will fall *gradually* to zero. The coil voltage will jump to E and then fall off. Notice that the switch must be "instantly" switched to do this. In practice, if you built a circuit such as this and attempted to switch the current off, a *spark* would probably appear at the switch as soon as the circuit was broken. A special "make before break" switch can be used to avoid this. This "sparking" effect will be explained later in the lesson.

Example: Time Constant Calculation — You are fairly familiar with the RC time constant and how it is calculated. Some examples of how the L/R time constant of a circuit such as that shown in Figure 14.40 can be calculated.

The time constant of this circuit can be found by substituting the circuit values into the time-constant formula, $T = L/R$. "L" is equal to 8.5 henries and R is 500 ohms. Performing the necessary calculations, T, the circuit time constant, is equal to 0.017 second, or 17 milliseconds. This means that it takes 17 milliseconds for the *circuit current to rise to 63% of its steady-state value.*

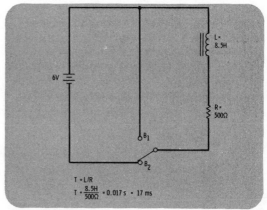

Figure 14.40

Current Rise — To calculate the steady-state value of current in this circuit, use Ohm's law in the form $I = E/R$, as mentioned before. Here $I = E/R = 6\text{ V}/500\ \Omega = 12$ mA. So, the circuit current rises as shown in Figure 14.41.

As in RC circuits, this L/R circuit also requires five time constants before the "steady-state" current value is reached, and no further change is taking place in the circuit. In this case, five time constants equal 5×17 milliseconds or 85 milliseconds. The graph shown in Figure 14.41 is a picture of the way a storage oscilloscope trace would illustrate the behavior of this circuit.

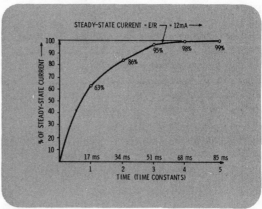

Figure 14.41

- **Current Fall with Resistor**
- **L/R Time Constant for an Open Circuit**

Current Fall with Resistor — If the switch is *instantaneously* moved to position B_1 as shown in Figure 14.42, the coil is connected in series with 500 ohms of resistance, and the current source is removed. When this is done, it will be seen that the current follows a reverse time constant behavior, and gradually falls to zero, after five time constants. After one time constant, the current has fallen to 37% of its final value.

Once again, when the drop in current is discussed, it is carefully specified that the switch must be "instantaneously" switched to position B_1. This is because most switches would *open* the circuit for a little while before the contacts reached position B_1. Opening a current-carrying circuit containing a coil produces an interesting, important, and somewhat drastic effect. As has been said before, a coil opposes changes in the current through a circuit. The more drastic the current change is, the greater the coil's opposition to it will be. When a circuit containing a coil is broken or opened, an infinite resistance is placed in the circuit. Stop for a moment and think about the effect this has on the time constant of the circuit.

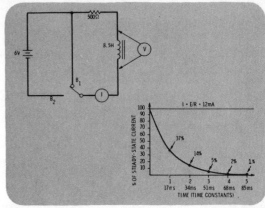

Figure 14.42

L/R Time Constant for an Open Circuit — Using the time constant formula $T = L/R$, notice that when R becomes equal to infinity, then the time constant for the circuit will become zero, because *any number divided by infinity is zero*, as shown in Figure 14.43. Now think: with a *zero time constant*, the current in the circuit will try to fall to zero *instantly*. This is a very drastic current change, and as you recall, a coil will oppose *any current change* and attempt to keep current flow constant through a circuit. The more drastic the change, the greater the coil will try to oppose it.

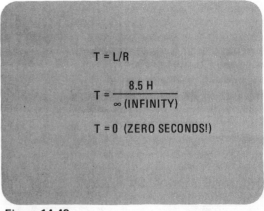

$$T = L/R$$

$$T = \frac{8.5\ H}{\infty\ (INFINITY)}$$

$$T = 0\ (ZERO\ SECONDS!)$$

Figure 14.43

Ohm's Law in Open Inductive Circuit — However, the open circuit has an *infinite resistance*. In order to maintain any value of current at a constant level through an infinitely large resistance, the coil would need an *infinitely large voltage*. In theory, the coil should produce an infinite voltage as shown in Figure 14.44. In practice, *that is just what the coil tries to do*. The current flowing in the circuit before the switch was opened was 17 milliamps. When the circuit is opened, the coil will attempt to maintain current flow at 17 milliamps. In order to do this across an infinite resistance, the energy contained in the coil's magnetic field is converted to a very high voltage, perhaps thousands of volts. The result is usually a spark somewhere in the circuit, probably at the switch. This phenomenon is affectionately called the "kick" of a coil. (If you should ever have you body connected across a current-carrying inductor when the circuit is opened, you will know how it got that name.)

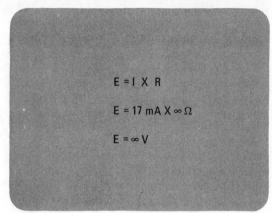

$$E = I \times R$$

$$E = 17 \text{ mA} \times \infty\, \Omega$$

$$E = \infty\, V$$

Figure 14.44

Inductive Kickback Circuit — To illustrate this high voltage "kick," a circuit may be connected as shown in Figure 14.45. Two special neon glow lamps are now connected across the inductor and resistor in a series RL circuit, just like the one investigated previously. This circuit will demonstrate the high voltage produced by a current-carrying coil when the circuit is opened. Each of the neon lamps requires about 70 to 75 volts in order to turn "on" and flash. Together they will require 140 volts or more to light at all. Until the voltage across the lamps reaches at least 140 volts, these two lamps will not operate. Notice that the power supply in this circuit is the same one considered earlier. It has an output of only

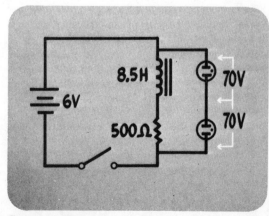

Figure 14.45

6 volts. When the switch is closed, 6 volts are applied to the circuit. Current flow gradually builds up until after five time constants, 17 milliamps of steady-state current flows in the circuit. At this point, the magnetic field has completely built up in the coil. The bulbs cannot light as yet because up to this point there is no voltage in the circuit anywhere near 140 volts. However, if the switch in the circuit is *opened*, energy from the coil's magnetic field will be abruptly dumped back into the circuit in the form of a very high voltage. Both of the neon bulbs will flash, indicating that a voltage of at least 140 volts was produced. In actuality, a much higher voltage than that is produced in this circuit.

Coil and Capacitor "Special Effects" — The high voltage "kick" effect is very important and finds many applications in electricity and electronics. You have now seen that a *coil* can produce a burst of *very high voltage* for a short period of time. This is similar to the effect shown in the preceding lesson, where a *capacitor* was used to produce a *large burst of current* for a short time (Figure 14.46).

    Both of these effects have many uses in electrical applications. Coils are used to produce high voltages for firing fluorescent lights, in electric fences, and as was seen in an earlier lesson, for firing the spark plugs in an automotive ignition system. As a technician, it is necessary for you to keep in mind that sometimes the high-voltage "kick" a coil produces can be an *undesirable side effect* of having a coil in a circuit. For example, a circuit containing a relay may be damaged when the relay is shut off and a high-voltage burst appears across it. For this reason, relays often have special protective devices across their terminals to short-out and eliminate this high voltage. More than one expensive piece of electronic gear has been "wiped out" by high voltages from relays and other inductive devices.

A COIL: CAN PRODUCE A BURST OF VERY HIGH **VOLTAGE**.

A CAPACITOR: CAN PRODUCE A LARGE BURST OF **CURRENT**.

Figure 14.46

Automotive Ignition System — You have seen a coil in action in an earlier lesson in this course; a portion of an automobile electrical system was shown. Your ignition system contains an "ignition coil" which produces the spark for your spark plugs, as well as an undesirable side effect. Figure 14.47 shows the basics of the circuit. The "points" in your ignition system perform the same function as the switch that provides current to this coil.

When the "points" in an automobile engine close, current flows through the ignition coil and builds up the magnetic field inside it. The coil is designed so that when the points open, this magnetic field inside the coil collapses, producing a high-voltage arc or spark that appears across the spark plug. In addition, since the points are part of an inductive current-carrying circuit, when they open the circuit, an electrical discharge or spark can be expected to appear across the points also. Unfortunately, this is not a good or desirable effect and can cause the points to become burned and age rapidly.

To stop the arcing across the points, a component that *opposes a change in voltage* can be inserted across them and control the action of the spark. This is the reason a *capacitor* is found in an automobile distributor connected directly across the points. The capacitor prevents the coil's induced voltage from damaging the points. This capacitor is often called a "buffer" capacitor, and capacitors of this sort are often employed where a switch or a "set of points" is used to interrupt the magnetic field produced by a coil.

Summary — In this lesson a new electrical component, the coil, and the L/R time constant have been introduced and discussed. You have seen what coils are and examined the key factors that affect their behavior in dc circuits. In many ways coils are seen to operate in "reverse" fashion to capacitors. As will be seen in any ac circuits course, and later electronics courses, capacitors and inductors are very useful and integral parts of almost every electronic circuit. In your ac courses, you will explore the reasons why inductors behave the way they do in greater detail.

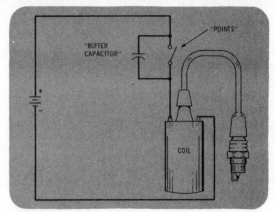

Figure 14.47

LESSON 14. INDUCTORS AND THE L/R TIME CONSTANT

● **Worked Through Examples**

1. Describe the magnetic field around a simple coil of the type shown in the figure below. What is the key effect of a coil's magnetic field on the behavior of coils in dc circuits?

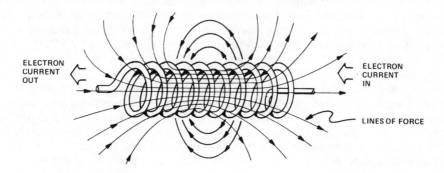

Solution: A magnetic field surrounds any wire carrying current. When this wire is wound into a coil, the magnetic field is concentrated inside the coil as shown by the magnetic lines of force drawn in the figure. This concentrated magnetic field is in effect an energy storage reservoir. Energy is stored when current attempts to increase through the coil, and this energy is released back into the circuit when current attempts to decrease through the coil. For this reason, coils are said to *oppose changes in current* in circuits.

2. Find the following values for the circuit shown below:

    a. Time constant

    b. Maximum steady-state current

    c. Voltage across the resistor after two time constants

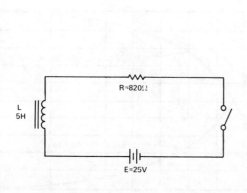

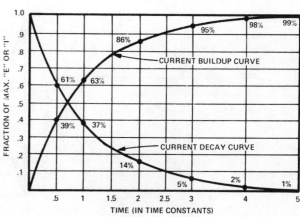

The time constant for this circuit may be found by using the inductive time constant formula, $T = L/R$. In this circuit, L is equal to 5 henries and R is equal to 820 ohms. $5/820 = 0.0061$ second, or 6.1 milliseconds. This is one time constant for this circuit. Five time constants are required for the circuit to reach its steady-state condition. The maximum steady-state current in an inductive circuit is determined by using Ohm's law. The total voltage, E (here 25 volts), must be divided by the total circuit resistance R_T to give you the steady-state current. In this circuit, the total resistance is taken to be 820 ohms, the value of the resistor performing the calculation: $25 \text{ V}/820 \text{ } \Omega = 30.5 \text{ mA}$. This value of current will be flowing in the circuit after five time constants.

The value of current flowing after only two time constants may be found by using the universal time constant graph. First, locate the two time constant mark on the horizontal line. Trace the graph line up until it intersects the "current buildup" curve. The intersection point is labeled 86%. This means that at this point, the circuit current is at 86% of the steady-state value. So, the current value at 2 time constants may be found by multiplying 0.86 X 30.5 mA. The current flowing after two time constants is equal to 26.2 mA. The value of the current at any time constant point may be determined by using the universal time constant graph in the manner just presented. To find the voltage across the resistor at the end of two time constants, multiply the current at that point (26.2 milliamps), times the resistance (820 ohms), to get your answer (21.5 volts).

3. Find the following values for the circuit shown below:

    a. Time constant

    b. Maximum steady-state current

    c. Voltage across the resistor after 2 milliseconds (2 ms).

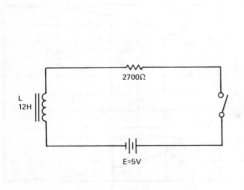

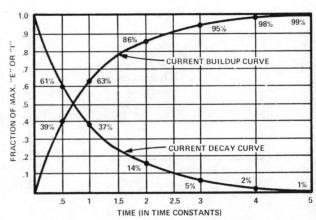

TIME (IN TIME CONSTANTS)

Solution:

a. $T = L/R$
     $T = 12/2700$
     $T = 4.44$ ms

b. $E_T/R_T = I_T$
     $5/2700 = 1.85$ mA = steady-state current

c.   To find the circuit current at 2 milliseconds, the first thing to do is locate 2 milliseconds on the horizontal axis of the time constant graph. This axis of the graph is measured out in terms of time constants. You must get the chart to read out in seconds. This may be done by dividing 2 milliseconds by 4.44 milliseconds, to determine the exact percentage 2 milliseconds is as compared to 4.44 milliseconds. Two ms/4.44 ms = 0.45. In terms of time constants, 2 milliseconds is equal to 0.45 (or 45%) of one time constant. Locate 0.45 on the horizontal axis of the graph. Trace upward until that graph line intersects the current buildup curve. The intersection occurs at approximately 37%. This indicates that the current flowing at this point is 37% of the steady-state current, or 0.37 X 1.85 mA which is equal to 0.68 mA. To find the voltage across the resistor, multiply this current (0.68 milliamps) times the resistance (2700 ohms) to yield the voltage (1.84 volts).

LESSON 14. INDUCTORS AND THE L/R TIME CONSTANT

- **Practice Problems**

Solve the following problems related to inductance and the L/R time constant, using the time constant formula and the universal time constant graph given below. Fold over the sheet to check your answers.

Depending upon the approach you use in solving these problems and how you round off intermediate results, your answers may vary slightly from those given here. However, any differences you encounter should only occur in the third significant digit of your answer. If the first two significant digits of your answers do not agree with those given here, recheck your calculations.

Fold Over

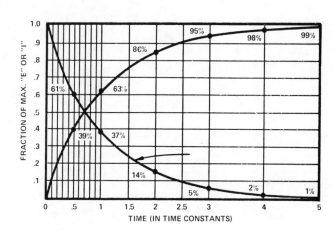

1.

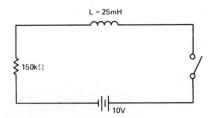

Circuit time constant = _____

I_{max} = _____

Voltage across the 150-kilohm resistor

after two time constants = _____

2.

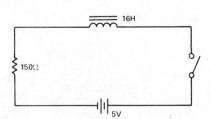

Circuit time constant = _____

I_{max} = _____

Voltage across the 150-ohm resistor

after 50 milliseconds = _____

Answers

1. Circuit time constant = 167 nanoseconds

   I_{max} = 66.7 microamps

   Voltage across the 150-kilohm resistor

   after two time constants = 8.6 volts

2. Circuit time constant = 107 milliseconds

   I_{max} = 33.3 milliamps

   Voltage across the 150-ohm resistor

   after 50 milliseconds = 1.86 volts

Fold Over

3.

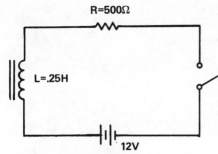

Circuit time constant = _____

I_{max} = _____

Voltage across the 500-ohm resistor

after 1 millisecond = _____

4.

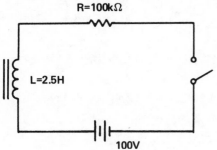

Circuit time constant = _____

I_{max} = _____

Voltage across the 100-kilohm resistor

after three time constants = _____

5.

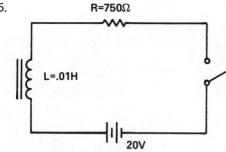

Circuit time constant = _____

I_{max} = _____

Voltage across the 750-ohm resistor

after 25 microseconds = _____

Answers

3. Circuit time constant = 500 microseconds

    I_{max} = 24 milliamps

    Voltage across the 500-ohm resistor

    after 1 millisecond = 10.3 volts

4. Circuit time constant = 25 microseconds

    I_{max} = 1 milliamp

    Voltage across the 100-kilohm resistor

    after three time constants = 95 volts

5. Circuit time constant = 13.3 microseconds

    I_{max} = 26.7 milliamps

    Voltage across the 750-ohm resistor

    after 25 microseconds = 17 volts

1. Coils or inductors are commonly used at high frequency when they:
   a. Have an iron core
   b. Have an air core
   c. When they are wound backwards
   d. None of the above

2. Coils oppose:
   a. Changes in current
   b. Changes in voltage
   c. Changes in resistance
   d. Changes in direction

3. Whenever current flows in a conductor, a _____ field is set up around the conductor.
   a. Voltage
   b. Current
   c. Electrostatic
   d. Magnetic

4. When many loops of current-carrying wire are wrapped into a coil, a strong _____ is created inside the coil.
   a. Current
   b. Voltage
   c. Electromagnetic field
   d. Bond

5. Magnetic fields store _____
   a. Coulombs
   b. Current
   c. Voltage
   d. Energy

6. It takes _____ for current to build up in a series circuit containing a coil than it does in a circuit with no coil.
   a. A shorter time
   b. Longer
   c. Forever
   d. None of above

7. In a coil with steady-state current flowing, the magnetic field has _____ on the current.
   a. Lots of effect
   b. No effect
   c. A new dependence
   d. None of the above

8. In a circuit with a coil, a resistor, a battery and an open switch, when the switch is closed the current rises:
   a. Instantaneously
   b. In a step function
   c. Gradually
   d. The same as the voltage

9. The final value of current in the circuit of question 8 is determined by:
   a. Ohm's Law
   b. The L and R ratio
   c. LR
   d. The amount of inductance

10. The time it takes for the current to attain 63% of its final value in a circuit containing inductance and resistance (besides a battery) is called:
    a. The capacitive time constant
    b. A coulomb
    c. The first step
    d. The L/R time constant

11. Inductance is measured in units called:
    a. Millivolts
    b. Henries
    c. Nanoseconds
    d. Gigahertz

12. When a switch opens the circuit with a steady-state current flowing through a coil, the coil will cause _____ voltage to appear across the infinite resistance of the open circuit.
    a. Twice the battery
    b. A very large
    c. A very small
    d. 3 Millivolts of

13. A coil can produce a burst of:
    a. Very high voltage
    b. Very low voltage
    c. Very large current
    d. Very small current

14. A capacitor can produce a burst of:
    a. Very high voltage
    b. Very low voltage
    c. Very large current
    d. Very small current

15. If more series resistance is added to a series R-L circuit, its time constant:

    a. Increases
    b. Stays the same
    c. Decreases
    d. None of above

16. The time constant for an R-L circuit is 25 milliseconds. Steady-state current is flowing. When the current is turned off it reaches approximately zero in:

    a. 25 Milliseconds
    b. 50 Milliseconds
    c. 75 Milliseconds
    d. 125 Milliseconds

Calculate the indicated unknown quantities:

17.   L = 2.5 H   R = 600 Ω

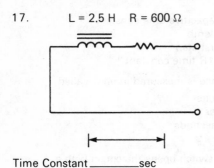

Time Constant _____ sec

18.   L = 100 mH

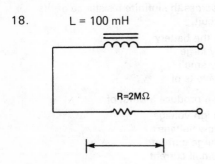

R=2MΩ

Time Constant _____ sec

19.   L = 15 H

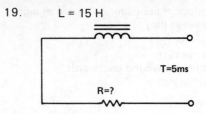

T=5ms

R=?

R _____ ohms

20.   L = ?

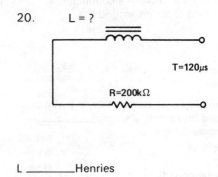

T=120μs

R=200kΩ

L _____ Henries

Appendices

---

1. Interpreting the Resistor Color Code A-2

2. Preferred Values for Resistors and Capacitors A-3

3. Resistor Size Comparison A-4

4. Scientific Notation and the Metric Prefixes A-5

5. Basic Schematic Symbols A-6

6. How to Use Square Root Tables A-7

7. How to Extract Square Roots Manually A-10

8. The Universal Time Constant Graph A-14

9. Charge and Discharge Curve Calculations A-17

10. Capacitor Color Codes A-18

11. Unit Conversion Charts A-22

12. The Greek Alphabet A-25

13. Basic Formulas of Basic Electricity A-26

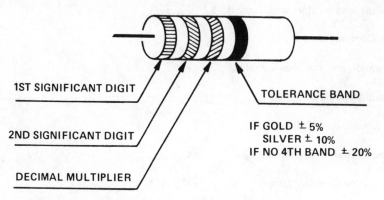

1ST SIGNIFICANT DIGIT

2ND SIGNIFICANT DIGIT

DECIMAL MULTIPLIER

TOLERANCE BAND

IF GOLD ± 5%
SILVER ± 10%
IF NO 4TH BAND ± 20%

(# OF ZEROS TO PLACE AFTER FIRST TWO DIGITS)

	Significant Digit	Decimal Multiplier (Put These Zeros Behind First Two Digits)	(Power of Ten)
Black	0	1	10^0
Brown	1	1 0	10^1
Red	2	1 00	10^2
Orange	3	1 000	10^3
Yellow	4	1 0000	10^4
Green	5	1 00000	10^5
Blue	6	1 000000	10^6
Violet	7	1 0000000	10^7
Gray	8	1 00000000	10^8
White	9	1 000000000	10^9
Gold	—	Multiply by 0.1	10^{-1}
Silver	—	Multiply by 0.01	10^{-2}

APPENDIX 2. PREFERRED VALUES FOR RESISTORS AND CAPACITORS

The numbers listed in the chart below, and *decimal multiples* of these numbers, are the commonly available resistor values at 5%, 10%, and 20% tolerance.

20% Tolerance (*No* 4th Band)	10% Tolerance (*Silver* 4th Band)	5% Tolerance (*Gold* 4th Band)
10*	10	10
		11
	12	12
		13
15	15	15
		16
	18	18
		20
22	22	22
		24
	27	27
		30
33	33	33
		36
	39	39
47	47	47
		51
	56	56
		62
68	68	68
		75
	82	82
		91
100	100	100

APPENDIX 3. RESISTOR SIZE COMPARISON

(By Wattage Rating)

$\dfrac{1}{10}$ watt

$\dfrac{1}{4}$ watt

$\dfrac{1}{2}$ watt

1 watt

2 watt

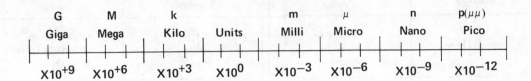

1 unit = 1 .

. 0 0 1 = 1 milli

1 kilo = 1 0 0 0 .

. 0 0 0 0 0 1 = 1 micro

1 mega = 1 0 0 0 0 0 0 .

. 0 0 0 0 0 0 0 0 1 = 1 nano

1 giga = 1 0 0 0 0 0 0 0 0 0 .

. 0 0 0 0 0 0 0 0 0 0 0 1 = 1 pico

STANDARD FORM: $\text{X.XX} \times 10^{+\text{exponent}}$			
Symbol	Prefix	Value	Power of 10
G	giga	1,0 0 0, 0 0 0, 0 0 0 .	$\times 10^{+9}$
M	mega	1, 0 0 0, 0 0 0 .	$\times 10^{+6}$
k	kilo	1, 0 0 0 .	$\times 10^{+3}$
—	(units)	1 .	$\times 10^{0}$
m	milli	.0 0 1	$\times 10^{-3}$
μ	micro	.0 0 0 0 0 1	$\times 10^{-6}$
n	nano	.0 0 0 0 0 0 0 0 1	$\times 10^{-9}$
p $(\mu\mu)$	pico	.0 0 0 0 0 0 0 0 0 0 0 1	$\times 10^{-12}$

Symbol	Device	Symbol	Device
	Battery or DC Power Supply		Push Button Normally Open (PBNO)
	Resistor		Push Button Normally Closed (PBNC)
	Potentiometer		Earth Ground
	Rheostat		Chassis Ground
	Tapped Resistor		Capacitor
V A mA	Meters — Symbol to Indicate Function		Capacitor, Polarized (Electrolytic)
	Lamp		Coil, Air Core
	Switch SPST		Coil, Iron Core
	Switch SPDT		Fuse
	Switch DPST	Conductor, General No Connection	
	Switch DPDT	Connection	

APPENDIX 6. HOW TO USE SQUARE ROOT TABLES

The following table can be used to find the square root or square of most any number. Numbers from 1 to 120 can be read directly from the table. But what about a number such as 150? How can its square or square root be found? The secret to the use of this table is in the understanding of *factoring*. Factoring a number means to break the original number up into two smaller numbers, that, when multiplied together, give you back the original. For example, 150 is equal to 10 times 15. Ten and 15 are said to be *factors* of 150. If 10 times 15 is equal to 150, then the square root of 10 times the square root of 15 is equal to the square root of 150. Both 10 and 15 are listed on the square and square root table. The square root of 10 from the table is equal to 3.162. The square root of 15 is equal to 3.873; 3.162 times 3.873 is equal to 12.246426, which should be the square root of 150. You can test this number by multiplying it by itself. Thus, 12.246426 squared is equal to 149.97, etc., — very close to 150. (Small errors due to rounding will normally occur when using the tables.) The factoring procedure written out mathematically would then be:

$$150 = 10 \times 15$$

$$\sqrt{150} = \sqrt{10} \times \sqrt{15} \quad \text{(Look up } \sqrt{10}, \sqrt{15} \text{ in tables)}$$

$$\sqrt{150} = 3.162 \times 3.873$$

$$\sqrt{150} = 12.246 \ldots \ldots$$

Try another number now, say, 350. First, factor 350:

$$350 = 35 \times 10$$

The square root of 350 must equal the square root of 35 times the square root of 10.

$$\sqrt{350} = \sqrt{35} \times \sqrt{10}$$

Go to the tables and look up the square roots of 10 and 35:

$$\sqrt{350} = 5.9161 \times 3.162$$

Multiply the square roots of 10 and 35, and you have found the square root of 350.

$$\sqrt{350} = 18.706 \ldots \ldots$$

To check the accuracy of your calculations, multiply 18.706 by itself.

$$18.706^2 = 349.91$$

Again, very close to the original number.

Try one more number, this time 1150.

First, factor 1150.

$$1150 = 115 \times 10$$

The square root of 1150 must equal the square root of 115 times the square root of 10.

$$\sqrt{1150} = \sqrt{115} \times \sqrt{10}$$

APPENDIX 6. HOW TO USE SQUARE ROOT TABLES

Look up the square roots of 115 and 10 from the tables.

$$\sqrt{1150} = 10.7238 \times 3.162$$

Multiply the square roots of 115 and 10, and you have the square root of 1150.

$$\sqrt{1150} = 33.908$$

To check the validity of this number, square it. It should be very close to 1150.

APPENDIX 6. HOW TO USE SQUARE ROOT TABLES

N	$\sqrt{N}$	N^2	N	$\sqrt{N}$	N^2	N	$\sqrt{N}$	N^2
1	1.000	1	41	6.4031	1681	81	9.0000	6561
2	1.414	4	42	6.4807	1764	82	9.0554	6724
3	1.732	9	43	6.5574	1849	83	9.1104	6889
4	2.000	16	44	6.6332	1936	84	9.1652	7056
5	2.236	25	45	6.7082	2025	85	9.2195	7225
6	2.449	36	46	6.7823	2116	86	9.2736	7396
7	2.646	49	47	6.8557	2209	87	9.3274	7569
8	2.828	64	48	6.9282	2304	88	9.3808	7744
9	3.000	81	49	7.0000	2401	89	9.4340	7921
10	3.162	100	50	7.0711	2500	90	9.4868	8100
11	3.3166	121	51	7.1414	2601	91	9.5394	8281
12	3.4641	144	52	7.2111	2704	92	9.5917	8464
13	3.6056	169	53	7.2801	2809	93	9.6437	8649
14	3.7417	196	54	7.3485	2916	94	9.6954	8836
15	3.8730	225	55	7.4162	3025	95	9.7468	9025
16	4.0000	256	56	7.4833	3136	96	9.7980	9216
17	4.1231	289	57	7.5498	3249	97	9.8489	9409
18	4.2426	324	58	7.6158	3364	98	9.8995	9604
19	4.3589	361	59	7.6811	3481	99	9.9499	9801
20	4.4721	400	60	7.7460	3600	100	10.0000	10000
21	4.5826	441	61	7.8102	3721	101	10.0499	10201
22	4.6904	484	62	7.8740	3844	102	10.0995	10404
23	4.7958	529	63	7.9373	3969	103	10.1489	10609
24	4.8990	576	64	8.0000	4096	104	10.1980	10816
25	5.0000	625	65	8.0623	4225	105	10.2470	11025
26	5.0990	676	66	8.1240	4356	106	10.2956	11236
27	5.1962	729	67	8.1854	4489	107	10.3441	11449
28	5.2915	784	68	8.2462	4624	108	10.3923	11664
29	5.3852	841	69	8.3066	4761	109	10.4403	11881
30	5.4772	900	70	8.3666	4900	110	10.4881	12100
31	5.5678	961	71	8.4261	5041	111	10.5357	12321
32	5.6569	1024	72	8.4853	5184	112	10.5830	12544
33	5.7446	1089	73	8.5440	5329	113	10.6301	12769
34	5.8310	1156	74	8.6023	5476	114	10.6771	12996
35	5.9161	1225	75	8.6603	5625	115	10.7238	13225
36	6.0000	1296	76	8.7178	5776	116	10.7703	13456
37	6.0828	1369	77	8.7750	5929	117	10.8167	13689
38	6.1644	1444	78	8.8318	6084	118	10.8628	13924
39	6.2450	1521	79	8.8882	6241	119	10.9087	14161
40	6.3246	1600	80	8.9443	6400	120	10.9545	14400

This procedure outlines, step by step, how to extract square roots manually.

Problem

Compute $\sqrt{4139}$

Solution

Step 1: Begin at the decimal point (which is to the right of the last digit) and divide the number into two-digit groups (underlining indicates the groups).

$$\underline{41}\,\underline{39}.\underline{00}$$

Step 2: Place the decimal point for the square root directly above the decimal point that appears under the radical sign.

$$\sqrt{41\,39.00}\;\overset{.}{}$$

Step 3: Find the largest number that *when multiplied by itself will give a product equal to or less than* the first pair of digits. In this case, 6 X 6 = 36, which is the largest perfect square that does not exceed 41. Place 6 on the radical sign above 41.

$$\overset{6\quad .}{\sqrt{41\,39.00}}$$

Step 4: Square 6 to obtain 36 and place it below the first two digits (41). Subtract 36 from 41 to obtain 5. Bring down the next pair of digits (39).

$$\begin{array}{r} 6\quad. \\ \sqrt{41\,39.00} \\ \underline{36} \\ 539 \end{array}$$

Step 5: Double the first digit of the answer, 6, to obtain a trial divisor of 12. Place 12 to the left of 539 as shown.

$$\begin{array}{r} 6\quad. \\ \sqrt{41\,39.00} \\ \underline{36} \\ 12\overline{\big)\,539} \end{array}$$

Step 6: Divide the trial divisor (12) into *all but the last digit* of the modified remainder 539. It will divide into 53 four times. This will be the next digit of the answer. *Place the 4 above the second pair of digits and also place the 4 to the right of the trial divisor.* The completed divisor is 124. Multiply 124 by 4 to obtain 496. Subtract 496 from 539 to obtain 43. Bring down the next pair of digits (.00).

```
              6  4.
          √ 4139.00
              36
     124 | 539
           496
          4300
```

Step 7:   Double the first two digits of the answer (64) to obtain the new trial divisor (128). Place 128 to the left of 4300 as shown.

```
              6  4.
          √ 4139.00
              36
     124 | 539
           496
     128 | 4300
```

Step 8:   Divide the trial divisor 128 into all but the last digit of the modified remainder 4300. It will go into 430 three times. This will be the next digit of the answer. Place the 3 on the radical sign over the next pair of numbers. Also, place the 3 to the right of the trial divisor 128. The completed trial divisor is 1283. Multiply 1283 by 3 to obtain 3849. Subtract 3849 from 4300. The remainder is 4.51.

```
              6  4.3
          √ 4139.00
              36
     124 | 539
           496
    1283 | 4300
           3849
            451
```

Note: If greater accuracy is required, the number may be carried out by adding more pairs of zeros to the right of the decimal place and performing Steps 7 and 8 until the desired accuracy is obtained.

Step 9.   The answer may be checked by multiplying the answer by itself and adding the remainder from the last step, 64.3 times 64.3 plus 4.51 is equal to 4139.

$$64.3 \times 64.3 = 4134.49 + 4.51 = 4139$$

Problem

Find the square root of 240.25

Solution

Step 1:   Begin at the decimal point and divide the number into digit groups in both directions. (Notice that a zero was added in front of the two in order to make a pair.)

$$\sqrt{\overline{02}\,\overline{40}.\overline{25}}$$

Step 2:   Place the decimal point for the square root directly above the decimal point that appears under the radical sign.

$$\sqrt{\overline{0240}.\overline{25}}$$

Step 3:   Determine the largest number that when multiplied by itself will give a product equal to or less than the first pair of digits, 02. The number 1 is the only number that meets these requirements. Place 1 over the first pair of digits.

$$\overset{1}{\sqrt{\overline{02}\,\overline{40}.\overline{25}}}$$

Step 4:   Square 1 to obtain 1. Place this number below the first two digits, 02. Subtract 1 from 02 to obtain 1. Bring down the next pair of digits (40).

$$\begin{array}{r} 1 \\ \sqrt{\overline{02}\,\overline{40}.\overline{25}} \\ \underline{1} \\ 140 \end{array}$$

Step 5:   Double the first digit of the answer 1 to obtain a trial divisor of 2. Place the 2 to the left of 140 as shown.

$$\begin{array}{r} 1 \\ \sqrt{\overline{02}\,\overline{40}.\overline{25}} \\ \underline{1} \\ 2 \,\rfloor\, 140 \end{array}$$

Step 6:   Divide the trial divisor (2) into all but the last digit of the modified remainder 140. Two will divide into 14, seven times. This will be the next digit of the answer. Place the 7 on the radical sign above the second pair of digits and also place a 7 to the right of the 2 in the trial divisor. The completed trial divisor is now 27. Multiply 27 by 7 to obtain 189. Oops! 189 will not subtract from 140. Now you know why the *trial* divisor is so named! At this point go back to the trial divisor, subtract one from it, and try again. Notice that one was also subtracted from the answer on the radical sign. You now have a trial divisor of 26, and the last digit of the answer is 6; 26 times 6 is equal to 156. Unfortunately, 156 will not subtract from 140. Take 1 from both the trial divisor and the last digit of the answer. You now have a trial divisor of 25 and the last digit of the answer is 5. Multiply 25 by 5 to get 125. Fortunately, 125 *will* subtract from 140 to leave a remainder of 15. Bring down the next pair of digits (25).

```
           15 .
        √0240.25
           1
    25 | 140
       | 125
         1525
```

Step 7: Double the first two digits of the answer 15, to obtain the new trial divisor of 30. Place 30 to the left of 1525 as shown.

```
           15 .
        √0240.25
           1
    25 | 140
       | 125
    30 | 1525
```

Step 8: Divide the trial divisor, 30, into all but the last digit of the modified remainder 1525; 152 divided by 30 is equal to 5. This will be the next digit of the answer. Place the 5 above the next pair of digits in the number whose square root is being extracted. Also, place the 5 to the right of the 30 in the trial divisor. The new trial divisor is 305. Multiply 305 by 5 to obtain 1525. Subtract 1525 from 1525 to obtain zero. The square root of 240.25 is 15.5.

```
           15 .5
        √0240.25
           1
    25  | 140
        | 125
    305 | 1525
        | 1525
            0
```

Step 9: Check your answer by multiplying 15.5 by 15.5 and adding the remainder, if any, to the product.

$$15.5 \times 15.5 = 240.25$$

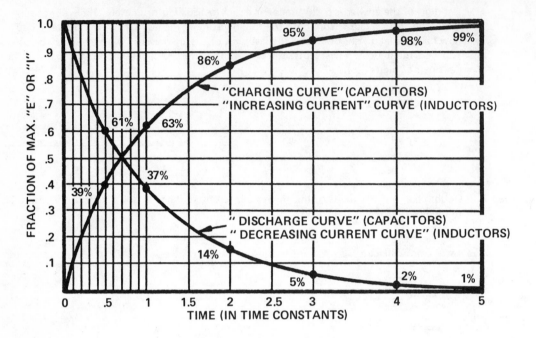

How to Use This Chart

This chart can be used to graphically determine the voltage or current at any point in time for an RC or L/R circuit, during charging (or current buildup), or discharge (or current collapse).

The examples shown below illustrate the use of the chart.

1. Find the voltage across the capacitor shown in the circuit below, 1 second after the switch is thrown.

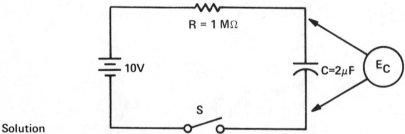

Solution

a. First find the circuit time constant

$T = RC$

$T = (1 \times 10^6) \times (2 \times 10^{-6}) = 2$ seconds

b. Express the time (t) at which the capacitor voltage is desired in *time constants*.

Here you want the voltage after 1 second and the time constant is 2 seconds, so t = 1/2 (the time constant)

or t = 0.5T

c. Look at the chart, on the horizontal axis and locate 0.5 time constants.

d. Move up the vertical line until it reaches the appropriate curve (in this case the charging curve). Read from the vertical axis the fraction of the applied voltage at the time (here 39%).

e. At t = 1 second, the voltage across the capacitor equals 39% of 10 volts or

$$E_C = 0.39 \times 10$$
$$E_C = 3.9 \text{ volts}$$

2. Find the voltage across the capacitor shown in the circuit below 2 seconds after the switch, S, is thrown. The capacitor is charged to 20 volts before the switch is thrown.

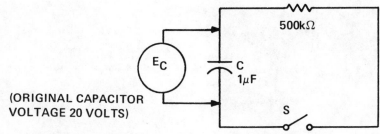

(ORIGINAL CAPACITOR VOLTAGE 20 VOLTS)

Solution

a. Find the circuit time constant

$$T = RC$$
$$T = (500 \times 10^{+3}) \times (1 \times 10^{-6})$$
$$T = 0.5 \text{ seconds}$$

b. Express the time at which the capacitors voltage is desired in time constants. Here, 2 seconds divided by 0.5 seconds is 4; 2 seconds is 4 time constants for this circuit.

$$t = 4T$$

c. Look at the chart, locate 4 time constants on the horizontal axis.

d. Move up the vertical line until it reaches the appropriate curve (the discharge curve). Read the fraction of the original voltage from the vertical axis (2%).

e.   AT t = 2 seconds, the voltage across the capacitor is at 2% of the original voltage or is at 2% of 20 volts.

$$E_C = 0.02 \times 20$$
$$E_C = 0.40 \text{ volts}$$

Remember that 5 time constants is required for a 100% charge (full charge or discharge for RC circuits, maximum or zero current for L/R circuits).

APPENDIX 9. CHARGE AND DISCHARGE CURVE CALCULATIONS

The voltage at any point along a charge or discharge curve may be calculated by using one of these two mathematical formulas:

Charge: e (at time t) $= E_{app} (1 - \epsilon^{-t/RC})$

Discharge: e (at time t) $= E_{app} (\epsilon^{-t/RC})$

The scientific calculator greatly reduces the degree of difficulty in the solution of problems of this type. For example, the *charge formula* shown above may be solved by using a calculator such as the SR-50, and this procedure:

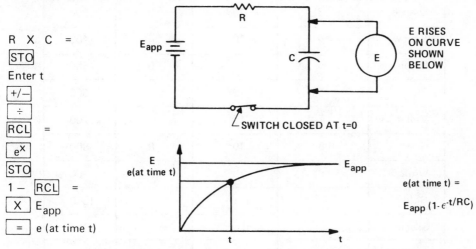

R   X   C   =
STO
Enter t
+/–
÷
RCL   =
eˣ
STO
1 –   RCL   =
X E_{app}
=   e (at time t)

E RISES ON CURVE SHOWN BELOW

e(at time t) = E_{app} (1- $\epsilon^{-t/RC}$)

The decay of a capacitor's charge (discharge) may be calculated by using this calculator sequence:

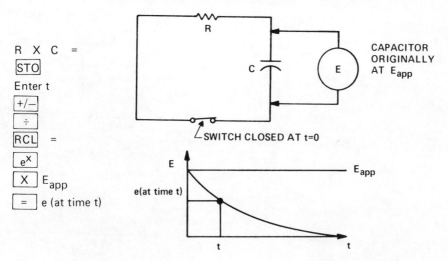

R   X   C   =
STO
Enter t
+/–
÷
RCL   =
eˣ
X E_{app}
=   e (at time t)

CAPACITOR ORIGINALLY AT E_{app}

CAPACITOR COLOR CODE CHART

Color	Significant Digit	Decimal Multiplier	Tolerance in %	Voltage Rating
Black	0	1	20	
Brown	1	10	1	100
Red	2	10^2	2	200
Orange	3	10^3	3	300
Yellow	4	10^4	4	400
Green	5	10^5	5	500
Blue	6	10^6	6	600
Violet	7	10^7	7	700
Gray	8	10^8	8	800
White	9	10^9	9	900
Gold		0.1		1000
Silver		0.01		2000
No Color			20	500

APPENDIX 10. CAPACITOR COLOR CODES

- **Mica Capacitors**

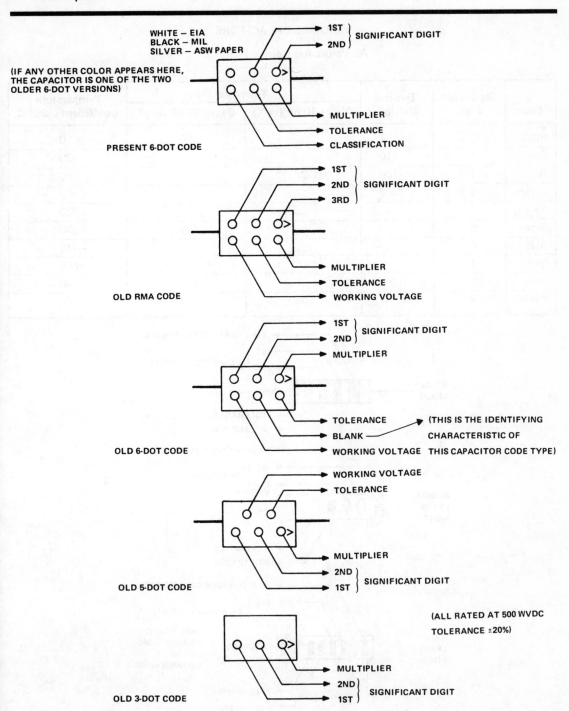

WHITE — EIA
BLACK — MIL
SILVER — ASW PAPER

(IF ANY OTHER COLOR APPEARS HERE, THE CAPACITOR IS ONE OF THE TWO OLDER 6-DOT VERSIONS)

1ST
2ND } SIGNIFICANT DIGIT

MULTIPLIER
TOLERANCE
CLASSIFICATION

PRESENT 6-DOT CODE

1ST
2ND } SIGNIFICANT DIGIT
3RD

MULTIPLIER
TOLERANCE
WORKING VOLTAGE

OLD RMA CODE

1ST } SIGNIFICANT DIGIT
2ND }
MULTIPLIER

TOLERANCE
BLANK ——→ (THIS IS THE IDENTIFYING CHARACTERISTIC OF THIS CAPACITOR CODE TYPE)
WORKING VOLTAGE

OLD 6-DOT CODE

WORKING VOLTAGE
TOLERANCE

MULTIPLIER
2ND } SIGNIFICANT DIGIT
1ST

OLD 5-DOT CODE

(ALL RATED AT 500 WVDC
TOLERANCE ±20%)

MULTIPLIER
2ND } SIGNIFICANT DIGIT
1ST

OLD 3-DOT CODE

A-19

APPENDIX 10. CAPACITOR COLOR CODES

- **Ceramic Capacitors**

CERAMIC CAPACITORS
All Values Are Read in Picofarads

Color	Significant Digit	Decimal Multiplier	Tolerance		Temperature Coefficient ppm/°C
			Above 10 pF (in %)	Below 10 pF (in pF)	
Black	0	1	20	2.0	0
Brown	1	10	1		−30
Red	2	100	2		−80
Orange	3	1000			−150
Yellow	4				−220
Green	5		5	0.5	−330
Blue	6				−470
Violet	7				−750
Gray	8	0.01		0.25	30
White	9	0.1	10	1.0	500

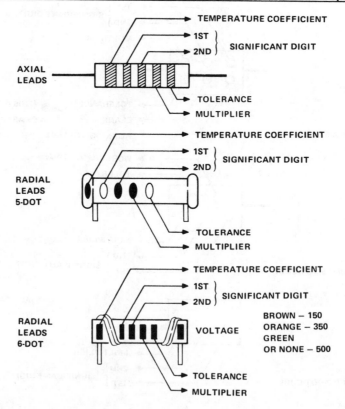

AXIAL LEADS
- TEMPERATURE COEFFICIENT
- 1ST
- 2ND } SIGNIFICANT DIGIT
- TOLERANCE
- MULTIPLIER

RADIAL LEADS 5-DOT
- TEMPERATURE COEFFICIENT
- 1ST
- 2ND } SIGNIFICANT DIGIT
- TOLERANCE
- MULTIPLIER

RADIAL LEADS 6-DOT
- TEMPERATURE COEFFICIENT
- 1ST
- 2ND } SIGNIFICANT DIGIT
- VOLTAGE
- TOLERANCE
- MULTIPLIER

BROWN — 150
ORANGE — 350
GREEN
OR NONE — 500

APPENDIX 10. CAPACITOR COLOR CODES

● **Ceramic Capacitors**

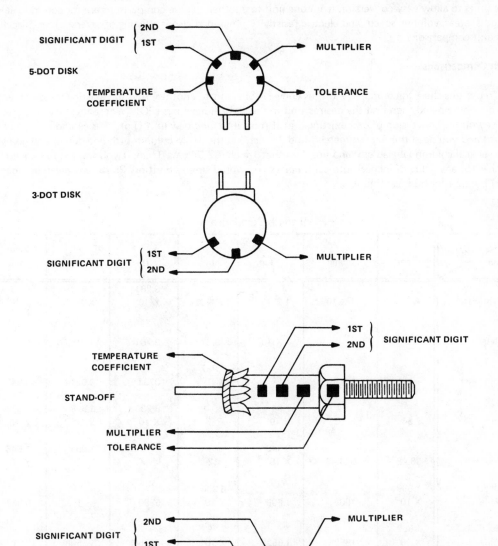

APPENDIX 11. UNIT CONVERSION CHARTS

The following charts are listed to give a convenient method for comparing various common English and metric units to allow easy conversion from one unit to another. These comparisons are for common values of lengths, areas, volume, speed, and electric resistivity. Included also is a listing of several other miscellaneous unit comparisons.

Length Comparisons

To use this chart to compare (and thus convert) one unit to another, find the existing measurement in the From column and then find the desired unit in the vertical headings (TO). Where these two intersect will give you the conversion of *one* existing unit (From) into *one* new unit (To). For example, if you have *one inch* and you need this *in centimeters*; find "1 inch" in the From column (4th line down) and go over to the vertical column labeled cm; and you find that 1 inch = 2.54 cm. Then, if you wanted to convert 25 inches (or any value of inches) into centimeters you would simply multiply 25 (or any given number of inches) by 2.54 for 63.5 centimeters.

Length Comparisons

From \ To	cm	meter	km	in	ft	mile	naut. mile
1 Centimeter	1	1×10^{-2}	1×10^{-5}	0.3937	3.281×10^{-2}	6.214×10^{-6}	5.40×10^{-6}
1 Meter	100	1	1×10^{-3}	39.37	3.281	6.214×10^{-4}	5.40×10^{-4}
1 Kilometer	1×10^5	1×10^3	1	3.937×10^4	3281	0.6214	0.540
1 Inch	2.54	2.54×10^{-2}	2.54×10^{-5}	1	8.333×10^{-2}	1.578×10^{-5}	1.371×10^{-5}
1 Foot	30.48	0.3048	3.048×10^{-4}	12	1	1.894×10^{-4}	1.646×10^{-4}
1 Statute Mile	1.609×10^5	1609	1.609	6.336×10^4	5280	1	0.8670
1 Nautical Mile	1.852×10^5	1852	1.852	7.293×10^4	6076.1	1.1508	1

APPENDIX 11. UNIT CONVERSION CHARTS

The charts that follow are used in the same manner as the length comparison chart with the "From" in the left column and the "To" conversions listed in the following vertical columns.

Area Comparison

From \ To	$meter^2$	cm^2	ft^2	in^2	circ mil
1 square meter	1	1×10^4	10.76	1550	1.974×10^9
1 square centimeter	1×10^{-4}	1	1.076×10^{-3}	0.1550	1.974×10^5
1 square foot	9.290×10^{-2}	929.0	1	144	1.833×10^8
1 square inch	6.452×10^{-4}	6.452	6.944×10^{-3}	1	1.273×10^6
1 circular mil	5.067×10^{-10}	5.067×10^{-6}	5.454×10^{-9}	7.854×10^{-7}	1

Volume Comparison

From \ To	$meter^3$	cm^3	1	ft^3	in^3
1 cubic meter	1	1×10^6	1000	35.31	6.102×10^4
1 cubic centimeter	1×10^{-6}	1	$1. \times 10^{-3}$	3.531×10^{-5}	6.102×10^{-2}
1 liter	1.000×10^{-3}	1000	1	3.531×10^{-2}	61.02
1 cubic foot	2.832×10^{-2}	2.832×10^4	28.32	1	1728
1 cubic inch	1.639×10^{-5}	16.39	1.639×10^{-2}	5.787×10^{-4}	1

Speed Comparison

From \ To	ft/sec	km/hr	meter/sec	miles/hr	cm/sec	knot
1 foot per second	1	1.097	0.3048	0.6818	30.48	0.5925
1 kilometer per hour	0.9113	1	0.2778	0.6214	27.78	0.540
1 meter per second	3.281	3.6	1	2.237	100	1.944
1 mile per hour	1.467	1.609	0.4470	1	44.70	0.8689
1 centimeter per second	3.281×10^{-2}	3.6×10^{-2}	0.01	2.237×10^{-2}	1	1.944×10^{-2}
1 knot	1.688	1.852	0.5144	1.151	51.44	1

APPENDIX 11. UNIT CONVERSION CHARTS

Electric Resistivity Comparison

To From	μohm- cm	ohm-cm	ohm-m	ohm-circ mil/ft
1 micro-ohm-centimeter	1	1×10^{-6}	1×10^{-8}	6.015
1 ohm-centimeter	1×10^6	1	0.01	6.015×10^6
1 ohm-meter	1×10^8	100	1	6.015×10^8
1 ohm-circular mil per foot	0.1662	1.662×10^{-7}	1.662×10^{-9}	1

Miscellaneous Unit Comparisons

1 fathom = 1 ft

1 yard = 3 ft

1 rod = 16.5 ft

1 U.S. gallon = 4 U.S. fluid quarts

1 U.S. quart = 2 U.S. pints

1 U.S. pint = 16 U.S. fluid ounces

1 U.S. gallon = 0.8327 British imperial gallon

1 British imperial gallon = 1.2 U.S. gallons

1 liter = 1000 cm^3

1 knot = 1 nautical mile/hr

1 mile/min = 88 ft/sec = 60 miles/hr

1 meter = 39.4 in = 3.28 ft

1 inch = 2.54 cm

1 mile = 5280 ft = 1.61 km

1 angstrom unit = 10^{-10} meters

1 horsepower = 550 ft-lb/sec = 746 watts

APPENDIX 12. THE GREEK ALPHABET

The Greek Alphabet
(Including common use of symbols in basic electricity)

Letter	Capital	Common Use of Symbol	Lower	Common Use of Symbol
Alpha	A		α	
Beta	B		β	
Gamma	Γ		γ	
Delta	Δ	change in	δ	change in
Epsilon	E		ϵ	base of natural logs
Zeta	Z		ζ	
Eta	H		η	
Theta	Θ		θ , ϑ	angle (phase angle)
Iota	I		ι	
Kappa	K		κ	dielectric constant
Lambda	Λ		λ	wavelength
Mu	M		μ	micro
Nu	N		ν	frequency
Xi	Ξ		ξ	
Omicron	O		o	
Pi	Π		π	3.14159
Rho	P		ρ	specific resistance, resistivity
Sigma	Σ	sum of terms	σ , ς	
Tau	T		τ	
Upsilon	Υ		υ	
Phi	Φ		ϕ , φ	magnetic flux
Chi	X		χ	
Psi	Ψ		ψ	
Omega	Ω	ohms	ω	angular frequency
(Reversed Omega)	$(\mho)$	mho		

TERM	UNIT	SYMBOL	FORMULA		
			SERIES		PARALLEL
Charge	Coulomb	Q	1 coulomb = 6.28 X 10^{18} electrons		
Voltage (Potential difference, EMF)	Volt (V)	E	$E_T = E_1 + E_2 + E_3 + \ldots$	(E / I R) $E = IR$	$E_T = E_1 = E_2 = E_3 \ldots$
Current (Flow of charge)	Ampere (Amp) (A)	I	$I_T = I_1 = I_2 = I_3 \ldots$	(E / I R) $I = E/R$	$I_T = I_1 + I_2 + I_3 \ldots$
Resistance	Ohm (Ω)	R	$R_T = R_1 + R_2 + R_3 + \ldots$	(E / I R) $R = E/I$ $R = 1/G$	$R_T = \dfrac{1}{1/R_1 + 1/R_2 + 1/R_3 + \ldots}$ $R_T = \dfrac{R_1 R_2}{R_1 + R_2}$ $R_T = \dfrac{R_s}{N}$
Conductance	Mho (℧)	G	$G_T = 1/R_T$	$G = 1/R$	$G_T = G_1 + G_2 + G_3 \ldots$
Power	Watt (W)	P	$P = IE$ $P = E^2/R$ $P = I^2 R$	(P / I E) (E^2 / R P) (P / I^2 R)	$P = IE$ $P = E^2/R$ $P = I^2 R$
Capacitance	Farad (F)	C	$C_T = \dfrac{1}{1/C_1 + 1/C_2 + 1/C_3 + \ldots}$	$C = Q/E$ $T = RC$	$C_T = C_1 + C_2 + C_3 + \ldots$
Inductance	Henry (H)	L	$L_T = L_1 + L_2 + L_3 + \ldots$	$T = L/R$	$L_T = \dfrac{1}{1/L_1 + 1/L_2 + 1/L_3 + \ldots}$

Bibliography

Adams, J. E., *Electrical Principles and Practices*, New York, N.Y.: McGraw-Hill Book Co., 1963.

Bureau of Naval Personnel, *Basic Electricity*, New York, N.Y.: Dover Publications, Inc., 1970.

Cooke, N. M., *Basic Mathematics for Electronics*, Second Edition, New York, N.Y.: McGraw-Hill Book Co., 1960.

DeFrance, J. J., *Electrical Fundamentals*, Englewood Cliffs, New Jersey: Prentice-Hall, Inc., 1969.

Doyle, J. M., *An Introduction to Electrical Wiring*, Reston, Virginia: Reston Publishing Co., Inc., 1975.

Fiske, K. A., and Harter, J. H., *Direct Current Circuit Analysis Through Experimentation*, Third Edition, Seal Beach, California: The Technical Education Press, 1970.

Gillie, A. C., *Electrical Principles of Electronics*, Second Edition, New York, N.Y.: McGraw-Hill Book Co., 1969.

Graf, R. F., *Modern Dictionary of Electronics*, Indianapolis, Indiana: Howard W. Sams and Co., Inc., 1968.

Graham, K. C., *Fundamentals of Electricity*, Fifth Edition, Chicago, Illinois: American Technical Society, 1968.

Grob, B., *Basic Electronics*, Second Edition, New York, N.Y.: McGraw-Hill Book Co., 1971.

Halliday, D., and Resnick, R., *Physics for Students of Science and Engineering, Part II*, New York, N.Y.: John Wiley and Sons, 1960.

Harris, N. C., and Hemmerling, E. M., *Introductory Applied Physics*, Third Edition, New York, N.Y.: McGraw-Hill Book Co., 1972.

Herrick, C. M., *Unified Concepts of Electronics*, Englewood Cliffs, N.J.: Prentice-Hall, Inc., 1970.

Mileaf, H., *Electricity One-Seven*, New York, N.Y.: Hayden Book Co., Inc., 1966.

Mileaf, H., *Electronics One-Seven*, Rochelle, Park, N.J.: Hayden Book Co., 1967.

Naval Air Technical Training Command, *Basic Electricity*, Memphis, Tennessee: NavAirTech Training Center, 1967.

Oppenheimer, S. L., Hess, F. R., Borchers, J. P., *Direct and Alternating Currents*, Second Edition, New York, N.Y.: McGraw-Hill Book Co., 1973.

Philco Education Operations, *Basic Concepts and DC Circuits*, Fort Washington, Pennsylvania: Philco Corporation, 1960.

Shrader, R. L., *Electrical Fundamentals for Technicians*, New York, N.Y.: McGraw-Hill Book Co., 1969.

Singer, B. B., *Basic Mathematics for Electricity and Electronics*, Second Edition, New York, N.Y.: McGraw-Hill Book Co., 1965.

Siskind, C. S., *Electrical Circuits, Direct and Alternating Current*, Second Edition, New York, N.Y.: McGraw-Hill Book Co., 1965.

Staff of Buck Engineering Co., Inc. (DeVito, M. J., Project Supervisor), *Introduction to Electricity and Electronics*, Farmingdale, New Jersey: Buck Engineering Co., Inc., 1971.

Staff of Electrical Technology Department, New York Institute of Technology, Schure, A., Project Director, *A Programmed Course in Basic Electricity*, New York, N.Y.: McGraw-Hill Book Co., 1970.

Suffern, M. G., *Basic Electrical and Electronic Principles*, Third Edition, New York, N.Y.: McGraw-Hill Book Co., 1962.

Timbie, W. H., *Essentials of Electricity*, Third Edition, New York, N.Y.: John Wiley and Sons, Inc., 1963.

Tocci, R. J., *Introduction to Electric Circuit Analysis*, Columbus, Ohio: Charles E. Merrill Publishing Co., 1974.

Trejo, P.E., *DC Circuits*, Palo Alto, California: Westinghouse Learning Press, 1972.

Turner, R. P., *Basic Electricity*, Second Edition, New York, N.Y.: Holt, Rinehart, and Wilson, 1963.

Weick, C. B., *Principles of Electronic Technology*, New York, N.Y.: McGraw-Hill Book Co., 1969.

Wellman, W. R., *Elementary Electricity*, Second Edition, New York, N.Y.: Van Nostrand Reinhold Company, 1971.

Glossary

algebraic sum
All positive quantities in an expression added together and each negative quantity subtracted from that result.

alternating current
Current which continuously reverses direction, usually in periodic fashion.

ammeter
A meter connected in series with a circuit, branch, or component which measures the current flowing through that circuit, branch, or component.

ampere
The unit of measure for current flow which equals 1 coulomb of electrons passing one point in a circuit in 1 second.

atom
The smallest part into which an element can be divided and still retain the behavior of the element.

battery
A device which maintains a potential difference between its terminals by chemical action.

bleeder current
Current flow through the bleeder resistor in a voltage divider circuit. Used to stabilize the output voltage of the voltage divider.

bleeder resistor
A resistor found in a voltage divider circuit or power supply and used to stabilize the output voltage.

branch
Path for current flow in a circuit.

bridge circuit
A special type of parallel-series circuit in which the voltages in each branch may be balanced by adjustment of one component. A special version called a Wheatstone bridge may be used to accurately measure resistance.

capacitance
How well a capacitor stores charge. Equal to the quantity of stored charge (Q) divided by the voltage (E) across the device when that charge was stored. Unit of measurement is the farad.

capacitor
A device that can store a charge on conducting plates through the action of an electrostatic field between the plates.

cell
A single unit device which converts chemical energy into electrical energy.

chassis
A metal frame used to secure and house electrical components and associated circuitry.

choke coil
An inductor used to oppose changes in current flow.

circuit
A complete path for current flow from one terminal to the other of a source such as a battery or a power supply.

circuit analysis
A technique of examining components in circuits to determine various values of voltage, current, resistance, power, etc.

circuit breaker
An automatic device which, under abnormal conditions, will open a current-carrying circuit to help prevent unnecessary damage. Unlike a fuse, a circuit breaker may be reset to reconnect the circuit.

circuit reduction
A technique of circuit analysis whereby a complex resistive circuit is replaced by a single equivalent resistance.

circuit sense
An ability to recognize series or parallel portions of complex circuits to apply series and parallel circuit rules to those portions of the circuit for circuit analysis.

coil
A number of turns of wire that is wrapped around a core. (Also called an inductor.)

combining like terms
Algebraic addition of parts of an equation that each contain the same unknown quantity.

common point
A voltage reference point in a circuit. A point which is "common" to many components in the circuit.

condenser
See capacitor.

conductance
The ability to conduct or carry current. Conductance is equivalent to the reciprocal of (or one over) the resistance.

conductor
A material with many free electrons that will carry current.

constant current source
An idealized source whose output current does not change with changes in the load, but whose output voltage varies with the load connected to it.

coulomb
A large quantity of electrons that is convenient when working with electricity and equals 6.25 billion, billion electrons (or 6.25×10^{18} electrons).

current
"Electron current" is the flow of electrons through a material from negative to positive. "Conventional current" is the flow of positive charges from positive to negative. "Current flow" is a general term often used to mean either of the above. Symbol is I, unit is ampere.

dielectric
An insulating material with properties that enable its use between the two plates of a capacitor.

dielectric breakdown (in a capacitor)
Failure of an insulator to prevent current flow from one plate of a capacitor through the insulator to the other plate. Often causes permanent damage to the capacitor.

dielectric constant
A factor which indicates how much more effective a material is as compared to air in helping a capacitor store a charge (when used as the insulating material between the capacitor's plates). The abbreviation for dielectric constant is K; air has a K of 1.

dielectric strength
A factor which indicates how well a dielectric resists breakdown under high voltages.

direct current
Current that flows in only one direction.

direct relationship
One in which two quantities both increase or both decrease while other factors remain constant.

direct short
A circuit situation in which a conductor with little or no resistance is placed across a battery or power supply. Results in very high current which will damage the source if a protective device such as a fuse or circuit breaker is not included in the circuit.

dropping resistor
A resistor used to decrease a given voltage by an amount equal to the voltage dropped across the resistor.

dry cell
A cell with a paste-like electrolyte which can be used in any position as compared to a wet cell which must be used in an upright position.

earth ground
A point that is at the potential of the earth or something that is in direct electrical connection with the earth such as water pipes.

electricity

The flow of electrons through simple materials and devices.

electrolyte

A chemical (liquid or paste) which reacts with metals in a cell to produce electricity.

electromagnetic field

A field of force produced around a conductor whenever there is current flowing through it. This field can be visualized with magnetic *lines of force*.

electron

Negatively charged particles surrounding the nucleus of an atom which determine chemical and electrical properties of the atom.

electron shells

The specific paths of rotation, or orbits, which electrons follow as they revolve around the nucleus of the atom.

electrostatic field

A field of force that surrounds any charged object. This field can be visualized with electrostatic lines of force.

electrostatic force

A force which exists between any two charged objects. If the two objects each have the *same* type of charge, the force is a *repulsion*. If the two objects each have *different* types of charge, the force is an *attraction*.

element

One of the 106 different substances which is the basic building block of all matter, and cannot be divided into simpler substances by chemical means.

energy

The ability to do work. Unit commonly used in measuring energy is the joule; equal to the energy supplied by a 1-watt power source in 1 second.

equivalent resistance

The value of one single resistor that can be used to replace a more complex connection of several resistors.

exponent

A number written above and to the right of another number called the base. Example: 10^2, 10 is the base, 2 is the exponent. A number which indicates how many times the base is multiplied by itself. $10^2 = 10 \times 10 = 100$.

farad

The unit of capacitance. A capacitor has 1 farad of capacitance when it can store 1 coulomb of charge with a 1-volt potential difference placed across it.

filament
> A wire in an electric light bulb or electron tube which is heated by passing a current through it in order to make it glow or emit light, and/or electrons.

free electrons
> Electrons which are not bound to a particular atom but circulate among the atoms of the substance.

fuse
> A protective device usually containing a material with a low melting point which melts when current through it exceeds the ampere value for which it is rated and opens the circuit stopping the current flow.

giga
> The metric prefix meaning one billion or 10^9. Abbreviated G.

ground
> A voltage reference point in a circuit which may be connected to earth ground.

henry
> Unit of measure for inductance. A 1-henry coil produces 1 volt when the current through it is changing at a rate of 1 ampere per second. Abbreviated H.

horsepower
> A measure of power. One horsepower equals 746 watts. Abbreviated hp.

hot wire
> A wire which is connected to a source of voltage or current and is not grounded.

inductance
> The ability of a coil to store energy and oppose changes in current flowing through it.

inductor
> A number of turns of wire wrapped around a core used to provide inductance in a circuit. (Also called a coil.)

insulator
> A material with very few free electrons. A nonconductor.

inverse relationship
> A relationship between two quantities in which an increase in one quantity causes a decrease in the other quantity while other factors are held constant.

jumper cables
> Heavy wire conductors (usually stranded) used as an aid in starting a car with a weak battery.

junction
> A connection common to more than two components in a circuit. A node.

kilo

A metric prefix meaning 1000 or 10^3. Abbreviated k.

Kirchhoff's current law

One of many tools of circuit analysis which states that the sum of the currents arriving at any point in a circuit must equal the sum of the currents leaving that point.

Kirchhoff's voltage law

Another tool of circuit analysis which states that the algebraic sum of all the voltages encountered in any loop equals zero.

leakage resistance

The normally high resistance of an insulator such as a dielectric between the plates of a capacitor.

load

A device such as a resistor which receives electrical energy from a source and that draws current and/or has resistance, requires voltage, or dissipates power.

loop

A closed path for current flow in a circuit.

loop equation

The algebraic sum of all the voltages in a loop set equal to zero.

main line current

The total current in a parallel circuit.

mega

A metric prefix meaning one million or 1,000,000 or 10^6. Abbreviated M.

mesh

The simplest form of a loop, resembling a single window pane in a circuit.

mesh current

The current flowing in a mesh. Usually assumed to be flowing in a particular direction.

mho

The unit of conductance. Symbol ℧.

micro

A metric prefix meaning one millionth or 1/1,000,000 or 10^{-6}. Abbreviated with the Greek letter mu (μ).

milli

A metric prefix meaning one thousandth or 1/1000 or 10^{-3}. Abbreviated m.

Millman's theorem
A tool of circuit analysis which states that the voltage across several branches of a multisource parallel circuit that has no series resistance between the branches equals the sum of the branch currents divided by the total conductance of the circuit.

nano
A metric prefix meaning one billionth or 1/1,000,000,000 or 10^{-9}. Abbreviated n.

negative ion
An atom which has gained one or more electrons.

node
A junction. A connection common to more than two components in a circuit.

node current equations
A mathematical expression of Kirchhoff's current law at a junction or node.

node voltage
The voltage at a node with respect to some reference point in the circuit.

ohm
The unit of resistance. Symbol Ω.

ohmmeter
An instrument used to measure resistance.

Ohm's law
A basic tool of circuit analysis which states that in simple materials, the amount of current through the material varies directly with the applied voltage and varies inversely with the resistance of the material. Gives rise to three common equations for use in circuit analysis: $E = IR$, $R = E/I$, $I = E/R$.

open circuit
A circuit interruption that causes an incomplete path for current flow.

oscilloscope
An instrument that can visually display rapidly varying quantities as a function of time. Often used to measure voltage.

parallel circuit
A circuit that has two or more paths (or branches) for current flow.

parallel-series circuit
A circuit with several branches wired in parallel. Each branch contains one or more components connected in series, but no single component carries the total circuit current.

partial short
A path with essentially 0 ohms of resistance connected across part of a circuit but not connected directly across the source.

percent
A ratio of one part to the total amount. One part of a hundred.

pico
A metric prefix meaning one million millionth or 10^{-12}. Abbreviated p.

polarity of voltage
A means of describing a voltage with respect to some reference point, either positive or negative.

positive ion
An atom that has lost one or more electrons.

potential difference
A measure of force produced between charged objects that moves free electrons. Also called voltage or electromotive force. Symbol is E, unit is the volt (abbreviated V).

potentiometer
A resistance element with a sliding wiper contact used in applications where a division of resistance is required. (A *three*-terminal adjustable resistive divider.)

power
The rate at which work is done or the rate at which heat is generated (abbreviated P). The unit of power is the *watt* (abbreviated W), which is equal to 1 joule per second.

power dissipated
Power which escapes from a resistance in the form of heat by the convection of air moving around the component.

power rating of a resistor
How much power a resistor can dissipate (give off) safely in the form of heat in watts.

power supply
A device which is usually plugged into a wall outlet and can replace a battery in many applications by providing a known potential difference between two convenient terminals.

protons
Particles in the nucleus of the atom which has a positive charge equal to the electron's negative charge.

recall
Function key on a calculator which when pressed causes the calculator to display the contents of the memory.

reciprocal
Mathematical "inverse". The reciprocal of any number is simply that number divided into one.

resistance
Opposition to current flow which is a lot like friction because it opposes electron motion and generates heat. Symbol R. Unit is the ohm (Ω).

reference node
> A junction in a circuit from which all voltages are measured.

reference point
> An arbitrarily chosen point in a circuit to which all other points in the circuit are compared, usually when measuring voltages.

regulated voltage
> The output voltage of a power supply which contains special circuitry to keep the output voltage constant, even if the current drain on it is changing.

relay
> A switch (or combination of switches) activated by an electromagnetic coil.

rheostat
> An adjustable device with two terminals which can be used to produce a variable resistance in a circuit.

rounding off
> A procedure by which a number with many digits can be reduced to a number with only three significant digits. The first three significant digits are kept, and the fourth examined. If the fourth digit is 5 or greater, the third significant digit is raised by one. If the fourth digit is 4 or less, the first three digits are kept unchanged.

scientific notation
> A type of shorthand used to keep track of decimal places which utilizes powers of the number 10. Standard form for scientific notation is $D.DD \times 10^E$, where D represents each of the first 3 significant digits, and E represents the exponent, or power of ten.

series circuit
> A circuit with only one path through which current can flow.

series-parallel circuit
> A group of series and parallel components in which at least one circuit element lies in the path of the total current.

short circuit
> A path with little or no resistance connected across the terminals of a circuit element.

shunt
> Another term which means parallel. Often also refers to the low value of parallel resistance used in an ammeter for determining or changing the "range" of the meter.

significant digits
> Those digits within a number which have the greatest weight. In the decimal system digits to the left of any designated digit are more significant than those to the right.

sign of a voltage

A notation, either positive (+) or negative (−), in front of a voltage. (Important in solving loop equations and depends on whether the voltage aids or opposes current flow in a circuit.)

simultaneous equations

A series of equations which contain the same unknown quantities, and which can be manipulated to solve for each of the unknowns.

solenoid

A term used to mean coil or inductor, also used to mean a type of relay such as that used to switch the starter current in an automobile.

source

A device, such as a battery or dc power supply, which supplies the potential difference and electrical energy to the circuit.

specific resistance

The resistance of any material in a particular size and shape. The resistance of a piece of a substance that is 1 foot long and 1 mil in diameter at 20°C measured in ohms.

square root of a number

Another number which must be multiplied by itself to obtain the original number.

square of a number

That number multiplied by itself.

store

A calculator operation where the number in the display is transferred to the memory where it is held until it is recalled.

substitute

To replace one part of a formula or equation with another quantity which is its equal.

superposition theorem

A tool of complex circuit analysis which states that in a network with two or more sources the current or voltage for any component is equal to the algebraic sum of the effects produced by each source acting separately.

switch

A device that is used to open or close circuits, thereby stopping or allowing current flow in a circuit or through a component.

terminal

A connection point on a device or component.

Thevenin's theorem

A tool of circuit analysis which states that a complex circuit can be reduced to an equivalent series circuit with a single voltage source and a single series resistance, as long as all components are linear.

time constant
The time it takes in seconds for a capacitor to charge up to 63 percent of the applied voltage or the time it takes for a fully charged capacitor to discharge from 100 percent down to 37 percent of full charge. Equal to the product of R (in ohms) times C (in farads) in a resistive-capacitive circuit. Also a measure of the current rise and fall in inductive circuits. (Equal to the quotient of L/R in resistive-inductive circuits, L in henries, R in ohms.)

transposing
Moving a quantity from one side of an equation across the equal sign to the other side of the equation and changing its sign.

traverse
Move around a circuit or across a component. Usually refers to a mental process used for keeping track of various voltages encountered in a loop.

troubleshooting
A technique used to locate a problem in a circuit.

valence electrons
Those electrons in the outermost or valence shell of an atom.

valence shell
The outermost shell of an atom.

volt
The unit of voltage or potential difference. Abbreviated V.

voltage
A measure of the push on each electron which makes it move. Symbol E. Unit is the volt.

voltage divider
A type of circuitry that provides an economical way to obtain one or several lower voltages from a single higher voltage supply.

voltage drop
Change in voltage available between points in a circuit produced by current flow through resistors. Also called an IR drop. Unit is the volt.

voltmeter
An instrument used to measure voltage between two points in a circuit.

watt
The unit of power. Abbreviated W. Equal to 1 joule per second.

Wheatstone bridge
A specialized circuit, sometimes housed as an instrument, for measuring resistance very accurately, by comparison to a standard resistance.

working voltage
The recommended maximum voltage at which a capacitor should be operated.

Index

Adding and subtracting with equations, 11-23
Algebraic sum, 11-14, 11-15
Assigning current direction, 11-16
Automotive electrical system, 8-17, 8-18
Automotive wiring system, 8-19
   Ohm's law in, 8-20
   Parallel current formula, 8-24
   Series voltage formula, 8-21, 8-23

Bar magnet, 14-9
Basic formulas of basic electricity, A-26
Basic schematic symbols, A-6
Bleeder current, 10-15
   Rule of thumb for, 10-15
Bleeder resistor, 10-15
Bridge circuit, 12-9

Capacitance, 13-11
   Factors affecting capacitance, 13-11, 13-12
   Formula, 13-11, 13-16
   Units, 13-14
Capacitor, 13-5, 13-8
   Applications, 13-30
   Breakdown, 13-13
   Capacitor action, 13-8, 14-13
   Charge, 13-10, 13-15, 13-17, 13-20
   Color code, A-18 — A-21
   Construction, 13-5, 13-28, 13-29
   Dielectric, 13-5, 13-12
   Discharge, 13-15, 13-21, 13-22
   Electrolytic, 13-6, 13-28, 13-29
   Equivalent circuit, 13-9
   Fixed and variable, 13-28
   In parallel, 13-32
   In series, 13-31
   Leakage resistance, 13-30
   Plate area, 13-11
   Symbols, 13-6
   Time constant, 13-18
   Types, 13-26, 13-27
Charge and discharge curve calculations, A-17
Chassis,
   Grounding applications, 10-11
Circuit reduction, 8-10

Coil, 14-5
   Construction, 14-5, 14-6
   Demonstration circuit, 14-14, 14-15, 14-16
   Effect in a circuit, 14-11
   Energy stored in, 14-13
   Magnetic field around, 14-8
   Relay, 14-10
   Solenoid, 14-10
Combining like terms, 11-26, 11-37
Condenser, 13-5
Current,
   Conventional, 11-27
   Electron, 11-27

Dielectric constant, 13-13
Dielectric strength, 13-12
Dropping resistor, 8-17

Electromagnetic field, 14-7
Electrostatic field,
   In a capacitor, 13-8

Filament, 8-20
Fuse, 9-26

Greek alphabet, A-25
Ground,
   Chassis, 10-9
   Earth, 10-10
   Return path for current, 10-9
   Voltage reference, 10-9

Inductance, 14-18
   Unit, 14-18
Inductor, 14-5
   Construction, 14-5, 14-6
   Demonstration circuit, 14-14, 14-15, 14-16
   Effect in a circuit, 14-11
   Energy stored in, 14-13
   Magnetic field around, 14-8
   Relay, 14-10
   Solenoid, 14-10

Junction, 11-8

Kirchhoff's current law, 11-8, 11-28, 12-8
   At a junction, 11-8, 12-10
   In parallel circuits, 11-10
   In series circuits, 11-10

Kirchhoff's voltage law, 11-11, 11-28
  Alternate forms 11-13, 11-14, 11-15, 12-5
  In parallel circuits, 11-12
  In series circuits, 11-12
  Steps in using, 11-28, 11-30, 12-6

Leakage resistance, 13-30
Leyden jar, 13-7
Load, 10-13
Loop, 11-11, 12-5
Loop equation, 11-16, 11-20, 12-12
  Solving equations, 12-13 — 12-15, 11-21 —
  11-25
  Solving simultaneous equations, 11-33 —
  11-36
  Substitution in, 11-37

Magnetic lines of force, 14-7, 14-8
  Direction of, 14-8
Mesh current analysis, 12-24
  Mesh currents, 12-24, 12-25
  Mesh equations, 12-25, 12-26
  Rules for use, 12-66
  Sample solution, 12-68 — 12-71, 12-27 —
  12-29
  Where useful, 12-66
Metric prefixes, A-5
Millman's theorem, 12-35
  Method of use, 12-87
  Millman's formula, 12-36, 12-86
  Sample calculation, 12-89
  Where useful, 12-87
Multiplying and dividing with equations, 11-24

Node, 11-8, 12-30
  Principal node, 12-30
Node current equations, 11-8, 12-10, 12-30
Node voltage analysis, 12-30
  Method of use, 12-72 — 12-74
  Node current equation, 12-30
  Node voltage, 12-30
  Sample calculation, 12-31, 12-75, 12-76
  Where useful, 12-72

Norton's theorem, 12-34
  Constant current source, 12-35
  Equivalent circuit, 12-35, 12-83
  Method of use, 12-82
  Norton current, 12-34, 12-82
  Norton resistance, 12-34, 12-83
  Sample calculation, 12-84 — 12-86

Oscilloscope, 13-22

Parallel circuit,
  Laws of, 8-7, 8-8
Parallel-Series circuit, 8-5, 8-9, 8-25, 8-26, 9-5
  Circuit reduction, 8-10
  Ohm's law in, 8-10, 8-13, 8-14, 8-15, 8-16
  Parallel current formula, 8-30
  Parallel resistance formula, 8-13
  Procedure for analysis, 8-31
  Power in, 8-33
  Series current analysis, 8-27
  Series resistance formula, 8-11, 8-12
  Series voltage formula, 8-16, 8-17, 8-28
Polarity of voltage, 10-12, 10-13, 11-40, 11-41
Power,
  Basic formula, 10-31
  E^2-R-P formula, 10-33
  In parallel-series circuits, 8-33
  In series-parallel circuits, 9-34, 10-35
  P-I^2-R formula, 10-31
Power dissipated, 8-33
Preferred values, A-3

RC circuit, 13-22
  Compared to RL circuit, 14-19, 14-20
Relay, 14-10
Resistor size comparison chart, A-4
RL circuit, 14-17
  Automotive ignition system, 14-25
  Current fall, 14-21
  Current rise, 14-20
  Inductive kickback, 14-23
  Sample calculations, 14-21, 14-22
  Steady state, 14-20
  Time constant formula, 14-19
  Time constant of, 14-17, 14-18

Scientific notation, A-5
Series circuit,
  Laws of, 8-6, 8-7
Series-Parallel Circuit, 8-5, 9-5, 9-7
  Branch circuits, 9-11
  Calculating I_T, 9-10, 9-14
  Circuit reduction, 9-8, 9-9, 9-10
  Demonstration circuit, 9-20 — 9-23
  Equivalent resistance, 9-10
  Power in, 9-34
  Series resistance formula, 9-14
  Steps in analyzing, 9-7
  Voltage across series resistors, 9-16
  Voltage drops, 9-11
Signs, 11-13
  Changing all signs in an equation, 11-25
  Of voltage drops, 11-13, 11-19
  Of voltage sources, 11-17
Solenoid, 14-10
Solving simultaneous equations, 11-33
  Addition method, 11-33, 11-34
  Substitution method, 11-35, 11-36
Square roots,
  How to take square roots manually, A-10 —
  A-13
  Tables, A-9
  Using a calculator, 10-37
  Using square root tables, 10-39 — 10-42,
  A-7, A-8
Superposition theorem, 12-16, 12-17
  Limitations of, 12-17
  Sample calculations, 12-18 — 12-23
  Statement of, 12-17
Switch, 8-17
  Operation, 9-26, 9-27
Voltage across, 9-27, 9-28

Thevenin's theorem, 12-32
  Calculation of E_{TH}, 12-33, 12-78
  Calculation of R_{TH}, 12-33, 12-78
  Equivalent circuit, 12-33
  Method of use, 12-77
  Sample calculation, 12-79 — 12-81
  Where useful, 12-77

Time constant, 13-18
  Formula for RC circuit, 13-19
  Formula for RL circuit, 14-19
  Graph, 13-20
Transposing, 11-24
Traverse, 11-11, 11-13

Unit conversion charts, A-22 — A-24
Universal time constant graph, 13-20, A-14
  How to use, A-14 — A-16

Voltage,
  Polarity of, 10-12, 10-13
Voltage divider, 10-5, 10-6
  Basic design, 10-19
  Bleeder current, 10-16
  Calculations, 10-17 — 10-19, 10-21 —
  10-30
  Equation, 10-8
  Loaded, 10-14, 10-20
  Unloaded, 10-6, 10-7, 10-12

Wheatstone bridge, 12-9
Working voltage, 13-26

QUIZ ANSWERS — CHAPTERS 8-14

Lesson 8	Lesson 9	Lesson 10	Lesson 11
1. SP	1. SP	1. b	1. b
2. P	2. P	2. c	2. d
3. PS	3. SP	3. a	3. c
4. S	4. S	4. b	4. d
5. SP	5. SP	5. d	5. e
6. PS	6. 54K	6. 160mW	6. d
7. SP	7. 13.9	7. 400W	7. e
8. SP	8. 45.3	8. 25mA	8. a
9. PS	9. 84.6K	9. 9.6mW	9. b
10. PS	10. −1mA	10. 112V	10. d
11. 95Ω	11. −0.5mA	11. b	11. d
12. 123Ω	12. 15.1V	12. a	12. b
13. 133Ω	13. 222μA	13. b	13. a
14. 16.9Ω	14. 6mA	14. d	14. c
15. 24.5Ω	15. −820Ω	15. c	15. d
16. 1	16. −7.2V	16. c	16. a
17. R_4	17. −2mA	17. e	17. a
18. 3.15K	18. 19.7V	18. b	18. c
19. 10V	19. d		19. e
20. 1mA	20. d		20. d

Lesson 12	Lesson 13	Lesson 14
1. a	1. d	1. b
2. a	2. d	2. a
3. a	3. c	3. d
4. d	4. b	4. c
5. b	5. b	5. d
6. +320mA	6. b	6. b
7. +3.0A	7. a	7. b
8. −80mA	8. c	8. c
9. +30.5mA	9. b	9. a
10. −5mA	10. e	10. d
11. c	11. c	11. b
12. a	12. a	12. b
13. f	13. d	13. a
14. d	14. c	14. c
15. c	15. b	15. c
16. b	16. 1.03sec	16. d
17. b	17. 39x 10^{-9}	17. 4msec
18. a	18. 0.825sec	18. 50nsec
19. c	19. 12μF	19. 3K
20. b	20. 6μF	20. 24H